Electronic Switching: Central Office Systems of the World

OTHER IEEE PRESS BOOKS

Electromagnetic Horn Antennas, *Edited by A. W. Love*
Waveform Quantization and Coding, *Edited by N. S. Jayant*
Communication Satellite Systems: An Overview of the Technology, *Edited by the Satellite Systems Panel*
Literature Survey of Communication Satellite Systems and Technology, *Edited by J. H. W. Unger*
Solar Cells, *Edited by C. E. Backus*
Computer Networking, *Edited by R. P. Blanc and I. W. Cotton*
Communications Channels: Characterization and Behavior, *Edited by B. Goldberg*
Large-Scale Networks: Theory and Design, *Edited by F. T. Boesch*
Optical Fiber Technology, *Edited by D. Gloge*
Selected Papers in Digital Signal Processing, II, *Edited by the Digital Signal Processing Committee*
A Guide for Better Technical Presentations, *Edited by R. M. Woelfle*
Career Management: A Guide to Combating Obsolescence, *Edited by H. G. Kaufman*
Energy and Man: Technical and Social Aspects of Energy, *Edited by M. G. Morgan*
Magnetic Bubble Technology: Integrated-Circuit Magnetics for Digital Storage and Processing, *Edited by H. Chang*
Frequency Synthesis: Techniques and Applications, *Edited by J. Gorski-Popiel*
Literature in Digital Processing: Author and Permuted Title Index (Revised and Expanded Edition), *Edited by H. D. Helms, J. F. Kaiser, and L. R. Rabiner*
Data Communications via Fading Channels, *Edited by K. Brayer*
Nonlinear Networks: Theory and Analysis, *Edited by A. N. Willson, Jr.*
Computer Communications, *Edited by P. E. Green, Jr. and R. W. Lucky*
Stability of Large Electric Power Systems, *Edited by R. T. Byerly and E. W. Kimbark*
Automatic Test Equipment: Hardware, Software, and Management, *Edited by F. Liguori*
Key Papers in the Development of Coding Theory, *Edited by E. R. Berlekamp*
Technology and Social Institutions, *Edited by K. Chen*
Key Papers in the Development of Information Theory, *Edited by D. Slepian*
Computer-Aided Filter Design, *Edited by G. Szentirmai*
Laser Devices and Applications, *Edited by I. P. Kaminow and A. E. Siegman*
Integrated Optics, *Edited by D. Marcuse*
Laser Theory, *Edited by F. S. Barnes*
Digital Signal Processing, *Edited by L. R. Rabiner and C. M. Rader*
Minicomputers: Hardware, Software, and Applications, *Edited by J. D. Schoeffler and R. H. Temple*
Semiconductor Memories, *Edited by D. A. Hodges*
Power Semiconductor Applications, Volume II: Equipment and Systems, *Edited by J. D. Harnden, Jr. and F. B. Golden*
Power Semiconductor Applications, Volume I: General Considerations, *Edited by J. D. Harnden, and F. B. Golden*
A Practical Guide to Minicomputer Applications, *Edited by F. F. Coury*
Active Inductorless Filters, *Edited by S. K. Mitra*
Clearing the Air: The Impact of the Clean Air Act on Technology, *Edited by J. C. Redmond, J. C. Cook, and A. A. J. Hoffman*

Electronic Switching: Central Office Systems of the World

Edited by
Amos E. Joel, Jr.
Switching Consultant
Bell Laboratories

A volume in the IEEE PRESS Selected Reprint Series,
prepared under the sponsorship
of the IEEE Communications Society.

IEEE PRESS

The Institute of Electrical and Electronics Engineers, Inc. New York

Contents

Foreword

Once electronics was successfully applied to communication transmission, designers considered the possibility of applying the same technology to communication switching. Many such proposals were made in the mid and late 1930's. But it was not until the invention of the transistor and the development of bulk memories for data processing systems that serious efforts were made to develop such systems, and to prove their feasibility.

During the subsequent decade and a half, a new generation of switching system designers experimented with the application of electronics to both the network and control portions of communication switching systems. In the early 1960's, systems based on these experiments started to emerge from the laboratories into field experiments. Since then, ever-increasing numbers of electronic switching systems have been produced in quantity and placed in service throughout the world. Each of the principal manufacturers of central office equipment has designed and is producing and installing a variety of electronic switching systems for public central office application.

This book is an assemblage of papers describing 29 of those systems that have reached this state. Most of the systems are for use in local central office switching, but a few are for the switching of long distance or toll traffic.

There are many other areas where electronic switching systems have been experimented with, and where the same principles are also being applied, particularly for PABX, data, and military switching. Also, no articles are included on the studies made on the traffic or other engineering principles for electronic switching. It is not the purpose of this book to provide reprints on much of the fine work that has transpired in these fields. Rather, it is the purpose of this book to describe the central office switching systems which have gone into service in recent years so as to provide a historic record and background experiences for those designing for the next generation.

Even for the field of central office switching, there have been many excellent articles and special issues of company house-organs describing many of these systems in considerable detail, more detail than previous generations of switching equipment. In selecting the articles for this book, the Editor has tried to confine the material to those articles that most succinctly describe the techniques employed in each system. Supplementing most papers, a bibliography has been provided where one may find emphasis on details and other aspects, as well as a listing of articles describing experiences with these systems.

A table (Appendix B) is provided summarizing the techniques used in these systems, together with information on the extent of use as can best be gleaned from published information.

To the neophyte, understanding switching literature is made more difficult by the variety of names, symbols, and diagrams used in describing the systems. Included in this volume, ahead of most articles, is a new diagram employing an experimental form of symbolism of the type described in the paper by the Editor and reprinted in Appendix A.

It is hoped that with the publication of this book, the growing interest among communication engineers in the topic of switching will be further stimulated, and the most important accomplishments in this art in the past decade will be recorded in one volume. The Editor wishes to thank his many colleagues for their contributions and comments on the selection of this material.

AMOS E. JOEL, JR.
Editor

Paper 1

No. 1 Electronic Switching System (No. 1 ESS)

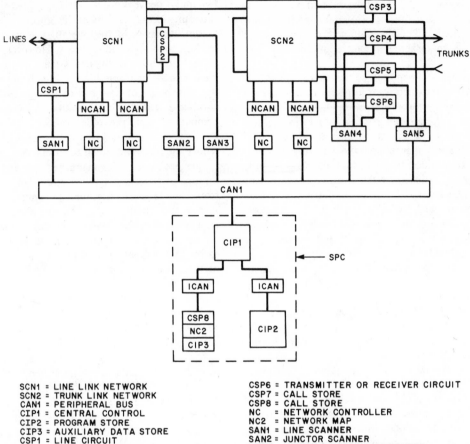

```
SCN1 = LINE LINK NETWORK          CSP6 = TRANSMITTER OR RECEIVER CIRCUIT
SCN2 = TRUNK LINK NETWORK         CSP7 = CALL STORE
CAN1 = PERIPHERAL BUS             CSP8 = CALL STORE
CIP1 = CENTRAL CONTROL            NC   = NETWORK CONTROLLER
CIP2 = PROGRAM STORE              NC2  = NETWORK MAP
CIP3 = AUXILIARY DATA STORE       SAN1 = LINE SCANNER
CSP1 = LINE CIRCUIT               SAN2 = JUNCTOR SCANNER
CSP2 = JUNCTOR CIRCUIT            SAN3 = JUNCTOR SIGNAL DISTRIBUTOR
CSP3 = CUSTOMER DIAL PULSE RECEIVER  SAN4 = TRUNK SCANNER
CSP4 = OUTGOING TRUNK CIRCUIT     SAN5 = TRUNK SIGNAL DISTRIBUTOR
CSP5 = INCOMING TRUNK CIRCUIT     SPC  = CENTRAL PROCESSOR
```

A new electronic switching system

The evolution of telephone switching systems is toward common control. This first commercial electronic system is centered about a stored-program real-time data processor that facilitates modifications and additions to future service at low cost

W. Keister, R. W. Ketchledge, H. E. Vaughan

Bell Telephone Laboratories, Inc.

Telephone switching systems have evolved through the years to meet ever-burgeoning communication needs. The evolution is marked by stages in which new switching machines are introduced to service needs that can no longer be adequately met by existing equipment. The No. 1 Electronic Switching System (No. 1 ESS) marks the attainment of such a stage today. It both meets the need for additional types of services and anticipates future needs at relatively low cost. Two-wire and/or four-wire switching for local, toll, or tandem applica-tions are provided at a cost economically competitive with present applications.

To achieve this flexibility, many new concepts of switch-ing-system organization and new kinds of apparatus were used, making No. 1 ESS the largest development project ever undertaken by Bell Laboratories for the Bell Telephone System.

This article covers some of the history and outlines the organization and objectives of the new system.

Reprinted from *IEEE Spectrum*, vol. 2, pp. 87–94, Feb. 1965.

History

The main trend of the evolution has been toward centralized or common control. Briefly, this means that complex equipment for processing information is used on each call only during the stage at which its processing capability is required. It is then released and made available to serve other calls. In this way, the construction of more sophisticated and costly equipment can be justified since its use is time-shared among a number of customers.

The first elements of common control were introduced in the Panel System, which went into service in the early 1920s. The important concepts were digit registration and translation. The No. 1 Crossbar System in the late 1930s was the next important advance in system philosophy. It contains a marker unit, the first truly common control unit. In addition to performing the decoder task of translating digits dialed by the customer, this system also locates idle trunks and controls the network that makes connection with the selected trunk. The network is completely free of constraints that might otherwise be imposed by the numbering system and can be engineered in an optimum way to meet traffic requirements.

The No. 5 Crossbar System, first placed in service in 1947, is the latest in the Bell System's evolution of common-control electromechanical systems.

All of these systems, however, were mechanical or electromechanical. Electronic techniques for switching were investigated as part of a research program begun in the middle 1940s. An experimental system, using a large central memory in a common control, named DIAD[1] (drum information assembler and dispatcher) was one result of this work. Its switching network used "one-at-a-time" operation with "end-marking" of reed-diode crosspoints. In parallel with this experiment, another group demonstrated that a good talking path could also be set up through a multistage network of special gas tubes.

An appraisal of the state of the art showed that the advantages of such a system did not justify development at that time. Later developments, such as the transistor and new memory techniques, stimulated the design of the world's first electronic switching office, which was operated at Morris, Ill., from 1960 to early 1962. The trial at Morris[2] demonstrated the value of many of the basic concepts used in No. 1 ESS; in particular, the use of stored program and the basic maintenance philosophy. The system at Morris provided customers with regular commercial-grade service in addition to some new services, establishing valuable guides for production design in hardware, data formats, and programming. Also, many young engineers obtained experience and training that later played a major role in the design of the No. 1 ESS. Two issues of the *Bell System Technical Journal* were devoted to their design contributions.[3]

Objectives

Economics. A new switching system must be at least the equivalent in service features of existing systems for some significant segment of the market. The basis of comparison must be today's market rather than some hypothetical market of the future, since the new system is introduced in an environment of a very large number of older systems; thus the general capability of the overall switching network will be determined largely by the capability of the majority of the offices.

Improvements in the overall system are gradual, extending over a period of years. However, the inherently greater capability of the new system means that improvement can be realized at a gradually increasing rate as the percentage of new offices increases. This points up another essential: compatibility. A new office must be compatible with the older offices with which it operates, since modifications of older units in service could reduce the economic advantages of a new office design.

The problem of achieving an economic balance over a range of sizes in the No. 1 ESS plan is quite different from that in electromechanical common-control offices such as the crossbar type. The electronic system is based on a single high-speed central processor that is essentially the same in both large and small offices. In a system such as No. 5 Crossbar, a multiplicity of control units must be used because of their slower speed. This allows the amount of control equipment--for instance, the number of registers and markers in the crossbar system—to be increased as the office grows so that the full burden of a control capable of handling a large office need not be borne by a small initial installation.

The new system must meet the standards of dependability that have been established by electromechanical systems. Where dependability is of prime importance, the operation of a complete office by a single central processor poses a definite problem. In a multimarker office of No. 5 Crossbar, the failure of a single marker merely reduces the traffic capacity of the office. However, in an office depending on a single central processor, the failure of the controller would make the office completely inoperative. The solution followed in No. 1 ESS is to duplicate all units essential to proper office operation.

The economic objectives of No. 1 ESS are being realized through a basic design stressing optimization of details and economy in production and operation over a period of years. The design of the equipment itself and its component parts was based on quantity manufacture. Through the use of the stored program, it was possible to plan a system that requires no wired options during manufacture, thus promoting production efficiency. And because system units were designed for a minimum of interconnections between frames, most of the wiring and much of the detailed testing can be done at the factory rather than during the process of installation.

Trouble detection and fault location have been highly automated through the use of stored program. Since most of the system logic involving telephone service features has been placed in the stored program, the introduction of new service features and the modification of existing features will be greatly simplified. In many cases, modifications will be possible by changing programs rather than by wiring changes.

I. Distribution by buildings of total Bell System lines in service

Total Lines, per cent	Number of Lines in Building
75	over 7500
50	over 19 000
25	over 32 000

II. Total central office building

Per Cent	Lines Served
25	less than 230
50	less than 750
75	less than 3000

Size

Determination of the range of sizes over which the system would be applicable is an important item in system planning. In the design of No. 1 ESS, two major parts were greatly influenced by size: the network, which had to serve the entire range with systematic growth from the smallest to the largest size encompassed by the design; and the central processor, whose call-processing capacity had to be both sufficient to handle the largest office and economical when used at only a fraction of its total capacity in smaller offices.

The appropriate size range was determined by a survey of the range of office sizes for which there is a demand.

Information for this survey was obtained from the operating telephone companies who provided information on the number of wire centers and the size of each wire center in their company. This information, covering a total of over 30 million lines in the Bell System, was analyzed by a digital computer to provide statistical information on the make-up of the potential market.

The general nature of the results is indicated in Tables I and II. Two things are apparent: (1) the large number of very small wire centers, and (2) the large volume of business handled by large wire centers. Approximately 50 per cent of the total lines are served from wire centers of 19 000 or more lines. However, an office large enough to accommodate the largest wire centers was not necessary, since the cost per line decreases as the office size increases and flattens out in the larger office sizes. For example, the cost of two 50 000-line units is not significantly higher than the cost of a single 100 000-line unit; hence, an upper size limit of 65 000 lines would be reasonable. This has been verified by a number of studies. The lower size limit is determined by pure economics; however, it should extend down to at least the 4000- to 5000-line size since the survey showed that a large number of offices are initially installed in this range.

From a traffic standpoint, the maximum size of the system is set by the capacity of the central processor for handling calls in real time. The capacity of the No. 1 ESS has been set at 100 000 calls in the busy hour. This figure was determined through studies of the cost and complexity of central processors of various designs,

weighed against the traffic needs in the wire centers of the Bell System. (The capacity of the central processor is determined by the basic speeds of the electronic circuits, its basic clock cycle time, the complexity of its individual logic operations, and the amount of processing done in parallel.)

Flexibility. The system has been planned for maximum use of the flexibility inherent in a stored program. The wired logic of central control represents basic logic operations that are related to telephone switching functions only through the sequences of instructions in the program. By means of the stored program, most of the logic decisions in call processing have been converted to basic logic operations.

This philosophy is extended to items such as trunk circuits. The physical equipment in a trunk circuit is limited in most cases to that necessary for detecting and generating the signals required on these trunk circuits, and for performing basic switching operations such as loop closure or loop reversal. All operational sequencing, including timing of the duration of signals, is performed by central control under instructions from the program. As a consequence, the variety of trunk circuits required has been reduced—and their cost has been reduced also, since changes in timing or sequence of operation can be made through changes in the program.

The switching network has been designed for flexibility in a variety of situations. Line frames and trunk frames are connected together by groups of junctors of three types: (1) junctors between line frames and trunk frames for connections between lines and trunks; (2) junctors from line frames back to line frames for line-to-line connections; and (3) junctors between trunk frames for tandem traffic and other trunk-to-trunk connections. The number of line frames and trunk frames can be varied independently and the junctor group sizes adjusted according to the mix of inter- and intraoffice and tandem traffic. The network has been designed so that frames of four-wire switches can be used without modification of the central processor complex or its basic network control programs. Hence, the single basic system design can be adapted to local, toll, and tandem applications that, in the past, have required quite different system designs.

System organization

Outline of system plan. The basic concept of the No. 1 ESS—a single high-speed electronic central processor operating with a stored program to control the actions of the central office on a time-sharing basis—is illustrated in Fig. 1. Through the switching network, interconnections can be made between system lines and trunks and access provided to the various service circuits required in handling telephone calls; these include tone sources, signaling detectors, and ringing sources. All information processing is handled by a central processor consisting of central control and the temporary and semipermanent memories. The temporary memory is used for storage of the transient information required in processing calls such as the digits dialed by the subscriber, or the busy and idle states of lines and trunks. The con-

A new electronic switching system

Fig. 1. Central information processor with stored program.

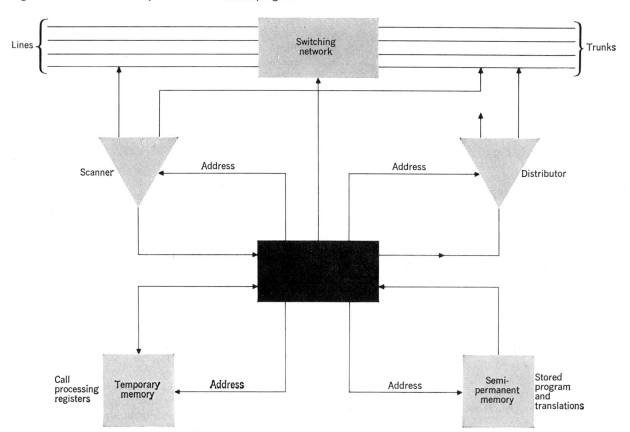

tents of the semipermanent memory, containing the stored program and translation information, do not change during the processing of a call. When the semipermanent information must be changed for any reason, the changes are made manually. The semipermanent memory also has the advantageous characteristic that its stored information cannot be erased by circuit malfunctions.

It is important to note that central control consists of wired logic for performing information-processing operations, organized on a word basis with a word length of 24 bits and operating on a basic cycle time of 5.5 μs. Since the telephone switching logic is also contained in the stored program, the hardware of the control complex is largely independent of the type of telephone service provided and the service treatments offered subscribers. Great flexibility is achieved in this manner, as the same equipment can be used with different programs to provide a variety of services.

Input information for the central processor is provided by scanners connected to various points in the system where information must be obtained; these include the lines, trunks, and signal receivers. The scanners are directed periodically to the lines to detect service requests, to the trunks to detect incoming calls, and to the signal receivers to detect dialed digits and other control data.

The distributor is the inverse of the scanner. It is connected to the various points in the system where actions

must be controlled by the central processor. Central control can address the distributor to a particular terminal where a flip-flop or other memory device can be set to start an action. At a later time, central control can address the distributor to terminate this action. The system handles this distributor action through two types of units: (1) the central pulse distributor, which is all electronic and is used for high-speed actions; and (2) the signal distributor, which uses a relay tree and is utilized for lower-speed actions such as the control of trunk relays.

To summarize, the facilities provided in the system are divided into four main categories:

1. Switching network, with its associated terminal circuits that perform the physical functions required in making connections, detecting, and producing signals.

2. Central processor, with its wired logic to perform basic information-processing functions.

3. Scanner and distributor, providing input and output communication for the central processor.

4. The stored program, containing instructions for performing all the switching tasks in ordered lists of instruction words.

Particular distinction must be made between the program and translation information contained in the semipermanent memory. The program is the lists of instructions for performing all of the service features. It is part of the basic design of the machine and is not influenced by the characteristics of the particular installation.

IEEE spectrum FEBRUARY 1965

Ordinarily, it will not be changed except for some significant change, either in its features or in the sequence in which actions are performed. The translation section contains the specific layout of facilities in the particular office; the association of subscriber directory numbers with the equipment location of their lines; the classes of service to be provided, such as individual and two-party, coin, extended area dialing, etc.; and specification of trunk routes, their location, and alternate routes to be used when available. This information must be changed periodically and means must be provided for making these changes on a routine basis.

Hardware. The equipment and apparatus of No. 1 ESS has been designed for large-volume manufacture at minimum cost. A volume of 1 million lines a year requires over 15 million ferreed crosspoints, 1½ million electronic circuit packages, 5 million transistors, 15 million diodes, etc. Such production rates call for high mechanization.

Equipment and apparatus should be adaptable to low-cost mechanized manufacture. Further, the high manufacturing volume justifies greater development effort and the creation of special devices and components. Thus, No. 1 ESS uses many items of apparatus developed for this particular application and whose design has been tailored for mass manufacture.

A good example of the ferreed switch used in the switching network is shown in Fig. 2.[4,5] It is manufactured as an 8 × 8 array of 64 crosspoints, with a minimum of individual handling of the crosspoints. The control coils are wound in simultaneous rows and columns from continuous lengths of wire.

Standardization and minimization of codes are other important steps to low-cost volume manufacture. In No. 1 ESS, strong efforts were made to standardize the hardware and achieve the necessary variability by program or translation methods. The network equipment is an example of equipment standardization. Only six codes of frames permit assembly of a switching network suitable for any local office. Two additional codes take care of four-wire networks for toll offices. The use of only two codes of transistors—the low-power 29A and the relatively higher power 20D—is an example of device standardization. The 29A is found in many logic circuits, audio amplifiers and oscillators, and in broad-band feedback amplifiers and regulators.

Standardization has also virtually eliminated wired options. Most electromechanical switching equipment makes liberal use of wired options to meet the variations of size and features of different installations; thus, the equipment is specially wired and tested at the factory. In No. 1 ESS, the factory makes a particular frame the same way each time, according to a fixed set of test requirements.

The need for special buildings is avoided through choice of seven-foot-high equipment design (instead of 11½ feet), which permits maintenance from the floor, without ladders. This also contributes to the objective of simplified installation and growth. To insure dependability and to permit reuse of existing buildings, air conditioning is not required for machine operability.

Power dependability has been enhanced through use of storage batteries. And by designing the equipment to operate over a ±10 per cent voltage variation, power equipment was simplified; and end cells, counter cells, and their associated switches eliminated.

Transmission received particular attention. All outgoing trunks include loop-compensation networks to improve return-loss characteristics. Tones are generated by precision transistor oscillators and are fed to lines and trunks out of precise balanced terminations. These and other similar measures, including careful control of noise, were taken in recognition of the role of the switching center in the maintenance and improvement of transmission objectives.

A No. 1 ESS office can be assembled from only 30 codes-of-equipment frames. Figure 3 shows two of the six frame codes used to assemble two-wire switching networks. These four-to-one concentration-line switch frames contain two stages of ferreed switches with their associated control circuits and scanners[6] to detect call originations.

Fig. 2. Ferreed switch used in the switching network.

Fig. 3. Line switching frames for four-to-one concentration ratio.

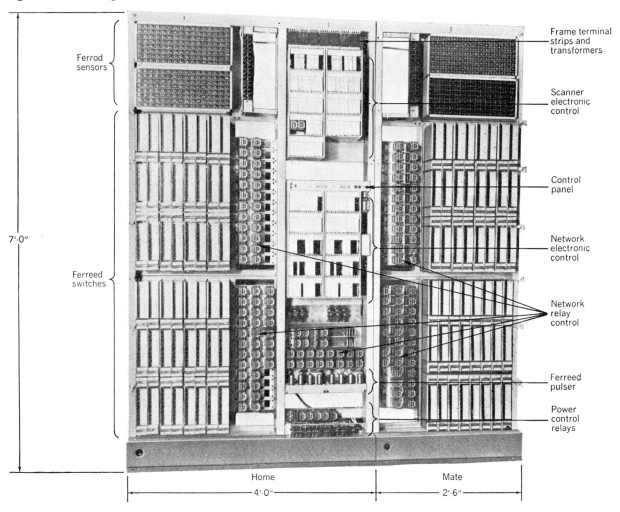

The duplicated network controllers in the four-to-one

III. Programs for Succasunna*

Type	Number of Programs	Number of Words
Operational		
Call	22	25 500
Administration	24	20 000
Special services	2	4 500
Subtotal	48	50 000
Maintenance		
Fault recognition	7	13 000
Diagnostics	7	14 500
Routine tests	11	12 400
Administration	12	12 100
Subtotal	37	52 000
Total	85	102 000

*Larger offices will require some additional programs with a maximum of about 150 000 words.

concentration-line switch frames serve both the home and mate frames. This allows the office to grow in steps of 512 lines, but spreads the controller cost across 1024 lines.

The central control shown in Fig. 4 comprises the logic portion of the system central processor. It includes approximately 2400 circuit packs, the majority of which contain low-level-logic circuits. This basic logic circuit, a diode-transistor AND–NOT gate, generates all logic functions and memory cells or flip-flops. Central control contains over 12 000 such gates.

The advent of nanosecond logic circuits has brought the circuit and equipment designer into closer cooperation than was previously necessary in relay switching systems. Wiring patterns and rules had to be developed to insure satisfactory switching speeds, circuit crosstalk protection, and a consistent manufactured product. Such requirements dictated dense packing of components.

A 23-bit bus system is used for data handling within the central control and this required an unconventional circuit pack organization. To provide uniform operation for all bits of a word and to meet timing requirements, no bus bit lead could exceed six feet in length. Apparatus for the various registers is distributed over several mounting plates. A particular register function also is distributed over several mounting plates, each bit occupying only a few circuit packs on each plate. This permits the assign-

Fig. 4. Central control utilizing functional logic unit.

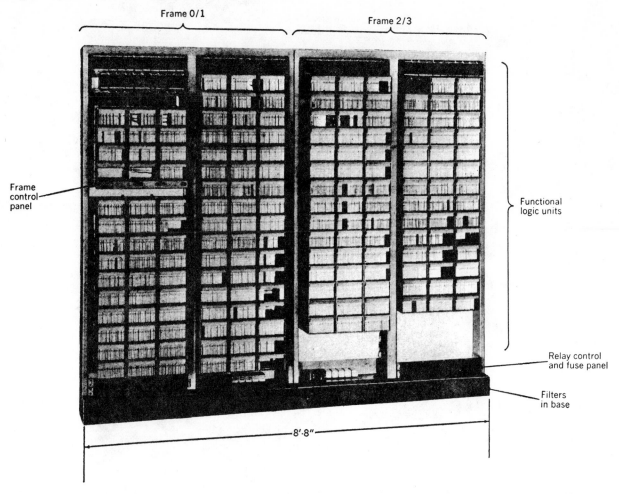

ment of the output gates of eight different registers associated with the same bus bit to the same circuit pack, thus minimizing bus lead length and simplifying flip-flop control leads and maintenance diagnosis.

The program store is the large, semipermanent memory for program and translation storage. It has a capacity of 131 072 words of 44 bits each, or 5.8×10^6 bits in all. The store shown in Fig. 5 consists of three frames. Two double-bay frames contain the twistor memory modules,[7] access circuits, and other related circuits, while the single-bay frame at the right contains circuits associated primarily with readout. Because of the high density of the memory modules, their frames are the heaviest in No. 1 ESS, with a weight of approximately 1900 pounds each.

The memory modules are arranged in a square 4×4 array to permit the 256×256 coordinate access wiring to be made on the rear with short jumpers between modules. Readout connections between modules are also relatively short with this arrangement. Readout connections are made on the front side of the store with cable running vertically in shielded ducts between the columns of modulus and horizontally in ducts between the first and second, and third and fourth rows of modules. Cables are further protected from noise pickups by use of close-

twisted pairs and by limiting to two inches the unshielded length of leads that connect to the twistor tapes.

Memory modules are mounted on the frame with three-point suspension to avoid distortion as a result of warping or twisting of the frame during shipping and installation.

Sliding covers are provided in front of the memory modules to protect memory cards from accidental damage. Each cover over a module containing program information is locked in place with a screw as a guard against accidentally disturbing the office program during translation changes.

Programs. As mentioned previously, the central processor is a real-time stored-program-control system. The stored programs are ordered sets of instructions to the processor on how to control a particular function, either internally or in cooperation with the peripheral equipment. One group—call programs—provides the solution to any problem a customer can present to the system through his telephone set, either directly or through some other switching system. An assembly of call programs must establish a tailor-made connection according to the demands of the customer.

When needed by an executive program, the processor can use multiprogramming, with the programs called in to determine what task must be performed at particular

A new electronic switching system

Fig. 5. Program store (semipermanent memory).

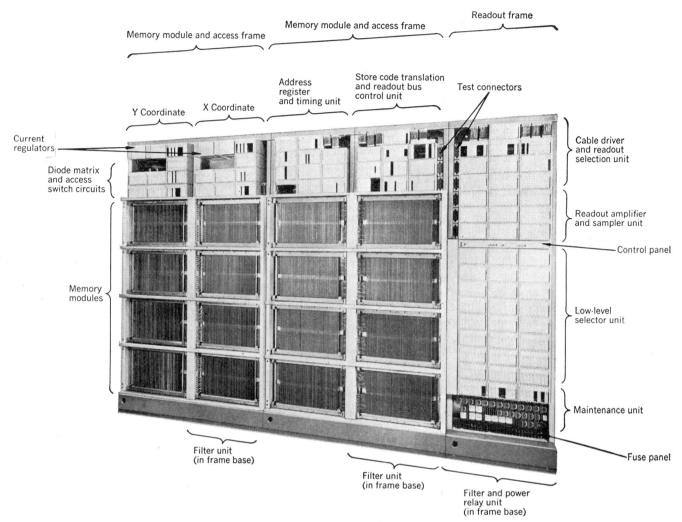

states of a call. Small delays of up to a tenth of a second in processing a call are unnoticed by customers. However, some input data, say dialing information, must be sensed and processed as it occurs in real time since any delay may cause an error. Processing of such data is called an undeferrable task and is handled by interrupting other programs if necessary at predetermined intervals. Other interruptions are used for maintenance. Call programs are a part of the operational group that includes several programs for general administration, traffic measuring, and some special services.

In addition to the operational programs, there are numerous maintenance programs to insure system dependability. More than half of the overall total instructions are for these maintenance programs. Table III gives the size of several programs by groups for the first office, installed at Succasunna, N.J.

Programs for a large number of different offices can be evolved from one of several approaches. A generic program, which is the same for each office, with detailed differences listed in a parameter table, is the approach used in No. 1 ESS. The generic program includes all features for a large number of offices, covering sizes from 2 000 to 65 000 lines and means for handling growth and changing traffic conditions. This approach simplifies record keeping, because only the parameter tables that specify present size and operating conditions are unique to each office. Additional data characterizing a particular office are also found in translation tables in the program store. Typically, 18 different sets of translations are required in each office. These include directory number to equipment number translations for lines and trunks, class of service, and special treatment for lines and trunks.

In the future, economics may dictate the need for several generic programs—for instance, one for small offices, one for large offices, one for four-wire offices, and perhaps some combination of these.

The development and preparation of programs for the system require the use of several utility programs written for a general-purpose digital computer. These programs are used to convert the language of the programmer to the language of the machine, to assemble and compile the individual pieces of call and maintenance programs, and to load information onto a tape which finally controls the writing of the magnets on the twistor cards. Additional programs are used to assemble, compile, and load parameters and translations.

Dependability

Objectives. Dependability, in a telephone office, is limited only by the state of the technology. Certainly a new system must at least be comparable to existing offices, which means outages of no more than a few minutes in 40 years. Heretofore, no large electronic machines have been able to approach this degree of dependability. In fact, the required dependability represented one of the major challenges of the No. 1 ESS development. Since No. 1 ESS is a large digital information processor, it is a cousin of the general-purpose digital computer. However, the required dependability dictated that No. 1 ESS be a system of a very different kind, with a much higher level of redundancy.

Comparison. The large size of No. 1 ESS and the unique dependability requirement implies that No. 1 ESS is a new kind of information processor, a kind that has never been developed before. One way of contrasting No. 1 ESS with a general-purpose computer is to compare the relative hazards of a machine data-processing error and a total machine failure. In a general-purpose computer, a machine stoppage is a nuisance; the problem must be rerun, but a data-processing error could be called a disaster because the results come out wrong. In No. 1 ESS, it is the other way around. A data-processing error may cause a particular call to be mishandled. This is a nuisance, particularly to the customer whose call must be redialed. A total machine failure, however, in a telephone office means no telephone service during the outage and the magnitude of such a disaster need not be argued. The key point is that the dependability demands on No. 1 ESS are both unusually severe and quite different from those on the general-purpose computer.

Duplication. Since some failures of individual components are bound to occur over decades of system service, duplication is essential. Every major system unit required to maintain service must be provided in duplicate. Not only must there be duplication but, to minimize exposure to system failure due to multiple troubles, troubles must be found and corrected quickly. This means that all units must be continually monitored so that trouble in the stand-by unit can be found just as quickly as in the unit giving service; in addition, both detection of troubles and switching of service when units fail must be automatic.[8]

Repair. When a trouble occurs in an operational machine, telephone actions are interrupted as briefly as possible. Then, on a less urgent basis, the defective unit is diagnosed by the system itself and the results printed on the maintenance teletypewriter.

Where offices are unattended during at least part of the day, alarms and a remote teletypewriter are provided at a location where 24-hour attendance is available.

Maintenance programs. As shown in Table III, more than half of the stored instructions are used for maintenance programs. These programs must provide the solution to any problem generated by the system's hardware. Some of these programs, in conjunction with logic wired into the hardware, detect and report faults and troubles; others control routine tests, diagnose troubles, and control emergency actions to insure a satisfactorily operating system, either by eliminating faulty subsystems or by reorganizing usable subsystems into a new operating combination. The classes of maintenance programs are arranged in a hierarchy of interrupt levels. When an error or a trouble is detected, the processor is forced to stop what it is doing; make a record in memory of where it is in the program and of all pertinent data; and, after the proper maintenance action is taken, retrieve the temporarily stored information and restore itself to normal operation. In the hierarchy, a higher class can interrupt any lower class of maintenance or operating program. Operational programs are at the lowest levels.

Status

The first set of No. 1 ESS equipment manufactured by Western Electric was installed as a laboratory model and has served as a hardware and program development vehicle since early 1963. The next system was installed at Succasunna in late 1963. It has undergone extensive testing and provided additional machine capacity for program development. This first regular office at Succasunna will be put into service early this year. Other two-wire installations still being tested are located in Chase, Md., and New York City. Installations have been started at other locations. In addition to these two-wire offices, several four-wire offices are being installed.

No. 1 ESS is a large undertaking, absorbing the efforts of many hundreds of people. Space limitations, however, preclude a listing of all who contributed in an important way. Even listing the numerous organizations within the Bell Laboratories would be difficult since this would exclude the many people in the Western Electric Company, the American Telephone and Telegraph Company, and the operating companies who have contributed in important ways.

REFERENCES

1. Malthaner, W. A., and Vaughan, H. E., "An Automatic Telephone System Employing Magnetic Drum Memory," *Proc. IRE*, vol. 41, Oct. 1953, pp. 1341–1347.

2. Keister, W., Ketchledge, R. W., and Lovell, C. A., *Proc. IEE*, vol. 107, pt. B, suppl. no. 20, 1960.

3. *Bell System Tech. J.*, vol. 43, no. 5, pts. 1 and 2, Sept. 1964.

4. Feiner, A., "The Ferreed," *Ibid.*, Jan. 1964, p. 1.

5. Feiner, A., Lovell, C. A., Lowry, T. N., and Ridinger, P. G., "The Ferreed—A New Switching Device," *Ibid.*, vol. 39, Jan. 1960, p. 1.

6. Freimanis, L., Guercio, A. M., and May, H. F., "No. 1 ESS Scanner, Signal Distributor and Central Pulse Distributor," *Ibid.*, vol. 43, Sept. 1964, p. 2255.

7. Stammerjohn, L. W., "An Evaluation of the Performance of the Permanent Magnet Twistor Memory," *Proc. Internat'l Conf. Nonlinear Magnetics*, Apr. 1964.

8. Downing, R. W., Nowak, J. S., and Tuomenoksa, L. S., "No. 1 ESS Maintenance Plan," *Bell System Tech. J.*, vol. 43, Sept. 1964, p. 1961.

A new electronic switching system

Supplementary Bibliography for Paper 1

NO. 1 ESS

SYSTEM GENERAL

BELL LABORATORIES RECORD - V 43 NO. 6 - JUNE 1965 PP194-280)
(ENTIRE ISSUE)

NEW ELECTRONIC SWITCHING SYSTEM WILL OFFER A VARIETY OF SERVICES
(ESS NO. 1)
BELL LAB REC 42. 379 (NOV 1964)

FULL-SCALE ELECTRONIC CENTRAL OFFICE PLANNED FOR NEW JERSEY
(ESS NO. 1)
BELL LAB REC 40. 38-30 (JAN 1962)

NO. 1 ELECTRONIC SWITCHING SYSTEM
KETCHLEDGE RW
IEEE TRANS COMMUN TECHNOL 13. 38-41 (MAR 1965)
INT SYMP GLOBAL COMMUN, 1964 PROC. P47 (T/I63D)

TRANSMISSION ASPECTS OF NO. 1 ESS
FEINER A
IEE CONF SWITCHING TECHNIQUES FOR TELECOMMUN NETWORKS APR 1969
CONF PUBL NO 52. P471-4

SERVICES AND FEATURES

ELECTRONIC SWITCHING SYSTEM FOR AUTOVON (ESS NO. 1)
BENSON GR + JACOBY JZ + SELLERS GA
IEEE COMMUN CONF. 1966 DIGEST P74

ON-LINE RETROFITTING OF ELECTRONIC SWITCHING SYSTEMS (NO. 1 ESS)
HASS RJ
IEEE TRANS COMMUN TECHNOL 17: 99-103 (APR 1969)

AMA FOR NO. 1 ESS
WICKHAM TF + NOLAN NS
BELL LAB REC 44. 271-6 (SEP 1966)

TRUNK AND LINE TESTING FOR NO. 1 ESS
BESMAN AI + BLCOM S
BELL LAB REC 369-72 (DEC 1967)

SUBSYSTEMS, COMPONENTS AND HARDWARE

REOPTIMIZATION OF CALL STORES FOR NO. 1 ESS
IRLAND EA
IEE CONF SWITCHING TECHNIQUES FOR TELECOMMUN NETWORKS APR 1969
CONF PUBL NO 52. P467-70

NEW METHOD OF DESIGNING LOW-LEVEL, HIGH-SPEED SEMICONDUCTOR

LOGIC CIRCUITS (ESS NO. 1)
CAGLE WB + CHEN WH
IRE WESCON CONV REC PART 2. 3-9 (1957)

DEVELOPMENT OF ESS MOLDED COIL-FORM
ESTES PM
WESTERN ELEC ENG 9 NO 4. 36-40 (OCT 1965)

MANUFACTURE OF NO. 1 ESS
ZWEIER P
INT CONF ELECTRON SWITCHING, 1966 PROC. PARIS, EDITION CHIRON.
P1319-34

COMPUTERIZED TESTING OF NO. 1 ESS NETWORK FRAMES ON THE
MANUFACTURING FLOOR.
GARDNER RA
WESTERN ELEC ENG 19: 11 (OCT 1975)

SOFTWARE

PATROL SURVEYS TRAFFIC FOR NO. 1 ESS OFFICES. (TIME
SHARED COMPUTER PROGRAMS)
HALL MS + PATTI GP
BELL LABS REC 51: 72-7 (1963)

GETTING THE MOST OUT OF STORED PROGRAM CONTROL. (NO. 1
ESS TSPS NO. 1)
POTTER RL
BELL LAB REC 51: 181-5 (L973)

SOFTWARE PROTECTION IN NO. 1 ESS
ALMQUIST RP + HAAS R J + HAGERMAN JR + PETERSON RW
+ STEVENS SL
P565-9 OF INT SWITCHING SYMP, MIT, 1972 (E173 I597)

DEVELOPMENT HISTORY OF NO. 1 ESS - SOFTWARE
VAUGHAN HE
IEE CONF SWITCHING TECHNIQUES FOR TELECOMMUN NETWORKS APR 1969
CONF PUBL NO 52. P475-8

GENERIC PROGRAMS FOR NO. 1 ESS
PHILLIPS SJ
BELL LAB REC 47: 210-14 (JUL 1969)

TRANSLATIONS AND RECENT-CHANGE INFORMATION IN NO. 1 ESS
CARRAN JH
BELL LAB REC 45. 83-6 (MAR 1967)

COMPUTER PROGRAM FOR NO. 1 ESS JUNCTOR ASSIGNMENTS
GIBSON TA + GRANTGES RF
BELL LAB REC 44. 192-6 (1966)

PERFORMANCE AND FIELD EXPERIENCES

PHILADELPHIA STORY.
ARNOLD D
BELL TEL MAG 52(3): 2-5 (1973)

INCREMENTAL CUTOVER OF A LARGE NO. 1 ESS.
GOODRICH EE
P61-5 OF IEEE FALL ELECTRONIC CONF, 1971 (E4 I095,
150841)

EMERGENCY ACTION FOR NO. 1 ESS. (PERIODIC AND AUTOMATIC
INVENTORY OF CRITICAL PORTIONS OF THE MEMORY)
NOWAK JS
BELL LAB REC 49: 176-9 (1971)

NO. 1 ESS PROCESSORS: HOW DEPENDABLE HAVE THEY BEEN.
CLEMENT GF + JONES WC + WATTERS RJ
BELL LAB REC 52: 21-5 (1974)

NO. 1 ESS SERVICE EXPERIENCE - HARDWARE.
STAEHLER RE
IEE CONF SWITCHING TECHNIQUES FOR TELECOMMUN NETWORKS APR 1969
CONF PUBL NO 52. P463-6

EARLY NO. 1 ESS FIELD EXPERIENCES. PART 1. TWO-WIRE SYSTEM
FOR COMMERCIAL APPLICATIONS.
HAUGK G
IEEE TRANS COMMUN TECHNOL 15. 744-50 (DEC 1967)

NO. 1 ESS SERVICE EXPERIENCE - SOFTWARE.
JOHANNESEN JD
IEE CONF SWITCHING TECHNIQUES FOR TELECOMMUN NETWORKS APR 1969
CONF PUBL NO 52. P459-62

SERVICE EXPERIENCE WITH NO. 1 ESS EQUIPMENT
KETCHLEDGE RW
INT CONF ELECTRON SWITCHING, 1966 PROC. PARIS, EDITION CHIRON.
P712-16

EARLY NO. 1 ESS FIELD EXPERIENCES. PART 2. FOUR-WIRE SYSTEM
FOR GOVERNMENT AND MILITARY APPLICATIONS
SECKLER HN
IEEE TRANS COMMUN TECHNOL 15. 751-4 (DEC 1967)

Paper 2

NO. 1 ESS LOCAL/TOLL/TANDEM

J. D. Johannesen
Bell Telephone Laboratories Inc.
Naperville, Illinois, USA

ABSTRACT

Though initially designed for local switching,
No. 1 ESS has been modified to provide switching
in a trunk-only environment. Primary application for this design will be in metropolitan
areas for inter-end office switching. In
addition, software and hardware features are
being developed which will enable the No. 1 ESS
machine to serve a moderately sized local
switching function (up to approximately 25,000
lines) with toll switching (1,000 to 2,000
intertoll trunks). This application results in
savings by the elimination of one switching
machine. Early versions of this machine will
use 2-wire networks for toll switching and
primary application will be in sparse areas
where the Class 5 and control switch point
functions are combined.

This paper will describe the new software and
hardware features required for the above
applications. Included is a description of
the new network configuration whose capacity
is approximately 250,000 switched CCS and
30,000 terminals.

INTRODUCTION

The latest generic program for No. 1 ESS called
Centrex 7 will permit No. 1 ESS machines to provide a vehicle for modern switching in the toll
network. This will extend the range of application of a 2-wire No. 1 ESS from local and small
local/tandem operation to local/toll/tandem and
large toll/tandem operation. See Table A for
definitions of terms. The toll features in this
generic provide most Class 4 functions. This
one generic program will cover all applications.
Local and local/toll/tandem offices will use
1024-trunk link networks (TLNs). Large tandem,

toll, or toll/tandem offices will use a new
2048-TLN configuration; no line link networks
will be required in the office for these applications.

In the design of No. 1 ESS, particular attention
was paid to the transmission characteristics of
the network. Consequently, the transmission is
toll grade quality. However, in tandem/toll
operation, intertoll-to-intertoll switching and
intertoll-to-toll connecting switching are required and balance considerations must be met.
No. 1 ESS 2-wire can meet tighter requirements
and, in fact, uses a simpler balancing procedure
than crossbar-tandem (XBT) machines. This procedure is described in more detail in a later
section.

Tandem features for No. 1 ESS were provided with
the first Centrex 1 program installed in the
Philadelphia Locust Street office in 1968.
Several other early applications as replacements
for step-by-step tandems were installed in
Nashville and Memphis, Tennessee, and in Atlanta,
Georgia. Due to program design restrictions, at
least one line link network had to be installed
for these tandem applications. Other features
such as incoming trunk overload protection,
network management features, traffic features,
and trunk maintenance features were either not
available or not suitable for offices with
15,000 to 30,000 trunks. The features required
for tandem and toll operation are now in Centrex
7 and will be described in more detail.

The early toll applications of No. 1 ESS, with
one exception, will be small local/toll machines.
In 1974, four such machines will begin operation
in Duluth, Minnesota, Greenville, Mississippi,
Wichita Falls, Texas, and Lake Charles,
Louisiana. These offices will serve local and
Class 4 toll traffic at a size and cost less
than their electromechanical alternatives.
These small machines require only 1024-TLNs and
the toll program features of Centrex 7.

This discussion concentrates on the large trunk-
only machines. The program features, the call-
carrying capacity, the 2048 network, and the
balancing procedures are described. Finally, a
discussion of space savings over electromechanical systems now in use is given.

Reprinted with permission from *1974 Int. Switching Symp. Rec.*, Sept. 9-13, 1974, pp. 526/1-526/4.

SOFTWARE FEATURES FOR LOCAL AND TOLL

Most program features incorporated into No. 1 ESS prior to the Centrex 6 generic program were subscriber line oriented. In order to permit operation of No. 1 ESS as a toll or tandem office, additional features such as network management controls and centralized automatic message account (CAMA) with automatic and operator number identification (ANI and ONI) of the calling number, were required. The capability to handle the additional dialing codes required in a toll center (operator and plant test codes) was also needed. Operator signalling, such as, rering to and from the toll network and compatibility with residual operator traffic from TSPS and traffic measurements, such as, receiver attachment delay, which is the equivalent of the dial pulse speed test in local offices, were not previously available. These features are now incorporated into the program.

To expand on one of these, network management controls will be able to implement trunk group controls after receiving dynamic overload control (DOC) signals from higher level offices or commands from a teletypewriter. Originating traffic to congested points on the network is controlled at the source by examining the dialed digits. This is called code blocking. Code blocking, initiated by a TTY request may be performed on the basis of a numbering plan area (NPA) and office code in the home NPA, an NPA office code combination, or on a 7- or 10-digit directory number. A maximum of 31 such combinations may be in effect at any one time. Included is the ability to generate DOC signals to subtending offices and to provide displays, data, and controls useful in reducing tandem and toll network congestion.

Improved trunk maintenance features such as, transmission test lines for checking signalling, noise, and echo suppressors have been added. Provision has also been made to move the supplementary trunk test frames a maximum of 1500 cable feet from the ESS office. This will allow trunk maintenance activity to be centralized. Supplementary trunk test frames are trunk test positions which are added to the office when the number of trunks in the office exceeds the testing capability of the master control center.

The remote office test line (ROTL) is an important maintenance feature which allows the office to receive trunk maintenance requests from a centralized automatic reporting on trunks (CAROT) or similar test center. Each ROTL in the office provides a terminating appearance which can be reached through the normal direct distance dialing (DDD) network. Once terminated, the test center can request that automatic transmission tests be conducted over any trunk outgoing from the ROTL office to the selected transmission test line at the trunk's incoming end. The test center can also remotely condition (make busy/make idle) outgoing or 2-way trunks under certain central office-imposed restrictions and may request trunk and trunk group status. Each ROTL frame is capable of routinely testing up to 6000 outgoing and 2-way trunks on an 8-hours-a-day, 5-days-a-week basis. The ROTL feature also allows installation of a program controlled trunk interrogator for doing ROTL transmission tests by manual request from a TTY or test position.

CALL CARRYING CAPACITY

Fig. 1 shows the increase in call carrying capacity that has been made by program changes. The upper and lower bounds shown represent the achievable ranges. The data representing the SP office capacities is from a survey of 60 existing central offices. The capacity spread is due to different traffic mixes between the sample offices, i.e., all call types are not equal in real time consumed. The solid line represents the average peak call carrying capacity of these offices. Note that the average capacity has increased and has more than made up for the loss of real time due to the introduction of new features each year.

Fig. 1 also shows the increase in call carrying capacity for tandem calls. Tandem features were first introduced into No. 1 ESS in 1968 with the first Centrex 1 generic program. The peak through-switched busy hour calls (BHC) for an all multifrequency (MF) tandem office is 102,000 in the Centrex 7 generic program. This corresponds to 112,000 attempts per hour or approximately 83% of the capacity of a No. 4A crossbar (4AXB) equipped with an electronic translator system (ETS). Offices with mixes of multifrequency, revertive, and dial pulse traffic will vary from this value.

Prior to the Centrex 5 program, the call carrying capacity of No. 1 ESS was limited by the real time capacity of the central control. With the issuing of the Centrex 5 generic program, the signal processor, which is the input/output device for large offices, began to be the capacity limiting factor in certain cases. This is largely dependent on office size and signalling mix. As the equipment to be scanned in the office is increased, more overhead is required for scanning and, thus, less real time is left for call processing.

Table B shows the SP capacity given the busy attempt rate per incoming trunk and signalling type. The number in parentheses indicates the corresponding maximum number of equipped terminals that can be accommodated for the various attempt rates using the SP-CTX-7 generic program equipped with 2048-TLNs.

2048 TRUNK LINK NETWORK

With recent improvements in real time processor capacity, the network capacity limit is being approached for the current fifteen 1024-TLN network configuration in a nonlocal office. Two methods could be employed to increase network capacity. One method would be to increase the maximum number of 1024-TLNs from 15 to 32. The second method would be to retain the limit of 15 and substitute 2048-TLNs. The development effort required for extending the 1024-TLN limit to 32 would have been much greater than the work required for the 2048-TLN network. Thus, program and hardware features for the 2048-TLN will be provided in Centrex 7 for offices requiring the greater network capacity. The 1024-TLN features will be retained in the program for those smaller offices which either already have 1024-TLNs or do not require the increased network capacity. Note that for both 1024- and 2048-TLN networks the number of TLNs is limited to 15 at this time.

The 2048-TLN is essentially two 1024-TLNs with a modified B-link wiring pattern. Thus, it has eight trunk switch frames (TSFs) and eight junctor switch frames (JSFs) in contrast to four TSFs and four JSFs in a 1:1 concentration ratio 1024-TLN. The 2048-TLN is only available in a 1:1 concentration ratio.

The switched CCS capacity of fifteen 2048-TLNs is 6944 erlangs when equipped 8-out-of-8 and 7361 erlangs when equipped 6-out-of-8. These capacities correspond to an average of .458 erlangs per equipped terminal and .647 erlangs per equipped terminal, respectively. The number of terminals in the first case is 30,720 and in the second case is 23,040. This can be compared with the switched capacity of fifteen 1024-TLNs which is 3888 erlangs when equipped 8-out-of-8 and 4166 erlangs when equipped 6-out-of-8.

TRANSMISSION BALANCE

When 2-wire switching systems are used for toll applications, special adjustments referred to as office balance are required to keep the reflected echo at the switch point within acceptable levels. Referring to Fig. 2, the impedance of the balancing network (Z_a) of the 2- to 4-wire terminating set must closely match that presented at the 2-wire point (Z_b). The impedance of the 2-wire point consists of a relatively fixed component at the so-called "point of good impedance" in series with the impedance of the cabling used in the switch path. This latter impedance is variable within the switching office.

The approach used in electromechanical systems is to build out all switched paths so that they are equivalent to the longest path in the office. An equivalent impedance in the balancing network referred to as the office network build out (NBO) is provided. There are several disadvantages associated with this approach. Except for the few trunks which have longer path lengths, all other trunks generally require adjustment to make their path lengths comparable to the longest lengths. If the office experiences unanticipated growth, causing the longest path length to increase significantly, all trunks require rebalancing to become equivalent to the new longer lengths.

The procedure used for No. 1 ESS is significantly different. It consists of providing a reference trunk of fixed path length; for No. 1 ESS the fixed path length is 400 feet. The office is balanced by connecting all of the terminating sets to the reference trunk and adjusting variable elements within the balancing network to obtain optimum balance. In conjunction with this, the path lengths of all trunks are controlled so that their deviation from the optimum 400-foot length will allow the overall balance to stay within acceptable limits. The deviation allowed is approximately 1000 feet.

With this procedure, the only trunks requiring adjustments are those intertoll trunks containing the 2- to 4-wire terminating sets. In general, toll connecting trunks require no special treatment comparable to the electrical build out required by the former approach. More importantly, even though the office may experience unanticipated growth, rebalancing of the previously balanced trunks would not be required since the plan does not rely on an office NBO.

This procedure is made possible by the dense equipment packaging associated with electronic systems. This packaging permits more equipment to be reached by shorter lengths of cabling. The larger space requirements of the older electromechanical systems would not permit the cabling length deviations to be maintained within such a close tolerance.

In addition to these functional differences, other aspects of the electronic systems help to reduce the effort associated with the office balance. Improperly applied hardware wiring options, perhaps the most common source of difficulty in obtaining good balance, are largely eliminated in the electronic systems. The options are instead being provided by the stored program.

SPACE

The small size of ferreed and remreed networks provides significant savings in floor space. Estimated floor space requirements are compared in Fig. 3 for a No. 4A crossbar, a crossbar tandem, and No. 1 ESS. These curves do not include space for power or transmission facilities but do include all frames associated with the switching machine and the trunk circuit frames. The data for the 4AXB and the crossbar tandem were obtained from installed offices. The discontinuity in the crossbar tandem curve occurs when a second unit is paired with the first. Two curves are given for No. 1 ESS, one for the case where all the incoming and outgoing trunks are 2-wire facilities, the other where all incoming and outgoing trunks are 4-wire facilities. In both cases, the network fabric is 2-wire. Those offices having a mix of 2- and 4-wire facilities fall between these bounds. The No. 1 ESS curves shown are based on ferreed TLNs since remreed TLNs were not available for the first three large tandem offices ordered. The application of remreed TLNs to offices of this type will provide significant additional savings in floor space.

SUMMARY

Program and hardware features available in the Centrex 7 program have extended the field of application of No. 1 ESS to large tandem and toll applications. Although No. 1 ESS can only handle 83% of the maximum switched traffic handled by 4A crossbar, this capacity is enough for many applications and provides, in addition, cost and space savings.

Additional toll, tandem, and maintenance features will be added to No. 1 ESS, as in the past, on a yearly basis. Other items, such as, cost reduction to trunks, addition of CCIS, and a 4-wire TLN are also under consideration. It is not expected that the call handling capacity of No. 1 ESS will increase markedly over its present value. However, the use of the 1A Processor[1] in No. 1 ESS will increase the call handling capacity and, hence, further extend the capabilities of the office.

At the time of writing this paper, the first large tandem is being installed in Williamsburg in Brooklyn, New York. This office has nine ferreed 2048-TLNs and will serve as a tandem office with 7600 incoming trunks and 7600 outgoing trunks, all 2-wire. It is scheduled for service by the third quarter of 1974.

Several additional large tandem offices are planned, including the Canal Street office in Chicago and the Jackson Street office in Houston. These are expected to be placed into service in the first quarter of 1975.

REFERENCES

[1] R. E. Staehler and T. S. Greenwood, "1A Processor - Development and Status," International Switching Symposium, Munich, Germany, September, 1974.

Table A   Definitions

LOCAL OFFICE   Connects subscriber's line
                      to another subscriber's
                      line or any trunk (Class 5)

TOLL OFFICE   Connects two trunks, one
                      of which is an intertoll
                      trunk (Class 4 or above)

TANDEM OFFICE   Connects two trunks,
                      neither of which is an
                      intertoll trunk

TABLE B SP CAPACITY

ATTEMPTS/INCOMING TRUNK/HR	9	12	15
INCOMING TRAFFIC MIX:			
50% MF/50% RP Peak Busy Hours Att.	99,000	112,400	123,000
(Equipped Term.)	(23,000)	(23,000)	(17,400)
50% MF/50% DP Peak Busy Hour Att.	79,600	91,000	99,000
(Equipped Term.)	(18,300)	(15,800)	(13,900)

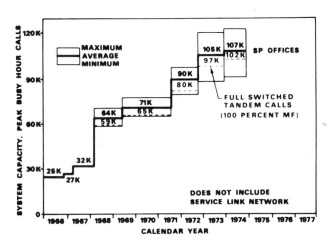

Fig.1   Call Carrying Capacity

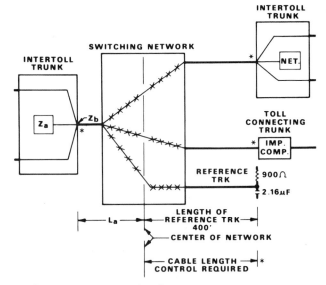

Denotes Point of Good Impedance

Fig.2   No. 1 ESS Toll/Tandem Office Balance

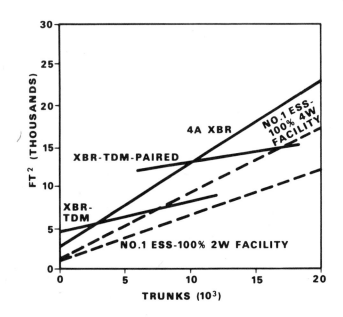

Fig.3   Tandem System Floor Space Comparison

ISS 74

16

Paper 3

No. 1 Electronic Switching System with Signal Processor and Service Link Network (No. 1 ESS)

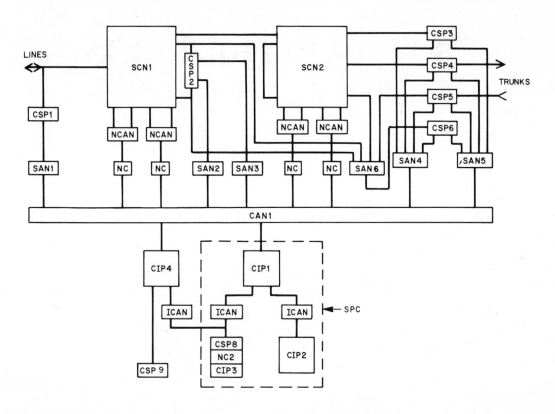

SCN1	=LINE LINK NETWORK		CAN 1	=PERIPHERAL BUS
SCN2	=TRUNK LINK NETWORK		NC	=NETWORK CONTROLLER
CIP1	=CENTRAL CONTROL		NC2	=NETWORK MAP
CIP2	=PROGRAM STORE		SAN1	=LINE SCANNER
CIP3	=TRANSLATION STORE		SAN2	=JUNCTOR SCANNER
CIP4	=SIGNAL PROCESSOR		SAN3	=JUNCTOR SIGNAL DISTRIBUTOR
CSP1	=LINE CIRCUIT		SAN4	=TRUNK SCANNER
CSP2	=JUNCTOR CIRCUIT		SAN5	=TRUNK SIGNAL DISTRIBUTOR
CSP3	=CUSTOMER DIAL PULSE RECEIVER		SAN6	=SERVICE LINK NETWORK
CSP4	=OUTGOING TRUNK CIRCUIT		SPC	=CENTRAL PROCESSOR
CSP5	=INCOMING TRUNK CIRCUIT			
CSP6	=TRANSMITTER OR RECEIVER CIRCUIT			
CSP7	=CALL STORE			
CSP8	=CALL STORE			
CSP9	=SIGNAL PROCESSOR CALL STORE			

A status report on this electronic switching system reveals that expansion of the number of offices, growth of call-handling capacity per office, institution of new services, improvements for easier maintenance, and reduction of costs characterize its recent history.

What's New in No. 1 ESS

John D. Johannesen and Robert E. Staehler

THE ELECTRONIC SWITCHING SYSTEM, No. 1 ESS, designed for medium-to-large telephone offices, has come a long way since the first office started service at Succasunna, New Jersey, on May 30, 1965. Six years later, more than 150 No. 1 ESS offices have cumulatively logged more than 2 million hours of operation. And the rate at which new offices are installed is steadily increasing.

Rapid expansion is only part of the No. 1 ESS story. Call-handling capacity of individual offices has increased substantially. New services have been added: Centrex, PBX Automatic Identified Outward Dialing (AIOD), no-deposit dial-tone-first coin service, multiparty service, international dialing. Finally, maintenance has been made easier and costs have been reduced.

Much of the increased capacity of electronic offices is due to the addition of a signal processing unit to the basic central processing unit to take over simple repetitive tasks (see *The No. 1 ESS Signal Processor*, RECORD, *April 1969*). In the early years of No. 1 ESS, most of the offices were of modest size, with about 30,000 to 40,000 call-per-hour capacity. These offices, therefore, required only the basic No. 1 ESS processing unit and are referred to as the central control (CC) type of office. Large metropolitan areas require large offices, however. Toward this end—to provide greater size and traffic capacity—a signal processor addition to the basic central processing unit was designed. New York's Pennsylvania 6 office in 1968 became the first of the signal processor (SP) type; since then, most of the offices installed have been SP offices. The largest to date is the 633-frame Atlantic office in Pittsburgh, which serves Pittsburgh Plate Glass Co. and U. S. Steel Corp.

A prime advantage of a stored-program switching system like No. 1 ESS is that new features can be added merely by modifying the program. The hardware additions that would be necessary in a comparable electromechanical system are minimized and in many cases avoided entirely. A corollary advantage is that the feature becomes avail-

Representative of the significant improvements in the No. 1 electronic switching system is the Atlantic office in Pittsburgh, which, with 633 frames, constitutes the largest of the ESS offices.

able almost immediately after the stored program has been developed; there is no lead time for manufacturing as with electromechanical switching systems. The impact of these advantages is evident in the number and diversity of the new No. 1 ESS services.

Centrex service, for example, now allows No. 1 ESS business customers to connect directly with the direct distance dialing network without the help of an attendant, who can thus spend her time more efficiently on those calls that do require assistance. Unlike standard PBX service, Centrex service permits direct inward dialing, direct outward dialing, and automatic message accounting without operator assistance. Moreover, a minimum of equipment is required on the customer's premises.

Centrex service was first offered in conjunction with ESS in Philadelphia's Locust office in 1968 (see *Centrex Service in No. 1 ESS, RECORD, No-*

vember 1968). This first installation served two groups of business customers with 1000 lines and four consoles. The largest ESS Centrex office now in service is in the Pentagon in Washington, with 17,000 lines and 74 consoles. The Pentagon ESS office is the only one to serve a single large Centrex group exclusively, with no "plain old telephone service", or POTS, customers.

With ESS-Centrex operation the attendant console connects to the ESS via a data link between the central office and the customer's premises. Through this link, the customer's console transmits information regarding its state to the central office or requests action from the system. In the other direction, the central office sends data for controlling the lamp display.

A recent variation of the basic ESS-Centrex service is the Common-Controlled Switching Arrangement (CCSA), which permits geographically dispersed organizations to connect their locations

the Locust office in Philadelphia, craftsman Gerald W. Curran ─usts relay and associated loop circuits of the Centrex at-─dant trunk circuit. In 1968, the Locust office became the first ─offer No. 1 ESS Centrex service, which provides direct dialing

facilities and automatic message accounting without an attendant's help, unlike standard PBX service. A further advantage is that Centrex requires minimal equipment on the customer's premises—only a "customer-premises unit" and a console.

via a switched private-line network with such features as a common numbering plan, alternate routing, and off-network access. The newest Centrex programs for No. 1 ESS provide the means for controlling POTS, Centrex, and CCSA in the same office.

The new PBX Automatic Identified Outward Dialing (AIOD) service provides a separate data path from a business customer's premises back to the central office so that the central office can record which extension is using a particular trunk at a given time.

For this AIOD service, an Automatic Number Identification (ANI) unit on the customer's premises detects and transmits the station number—that is, the extension of the calling party—over a data link to the AIOD equipment in the central office. Because No. 1 ESS is already designed to collect and process data on a time-shared basis, only a minimal amount of additional hardware is required. The cost of adding AIOD, therefore, is as little as ¼ that of adding this feature to the corresponding electromechanical system. The initial AIOD office was at Stockton, California. It was cut over on April 4, 1971.

The new dial-tone-first feature was developed to enable coin-telephone customers to dial certain calls without depositing a coin (see *No Dime Needed*, RECORD, *October 1969*). These include calls to the operator, toll calls costing more than ten cents, person-to-person calls, collect calls, credit card calls, some service calls, and calls to emergency numbers.

Again, most of the new system actions for dial-tone-first operation were implemented through program modifications, not through hardware changes. As a result, cost of adding the feature to No. 1 ESS is less than half that for a No. 1 or No. 5 crossbar system.

The initial No. 1 ESS dial-tone-first installation was in the Newark, New Jersey, Ironbound office. It was cut over on October 16, 1970.

With its new multiparty features, No. 1 ESS can provide fully selective or semiselective four-party service and semiselective eight-party service in addition to the previously available two-party service. The term "selective" indicates that each party customer can be rung with a common ringing code without ringing the telephones of other parties. "Semiselective" refers to an arrangement in which no more than two telephones are rung on a call to a multiparty line; different ringing codes are assigned to each party for identification. The various codes required for addressing the correct telephone are generated in No. 1 ESS solely by a new program control; no addition to the ex-

isting hardware is needed. The first ESS to provide this service is in the Amherst office, near Buffalo, New York, which was cut over on December 21 of last year.

For direct dialing to overseas telephones, No. 1 ESS programs have been designed to handle the access codes and longer dialing patterns of international calls. This service is scheduled for formal introduction this year.

Of the several developments that have produced a substantial increase in the traffic-handling capacity of No. 1 ESS, the streamlining of the program is perhaps the most significant. (See *Streamlined Programs and Expanded Use of Memory Boost No. 1 ESS Capacity*, page 174). It became clear that the central processor was spending most of its "real" time in network connection actions. To avoid this bottleneck, the service link frame was developed (see *Service Link Network Simpli-*

The service link network increases the call-handling capacity of No. 1 ESS offices by reducing the time that the system program is occupied in making ringing and digit-receiver connections, thus freeing it for other tasks. As a result, the service link network can increase calls per hour by about 15 percent.

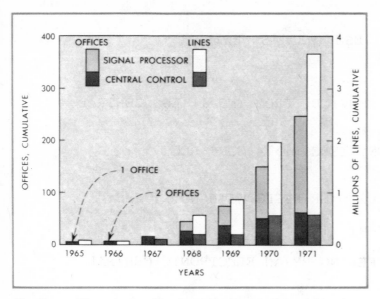

Starting with a single office in 1965, the number of No. 1 ESS offices has grown steadily. By the end of this year, 239 offices are expected to be in service, the great majority of them high-capacity signal-processor offices. The number of lines, too, has grown rapidly and will reach about 3.7 million at year's end.

fies *No. 1 ESS Call Handling,* page 171). This equipment in effect substitutes hardware for software and saves machine time spent in administering incoming and intra-office calls.

The field experience accumulated with No. 1 ESS in the few years since its introduction has been particularly fruitful in the case of maintenance. Based on this experience, better displays now help the craftsman to recognize trouble conditions, and more data are preserved to aid in trouble analysis (see *Emergency Action for No. 1 ESS,* page 176). Thus, a visual display now indicates that an emergency action is in process and an audible alarm indicates that the system is in the process of recovering. In addition, a printout shows the craftsman what recovery action took place, when it took place, and the state of the system.

There are other automatic maintenance features as well. One, the so-called data validation proce-

dure, is a program that continually searches the machine to determine whether the memory and hardware necessary to process calls are available. If they are not, and if the condition persists for a certain length of time, the program calls in appropriate "audit" programs to find the problem area to correct the situation. Audit programs, moreover, have been strengthened to audit redundant memory more completely and have been added for portions of memory that were not audited before.

Another example of improvements built into the system for ease of maintenance is the new CC diagnostic program and its companion trouble-location manual. These improve the capability of pinpointing a fault to a single circuit pack. The program was developed by first evaluating the results of deliberate insertion of faults to determine which circuits were inadequately tested by the diagnostic program. New tests were included in the program to specifically isolate these faults. After the new program was debugged, the physical fault insertion was repeated and the results indicate a substantial improvement in the ability to localize the fault to a single circuit pack.

One of the most difficult tasks in expanding ESS service is converting a CC office to an SP office without interrupting service. For this reason, procedures have been developed which permit frames to be added to in-service No. 1 ESS offices, without jeopardizing service. As early as October of 1969, for example, Bell Laboratories converted the Townsend office in Detroit, which serves the Chrysler Corporation, from a CC to an SP office. Hence, at the present time, standard growth procedures, usable by any installers for converting CC offices to SP offices for completing partially equipped offices, are available.

These and other new services, features, improvements, and cost reductions demonstrate that the stored program concept is the key to a flexible versatile, ever new No. 1 ESS. Besides these changes in No. 1 ESS already implemented, others are in various stages of development. Two modifications already well under way are the addition of PICTUREPHONE® service and remote maintenance of No. 1 ESS from centralized locations.

Supplementary Bibliography for Paper 3

NO. 1 ESS (WHAT'S NEW)

BUSINESS COMMUNICATIONS SERVICES FROM (NO 1) ESS CENTRAL
OFFICES.
HORENKAMP JJ + OEHRING H
P34C-1 OF INT CONF COMMUN, IEEE, 1974 CONF REC
CHO-858-9-CSCB

MEETING SMALL BUSINESS CUSTOMER NEEDS WITH NO. 1 ESS.
HOOD AA + OEHRING H
BELL LAB RECORD 52: 187-91 (1974)

NO. 1 ESS PBX SERVICE OFFERING BY AN ELECTRONIC CENTRAL
OFFICE.
OEHRING H + WICKHAM TF
P56 OF IEEE FALL ELECTRONIC CONF, 1971 (E4 I095, 150841)

SERVICE LINK NETWORK SIMPLIFIES NO. 1 ESS CALL HANDLING.
LISS WA
BELL LAB REC 49: 171-3 (1971)

STREAMLINED PROGRAMS AND EXPANDED USE OF MEMORIES BOOST
NO. 1 ESS CAPACITY.
LEE RC
BELL LAB REC 49: 174-5 (1971)

NEW MEMORY REDUCES NO. 1 ESS COST AND SIZE. (SILICON
INTEGRATED CIRCUITS FERRITE CORE MEMORIES)
CHEVALIER JG + ROLUND MW
BELL LAB REC 50: 120-3 (1972)

AUXILIARY PROGRAMS FOR NO. 1 ESS.
BELL LAB REC 50: 130 (1972)

UPGRADING MULTILOCATTION SERVICES WITH NO. 1 ESS.
RICHARDSON DB
BELL LAB REC 53: 264-71 (JUN 1975)

NO. 1 ESS SIGNAL PROCESSOR
DOBLMAIER AH + NEVILLE SM
BELL LAB REC APR 1969. P120-4

CENTREX SERVICE IN NO. 1 ESS
OEHRING H + WICKHAM JF
NAT ELECTRON CONF 1968, 24TH PROC. P661-6 (E4/N27)

INTRODUCING CAMA FEATURE TO NO. 1 ESS.
GARRATY WC
BELL LAB REC 53: 395-9 (NOV 1975)

Paper 4

No. 2 Electronic Switching System (No. 2 ESS)

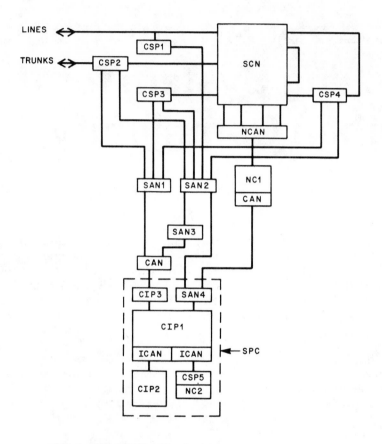

```
SCN   = LINE—TRUNK LINK NETWORK
CAN   = PERIPHERAL UNIT ADDRESS BUS
CIP1  = PROGRAM CONTROL
CIP2  = PROGRAM STORE
CIP3  = INPUT/OUTPUT CONTROL
CSP1  = LINE CIRCUIT
CSP2  = TRUNK CIRCUIT
CSP3  = SERVICE CIRCUIT
CSP4  = JUNCTOR CIRCUIT
CSP5  = CALL STORE
NC1   = NETWORK CONTROLLER
NC2   = NETWORK MAP
SAN1  = SCANNER
SAN2  = PERIPHERAL DECODER
SAN3  = SUPPLEMENTARY CENTRAL PULSE DISTRIBUTOR
SAN4  = CENTRAL PULSE DISTRIBUTOR
SPC   = CONTROL UNIT
```

No. 2 ESS complements No. 1 ESS by offering economical electronic switching service for medium size telephone offices. With stored program control, the system contains built-in flexibility to meet future demands for new features that are still difficult to anticipate.

No. 2 ESS: An Electronic Switching System for the Suburban Community

Philip C. Richards and John A. Herndon

OF THE MANY Bell Laboratories developments spawned by the invention of the transistor (see *25 Years of Transistors*, RECORD, *December 1972*), electronic switching ranks as one of the most significant for the Bell System. Bell Labs' development of the transistor, combined with an economical bulk memory to handle the enormous quantities of information needed to process and switch telephone calls, has led to an entire family of electronic switching systems (ESS). The new systems require less space and are easier to maintain than earlier, electromechanical systems. And, equally important, the systems are easy to modify when traffic and service requirements change. Ultimately, all older switching systems will be superseded by high-speed electronic switching systems.

The Bell System's first electronic machine for local switching offices, No. 1 ESS, was placed in service in 1965 (see *The No. 1 Electronic Switching System*, RECORD, *June 1965*). No. 1 ESS was designed to handle the heavy traffic loads and high density of telephone customers in metropolitan areas. For suburban communities, a smaller and more economical machine was needed. Consequently, Bell Labs engineers set about designing another machine, using the same basic principles, but geared to communities with local switching offices serving around 10,000 telephone lines. The result was No. 2 ESS, first placed in service in Oswego, Illinois in November, 1970.

No. 2 ESS, like No. 1 ESS, has one important feature which distinguishes it from electromechanical systems: stored program control—the control of switching functions by instructions stored in a memory. With stored program control, new service features may be added by changing the contents of the machine's memory. And customer services can be changed by feeding new data into the memory with a teletypewriter.

Like No. 1 ESS, No. 2 ESS contains three basic elements: (1) a switching network using high-speed ferreed switches (see *The Ferreed*, RECORD, *February 1964*); (2) a control unit, which directs the switching operations and maintenance in the system; and (3) two memories—a temporary memory (call store) for storing information such as the availability of circuits, called number, calling number, and type of call; and a semipermanent memory (program store) containing all the information the control unit needs to process the call and make a connection. The program store is semipermanent because it doesn't have to be changed as calls are processed by the system.

Two control units (the second one takes over in case trouble occurs in the first) and a maintenance frame make up the No. 2 ESS control complex. The various subunits that form a control unit include the program control, input-output control (of peripheral units such as switching networks), the call store, and the program store.

The program control is the central processing unit which executes the instructions contained in the program store. These instructions, for example, direct the program control to interpret the digits a customer dials, decide on the proper routing, and determine when the dialing has been completed. The program control follows every step in setting up and ultimately terminating a call.

To control a small electronic central office, the control unit of No. 2 ESS had to be designed for economy. Most of the instructions are general purpose, simple, and compact. Thus, little space is used to store the instructions. The compact instructions, in turn, reduce the size of other elements in the control unit. Reliability is enhanced because fewer components—with less complexity —are needed in No. 2 ESS (fewer components are needed because each program control has access to only one program store and call store).

Subroutines are widely used to limit the overall size of the program. Certain tasks are straightforward and can be accomplished by a sequence of operations—miniprograms within the program —which can be used in a number of different circumstances. Each time the program is used, different data are encountered. We have achieved additional economy in No. 2 ESS by "nesting" many levels of subroutines—that is, by having subroutines summon other subroutines during the execution of the program. Thus, the lowest-level subroutine accomplishes a very specific task in a straightforward manner—for example, performing some logic function on the contents of the call store. Higher-level subroutines perform large tasks, such as transferring data to peripheral units, by calling upon lower-level subroutines to perform each action.

A great many events occur between the time a customer originates a call and the time the call is completed. How does No. 2 ESS keep track of dialing, ringing, and answering, for example, and when does it know if something has gone wrong? Every call being processed by the system is assigned a "transient call record." This record calls upon a group of programs in the machine to monitor a call's progress, from dialing through ringing until an answer signal has been received and the customers begin talking. To perform this function, the record must keep track of various kinds of data, including: the identity of the calling and called customers; whether the connection is to a local line or an interoffice trunk; the number of the line or trunk; the address of the originating register, which receives and stores digits from the customer and also helps transmit the digits to another central office; and the identity of the circuit junctor—the link that is used to form a connection between the calling and called customers.

To process a telephone call, the control unit responds and completes a connection using the switching network and various types of trunks and service circuits, including dial pulse receivers, ringing circuits, and junctor circuits (see "Progress of a Call Through No. 2 ESS," page 134). Since the switching network is one of the more expensive parts of the system, the network was designed to grow in small increments. By providing access to all lines, trunks, and service circuits through a single type of network, we have minimized the amount of unused switching equipment in No. 2 ESS. And because there is only one kind of switching network, maintenance problems are reduced. Network connections are established via a simplified control circuit which, in response to a request from the control unit, completes a connection through the network and performs a check for circuit failures. A complete network connection is established by two such requests connecting two terminals through a junctor.

A complex switching machine with so many procedures to follow requires dependable maintenance. Because of good circuit design and the inherent reliability of its solid-state components, No. 2 ESS has a significantly lower trouble rate than general-purpose computer systems. However, the machine's complexity and high speed of operation have tended to place greater demands on the skills required by plant personnel to restore system operation and locate those troubles which the machine cannot isolate automatically.

To overcome these possible problems and also take advantage of potential cost savings, we have provided facilities and procedures which allow a

The peripheral decoder—a major feature of No. 2 ESS—is the first application of large scale integration (LSI) in a Bell System electronic switching system (several LSI chips are interconnected on the underside of the large white ceramic substrate). Advantages are obtained in size, reliability, and cost. The peripheral decoder, on the single circuit pack shown with front and rear views, controls relays in trunks and service circuits.

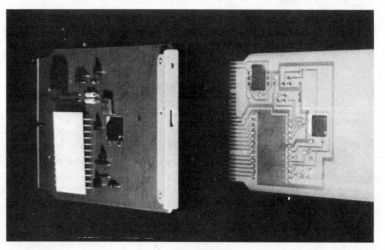

Information in the program store is updated by writing new data on a memory card. As services provided by the system are changed, or as lines and trunks are changed, the program data must also change. David J. Christensen is inserting a memory card into a card writer—part of the No. 2 ESS maintenance frame—to magnetize the card with the appropriate data. Further down the aisle is a processor frame—containing the program control, input-output, and call store units—and also several program store frames.

small group of well-trained people to administer and maintain several No. 2 ESS offices from a centralized point (the maintenance and administration center). Many repair operations, running of cross connections, and other tasks requiring physical contact with the equipment may be handled by semiskilled people, either dispatched from a central point to the equipment locations or assigned periodically to those locations.

A malfunction in the heart of No. 2 ESS—the control unit (including program control, program store and call store)—cannot interrupt the operation of the system because the unit is duplicated. The two control units run synchronously, with one acting as a standby. To assure rapid recovery from troubles and effective continuity of service, the off-line program control continually keeps its registers and associated call store contents up to date, ready to take over the on-line control unit's functions should trouble occur.

The major means of communication between Operating Company personnel and the switching machine is the teletypewriter. No. 2 ESS can be linked with as many as eight teletypewriters. Each teletypewriter station will produce only certain classes of messages and accept only a limited class of requests. For a typical No. 2 ESS office, four teletypewriters would be used as follows:

(1) local maintenance (at the No. 2 ESS site): for example, handling all messages before the office is put into service.

(2) remote maintenance (at the maintenance and administration center): reporting troubles detected, diagnosis results, etc.; and accepting all input messages.

(3) service orders (at a location called an assignment bureau): handling changes in customer telephone line information, such as type of telephone service, directory and billing numbers, etc.

(4) traffic: reporting traffic data, such as calling rate and circuit usage, according to a defined schedule.

In addition to offering good service, No. 2 ESS was also designed to enable Operating Companies to provide customers with the latest custom calling services:

• Speed calling, which allows a customer to call a frequently-used number by dialing only one or two digits instead of the full seven or more. For each customer who subscribes to speed calling, the system retains a list of numbers and the abbreviated code assigned to each. The system also accepts dialed instructions from customers enlarging or modifying their own lists.

• Three-way calling, which allows a customer to add a third party to a connection by flashing the switching system (momentarily depressing the switchhook button under the handset), and then dialing the number of the third party.

• Call waiting, which, with a tone, notifies a customer engaged in a call that an additional call is directed to his number. The customer can then flash the system to hold the original connection and connect the new call. Successive flashes then alternate connections between the customer and the two calls.

• Call forwarding, which allows a customer to direct the switching system to forward all calls to another number where he may be reached.

These features, in addition to many others, have been evaluated at the first four No. 2 ESS installations—Oswego, Illinois; Tucson, Arizona; North Madison, Connecticut; and Grand Island, New

Progress of a Call Through No. 2 ESS

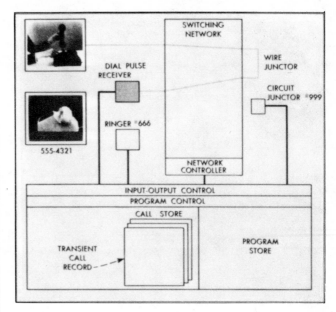

DIALING

termines which of the two control units will operate "on line" while the other "stands by." The maintenance frame also controls a card writer and up to eight teletypewriters. Using the card writer, a person can write new customer data on memory cards.

The relationship of the units in the switching system can be understood better by following the events which take place during a call:

The No. 2 electronic switching system (diagramed above) includes duplicated control units (center), a maintenance frame (lower center), teletypewriters, and the switching network (top). On one side of the switching network are a maximum of 30,000 input terminals for lines, trunks, and service circuits that can be connected to more than 7500 junctor terminals. The junctor terminals are interconnected in two ways: (1) wire junctors provide connections with trunk, receiver, and ringing circuits, etc. and (2) circuit junctors provide connections between two terminals in the switching equipment connected to customers' telephone lines. A scanner (below the switching network) feeds information to the control units on the activity of lines, trunks, and service circuits. The maintenance frame de-

Customer Action	Switching System Action
1. Lifts handset to call (See "Dialing")	Program control, working from information in the program store, selects a dial pulse receiver, which will detect the digits dialed by the customer, and selects a path between the dial pulse receiver and the calling customer (this path links two terminals in the switching system—one connected to the customer's incoming line and the other to the dial pulse receiver). Then program control directs the network controller to connect the path be-

York. More than eighteen installations are now providing good service. Only minor hardware and software problems have occurred in these offices.

New approaches to the design of No. 2 ESS programs have contributed to their excellent performance. For example, the system was put into service with an extensive set of audit programs, which continually verify records kept in the call

store and correct errors soon after they occur. If a software error causes the system to operate improperly, the audit programs rapidly identify the call that stimulated the error and disconnect it. Effective audit programs are one of the main reasons for the good performance record achieved by No. 2 ESS.

More and more, it is becoming apparent that

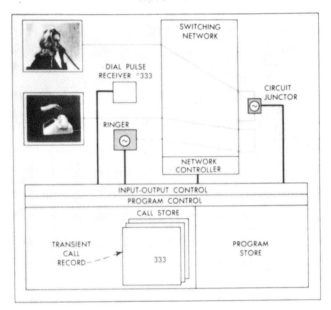

RINGING

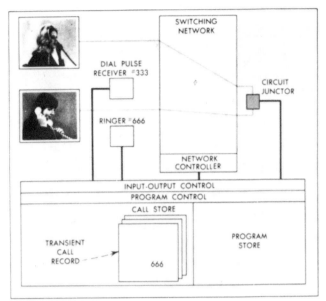

TALKING

tween the receiver and the calling customer, thus providing dial tone. In each case, data about the circuits selected are stored in the call store's transient call record.

| 2. Dials | Program control counts the pulses in the dial pulse receiver and stores them in the call store. |
| 3. Completes dialing (See "Ringing") | When all the digits have been received, program control selects a talking path, which is divided in two parts: one path links the calling customer to one side of a circuit junctor; the other links the called customer to the opposite side of the junctor. Program control directs the network controller to disconnect the dial pulse receiver and set up that part of the path connecting the calling customer. Program control selects a ringing circuit and a path to the circuit and directs the network controller to connect the circuit to the called customer's line. So the |

calling customer can "hear" the other party's phone ring, an audible ringback tone is delivered from the circuit junctor to the calling customer's line.

4. Called customer's phone rings	Program control makes the dial pulse receiver available for other calls and continually monitors both customers' lines in case the calling customer hangs up or the called customer answers.
5. Called customer answers (See "Talking")	Program control directs the network controller to disconnect the ringing circuit, making it available for another call. After connecting the called customer's part of the talking path, program control monitors the call for a termination.
6. Customers terminate call	Program control directs the network controller to disconnect the talking path between the customers, making the telephone lines and the talking path available for other calls.

flexibility is a very important objective for any new switching system. Years from now, the electronic switching systems of today will most likely be called upon to provide customers with services and operating features not known today. For this reason, every attempt was made to make No. 2 ESS flexible. The use of stored program control is a major step in providing this desired flexibility.

Additional flexibility comes from extensive use of modular equipment. Work is continuing on new features, including the addition of centrex features (by which calls to and from extensions in an office can be dialed directly without an attendant's assistance). And, anticipating future changes in telephone customer needs, we intend to continue investigating ways of further improving No. 2 ESS.

May 1973

Supplementary Bibliography for Paper 4

No. 2

SYSTEM GENERAL

GENERAL DESCRIPTION OF NO. 2 ELECTRONIC SWITCHING SYSTEM
VIGILANTE FS
IEE CONF SWITCHING TECHNIQUES FOR TELECOMMUN NETWORKS APR
1969
CONF PUB NO. 52 P479-82

SYSTEM ORGANIZATION AND OBJECTIVES OF NO. 2 ELECTRONIC
SWITCHING SYSTEM
SPENCER AE + VIGILANTE FS
BELL SYS TECH J 48: 2607-8 (OCT 1969) (ENTIRE ISSUE)

NO. 2 ESS: AN ELECTRONIC SWITCHING SYSTEM FOR THE SUBURBAN
COMMUNITY
RICHARDS PC + HERNDON JA
BELL LAB RECORD 51: 130-5 (MAY 1973)

DESIGN OF A MICROPROCESSOR CONTROL FOR A PROCESSOR (3ACC)
IN AN ELECTRONIC SWITCHING SYSTEM (ESS NO. 2B, ESS NO. 3)
T. F. STOREY
BELL SYSTEM TECHNICAL JOURNAL FEB. 1976 - P183-232

SYSTEM FEATURES AND SUBSYSTEMS

NO. 2 ESS UNIGAUGE RANGE EXTENSION
BEUSCHER HJ + DEISCH CW
IEEE TRANS COMMUN 21: 271-7 (APR 1973)

ADMINISTRATION OF NO. 2 ESS TRANSLATIONS
YATES JE
IEEE NATIONAL ELECTRONICS CONF (NEC) 1970 PROCEEDINGS P801-6

NO. 2 ESS TRANSLATIONS
RICHARDS PC + ROBERTS LR
NATIONAL ELECTRONICS CONFERENCE (NEC) 1970 PROCEEDINGS P807-11

Paper 5

No. 2B Electronic Switching System (No. 2B ESS)

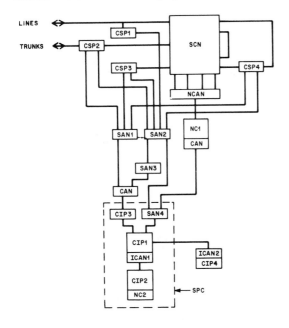

```
SCN    = LINE — TRUNK LINK NETWORK
CAN    = PERIPHERAL UNIT ADDRESS BUS
CIP1   = CENTRAL CONTROL (3ACC)
CIP2   = MAIN STORE
CIP3   = INPUT/OUTPUT CONTROL
CIP4   = TAPE (STORE)
CSP1   = LINE CIRCUIT
CSP2   = TRUNK CIRCUIT
CSP3   = SERVICE CIRCUIT
CSP4   = JUNCTOR CIRCUIT
CSP5   = CALL STORE
ICAN2  = TAPE DATA CONTROL
NC1    = NETWORK CONTROLLER
NC2    = NETWORK MAP
SAN1   = SCANNER
SAN2   = PERIPHERAL DECODER
SAN3   = SUPPLEMENTARY CENTRAL PULSE DISTRIBUTOR
SAN4   = INPUT/OUTPUT CONTROL
SPC    = CONTROL UNIT
```

No. 3 Electronic Switching System (No. 3 ESS)

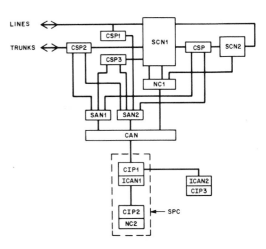

```
SCN1   = CONCENTRATOR GROUP
SCN2   = STAGE III
CAN    = FRAME INPUT/OUTPUT DISTRIBUTOR
CIP1   = CENTRAL CONTROL (3A)
CIP2   = MAIN STORE
CIP3   = TAPE (STORE)
ICAN2  = TAPE DATA CONTROL
NC1    = NETWORK CONTROLLER
NC2    = NETWORK MAP
SAN1   = SCANNER AND SCAN POINT
SAN2   = PERIPHERAL PULSE DISTRIBUTOR AND DECODER
SPC    = 3A PROCESSOR
```

NEW DEVELOPMENTS IN SUBURBAN AND RURAL ESS (NO. 2 AND NO. 3 ESS)

E. A. Irland and U. K. Stagg
Bell Telephone Laboratories Inc.
Naperville, Illinois, USA

ABSTRACT

Since its inception in November, 1970, the No. 2 ESS has been giving excellent service to a rapidly expanding market. First centrex service was given in 1974. Use of modular buildings has allowed factory-based total-office testing with shortened intervals. The ultimate size, however, has been limited by the real-time capacity of the processor.

Improvements planned for No. 2 ESS include use of semiconductor memory, 1A integrated circuits, and remnant reed switch networks. The central control, designed for use in small rural offices (No. 3 ESS) is self-checking and emulates No. 2 ESS programs by microprocessing with a 2-to-1 improvement in real-time capacity.

Another member of the ESS family - No. 3 ESS - is being developed to provide modern telephone service to Bell System customers living in sparsely populated areas. Although a difficult goal to achieve in the past, system organization tailored to the small office, micro-programmed integrated circuit central controls and low cost semiconductor memory now allow a stored program controlled system to be economically attractive down to office sizes of several hundred lines.

1. INTRODUCTION

No. 2 ESS Initial System

The first No. 2 Electronic Switching System[1] was placed in service on November 29, 1970, at Oswego, Illinois. As of February, 1974, the performance of over 50 offices in service has been excellent, with customer complaints below the Bell System average for central offices.

Immediately following the completion of the initial program called Local Office-1 (LO-1), a program to add centrex service and other features was planned. This program, called Extended Features-1 (EF-1), went into service without centrex customers in February, 1974, in Naperville, Illinois; and in April, 1974, the first centrex customer was put into service.

No. 2A ESS

In order to expedite installation, shorten the order-to-service interval and limit rising costs of buildings, a modular version of No. 2 ESS known as the No. 2A ESS has also been made available. Such central offices are shipped from the factory, pretested in building modules several of which can be fitted together to form a total building. Various facades have been used to adapt the overall architectural effect of the resulting buildings to a wide variety of locales. This arrangement has proved popular, especially in areas having high building costs or rapidly expanding population. There are no limitations on the ultimate size to which No. 2A ESS offices can be grown other than the limitation implicit in the design of the No. 2 ESS hardware or software, as additional building modules can readily be added to existing installations. Total sales of No. 2 and No. 2A ESS are shown in Fig. 1.

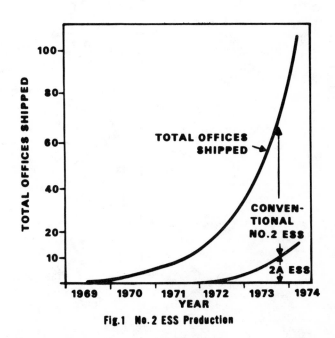

Fig.1 No. 2 ESS Production

2. NEW DEVELOPMENTS

In planning continued development to enhance the opportunities for use of electronic switching in this sector of the market (rural and suburban), two factors appeared predominant. (1) The required initial capital investment, including the cost of full stored program processor capability, did not encourage the use of ESS for offices of less than 1500 lines; and (2) the call handling capacity of No. 2 ESS (maximum engineered load of 19,000 calls per hour) generally limits the maximum usable size to much less than the 30,000 terminal maximum configuration of the network.

The feasibility of improving both the cost and capability of small-to-medium size ESS offices through the use of integrated circuit technology has now been established. A new system arrangement known as the No. 3 ESS has been optimized around the needs of the rural office. The new processor needed in this system not only capitalizes on the logic technology standardized for the 1A Processor[2] but also introduces a semiconductor memory at a cost per bit of about one-third that attainable in magnetic memories.

The order structure of the new central control is sufficiently flexible, through the use of a microprogram, to accommodate not only an optimized language for No. 3 ESS but also additional microcode which permits emulating existing No. 2 ESS programs. A faster machine cycle allows the new processor to achieve a 2-to-1 improvement in real-time performance when it is used as a replacement for the original No. 2 ESS Control Complex. In this application the processor is called the 2B Processor.

The New Central Control - 3A CC

The processing unit which is at the heart of both the 2B Processor and the 3A Processor is called the 3A Central Control (3A CC). This new central control embodies many features not previously used in ESS, as discussed below.

3A Processor

The 3A Processor is organized as shown in Fig. 2. In contrast to other ESS processors, the call, program and translation data are accessed through only one port per CC associated with a single Main Store community (MAS). Software and hardware interlocks assure that extraneous information cannot overwrite protected areas containing critical programs or translations.

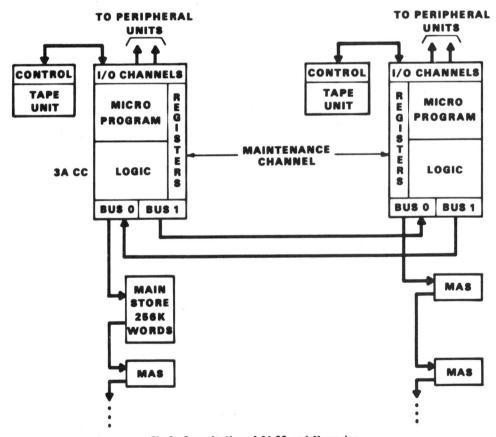

Fig.2 Organization of 3A CC and Memories

ISS 74

Since the MAS incorporates a random access read-write semiconductor memory, the programs and translations are also kept on a cartridge tape chosen for low cost and good operational stability. The tape serves both to back up the volatile main store and as a low-cost source of programs whose usage is low. Such programs may be loaded into the MAS on demand, thereby decreasing the required random access store size.

The data words are 16 bits in length with two additional bits supplying parity checks.

Microprogram Control

The order decoding of the 3A CC is carried out through use of a microprogram memory of 32 bits per word and a maximum capacity of 4096 words. The microcode required for the No. 3 ESS application including basic system initialization fits into 1024 words. The remaining store capacity can be made available for other uses and is largely used for emulation sequences and system recovery strategy when the CC is part of a 2B Processor.

The microcode is stored in a mask encoded LSI logic array of 1024 bits per chip. The CC cycle time consists of a variable number of microstore advances which occur in 150 ns steps. A basic machine cycle involving a main store access uses eight steps and thus occupies 1.20 microseconds.

Asynchronous, Self-Checking Operation

In order to permit the possibility of independent evolution of the CC and the associated memory, the main store is accessed asynchronously. Thus, the data returned from the store is accompanied by a completion signal and there is no precisely specified "time window."

The CCs and store controllers are organized and packaged so that single circuit failures generally create only single bit errors in the data. This organization allows a variety of error detecting schemes to be used rather than the cycle-by-cycle matching of other ESS processors. One CC, therefore, runs in control on-line and the other idles. The on-line CC writes into both main stores; so that, in the event of a switch, the off-line store contains up-to-date information on the state of the system. Periodic switching is used to assure that the CC on standby is functioning properly.

I/O Channels

A Flexible Input/Output Channel arrangement is supplied; so that, blocks of 20 channels may be added per single plug-in pack. The peripheral system control is thus accessed by a single serial channel per peripheral unit. The channel bits are transmitted one per 150 ns timing step. This technique greatly reduces the wiring complexity of peripheral control over that of the parallel peripheral busses used in No. 2 ESS.

Semiconductor Memory

The main store is built up from three-transistor cell MOS memory chips of 1024 bits per chip. Four of these chips are packaged together giving 4096 bits in a single dual in-line package (DIP). A memory plane then contains 16 DIPs or 64,000 bits. The improvements per bit in lower cost, frame space, power and weight for this memory compared to the ferrite sheet temporary memory and permanent magnet twistor memory which it replaces are shown in Fig. 3.

STORE	PER BIT COMPARISONS			
	COST	POWER	WEIGHT	VOLUME
FERRITE SHEET (8192 × 24-BIT WORDS)	100%	2.1 mW 100%	1.15 g 100%	2.19 cm³ 100%
PERMANENT MAGNET TWISTOR (65,536 × 22-BIT WORDS)	18%	0.32 mW 16%	0.44 g 38%	0.60 cm³ 28%
SEMICONDUCTOR (262,144 × 26-BIT WORDS)	6%	0.022 mW 1%	0.011 g 1%	0.021 cm³ 1%

Fig.3 Store Comparisons

No. 3 ESS Design Objectives

As previously mentioned, No. 3 ESS is being developed in order to bring to the rural community the kind of modern telephone features now available in urban and suburban areas through No. 1 and No. 2 ESS, and at a cost competitive with other alternatives. This market is now mainly served by step-by-step community dial offices.

More specific objectives are to develop a small electronic switching machine which allows short order-to-service intervals, involves less engineering effort by the telephone companies and Western Electric, has capability for unattended operation (which implies remote maintenance and administration facilities), is packaged for complete factory assembly and testing prior to shipping and minimizes the floor space and building requirements. The developments under way to achieve these ends include the 3A Processor described earlier, a new network topology using remnant reed switches, a new program developed for minimum size at the cost of real time, simple trunks, junctors and service circuits and minimization of circuit and feature options.

Peripheral System Design

The topology of the network has been optimized for the traffic characteristically observed in the rural Community Dial Office (CDO). Typically, the CDO has a high incidence of intraoffice traffic, a calling rate of one busy-hour call per main station and a busy-hour load of three CCS per main station. The maximum size network needs to serve only a few thousand lines. However, it must have a reasonably small growth unit, should not require junctor administration and should be relatively insensitive to unbalanced traffic loads. The final choice was a folded network with a fixed concentration ratio as shown in Fig. 4. Only three physical stages are provided; however, any call, line-to-line, line-to-trunk, trunk-to-line, traverses five sets of crosspoints due to the folded nature of the topology, passing through the first and second stage switches twice and once through the third stage.

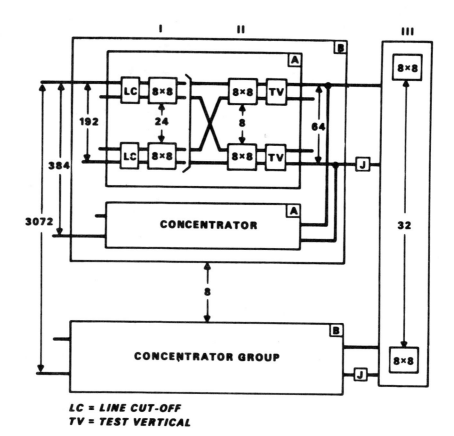

LC = LINE CUT-OFF
TV = TEST VERTICAL

Fig.4 No.3 ESS Network Topology

In every call, the connections between the second and third physical stages includes a circuit junctor as one element and a wire junctor as the other. Usually, the circuit junctor performs the line supervising function, thereby simplifying the trunk and service circuits. In addition, the junctor circuits provide access to tone and emergency announcement circuits permitting transmission of these messages to the customer at a minimum network occupancy penalty.

The simplification of the trunks and service circuits achieved by software tradeoffs and removing line supervision combined with the use of miniature wire spring relays has permitted design of all trunk circuits and some service circuits small enough to each fit on one printed wiring circuit pack. However, some of the service circuits (such as the customer dial pulse receiver) are more complex and will require two or more printed wiring circuit packs. As well as resulting in compactness, the simplification has also resulted in significantly lower cost trunks and service circuits than could otherwise have been obtained.

Continuing the theme of compactness, the network fabric uses the new remreed switch. Not only is the space required for the switch significantly reduced compared with that required for ferreed switches; but, because of complete electronic control of the remreed switch, the control hardware is also more

compact and more reliable than controllers using relay designs.

An organization of the peripheral hardware has been adopted which departs from the conventional approach. Historically, the network frames have contained only elements of the network fabric and its control. Other hardware such as trunks, junctors, service circuits, etc., have appeared in separately designated frames. No. 3 ESS organization is such that network, junctors, trunks and service circuits are combined in such a fashion that a single frame design is used both for initial and growth units. This frame contains the necessary network and circuit elements to provide service for approximately 300 lines offering typical traffic. Growth is accomplished by a simple addition of this frame, interconnecting it with the distributing frame and the control frame (which are always required and are provided at the time of the initial office installation). It is truly "add-on" in that appearances for the junctors are left on the control frame for the additions when less than the full-size system is provided. Hence, no junctor rearrangement is required. Since these frames are provided in increments serving approximately 300 lines each, and up to 15 of these frames can be provided, the range of application is approximately 300 to 4500 lines. Fig. 4 illustrates the arrangement for the typical CDOs up to approximately 2400 lines. Beyond this, additional concentrator groups are accommodated by additional third stage switches.

ISS 74

Software Organization

The software for the No. 3 ESS application is organized such that real time has been spent to reduce hardware cost. The resultant traffic handling capability appears to be still quite adequate for the CDO market because of the high speed of the 3A Processor. The trade-off is accomplished typically through "simple" (requiring little code) but time consuming algorithms and generous use of temporary memory. The allocation of real time to major classes of tasks is shown in Fig. 5. At zero traffic, base level tasks such as input processing use 15 percent of available real time, interrupt level tasks such as peripheral order distribution use 25 percent, deferrable tasks which include temporary memory audits use 45 percent and line scanning 15 percent. As offered traffic increases, the major change is a trade-off between interrupt level and deferrable tasks with some increase in base level tasks. As the load approaches the maximum, it is observed that line scanning falls off. This, plus reduction in input processing, reduces the new work accepted and processed by the system. This "negative feedback" is a self-limiting mechanism which protects the system during momentary peak overloads. The effect of this throttling is to introduce dial-tone delay to a few customers without introducing delay of any nature to calls already accepted and undergoing processing.

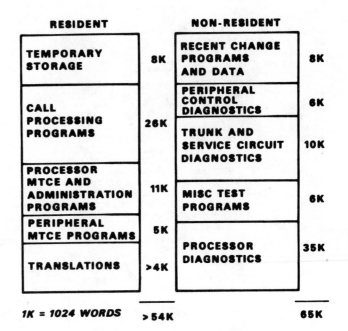

Fig.6 No.3 ESS Memory Organization

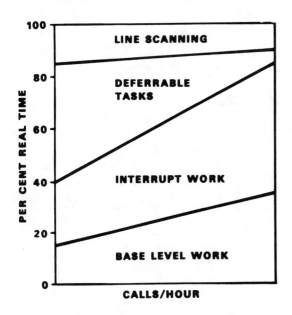

Fig.5 No.3 ESS Real Time (Simulated)

The organization of memory, both resident (in the random access memory) and nonresident (on the magnetic tape backup), is shown in Fig. 6. All resident code including translation is duplicated on the magnetic tape. The 8000 word temporary memory area of the MAS is not duplicated on tape. In addition to holding a copy of the resident code, the tape also is the repository of a large amount of diagnostic and other relatively infrequently used code which is loaded as required into a buffer area in the temporary memory. The need to bring this off-line code into the MAS is determined by resident fault detection code or by periodic requests for routine maintenance and exercising.

Fault recovery is accomplished by a carefully

designed interaction of software and hardware. All duplicated control circuits have error detection logic which begins recovery actions in response to fault detection. For processor errors, the first phase of the recovery is hardware controlled since program sanity is questionable. When the standby processor has been activated, control is returned to software to complete the recovery. For duplicated peripheral circuits, the entire recovery process is software controlled following initial hardware detection.

In the unduplicated peripheral area, such as in the network or the scanner matrix, error detection is more heavily dependent upon software action. This consists of interrogating the circuits used in the call setup procedure and analyzing parameters such as origination rates and call sequences to find abnormalities. Since many circuits may appear faulty with these schemes, a pattern recognition process is employed by the recovery software to identify the troublesome circuit. Once such a circuit has been identified, it is marked as unavailable for use in any further calls until repaired.

No. 2B ESS

Although the new processor provides reduced costs in the smaller size offices (No. 3 ESS), it also provides a means to increase the traffic handling capability of No. 2 ESS. With 2000 added words of microcode, the 3A CC acquires the ability to execute instructions in the format of No. 2 ESS programs. Although the No. 2 ESS call store word width is the same as that of No. 3 ESS, the program store uses 22 bit words. In the emulation mode, therefore, it is also necessary to add a few circuit packs to the CC to accommodate the added word size. To work with the No. 2 ESS peripheral equipment, it is also necessary for the processor to be adapted through interface circuits to the central pulse distributor and peripheral decoders.[1] When these adaptions (added microcode, wider store, CPD interface) have been made, the processor is called the 2B Processor.

When the No. 2 ESS system is equipped with the 2B Processor, it is known as the No. 2B ESS. Although the cycle rate of the 3A CC is about five times faster than that of the No. 2 ESS Program Control which it replaces, the net effect on call handling capacity will be about a 2-to-1 increase. This is because the 3A CC differs from the No. 2 Program Control in two ways which promote simplicity at a cost of reduced real-time capability. First, the use of one main memory requires that program words, translation data and call data be accessed serially, whereas the program store and call store of No. 2 ESS can be read simultaneously. Secondly, the No. 2 ESS Program Control operates in parallel with an I/O Processor which handles the routine scan data formatting. The I/O circuit has been eliminated in the 2B Processor.

In spite of the substantial differences between the 2B Processor and the No. 2 ESS Control Complex, the program emulation has been successful in saving large portions of the existing EF-1 generic program. Fig. 7 shows a comparison of emulated and new code required for No. 2B ESS.

Remnant Reed Network

In keeping with the use of the new remnant reed switches in No. 1 and No. 3 ESS, similar new network frames are being developed for No. 2 ESS, with a 3-to-1 reduction in floor space requirements. These frames have been designed to be completely compatible with existing software. They may, therefore, be used with either the original processor or the 2B Processor and may be intermixed with ferreed frames for growth.

3. CONCLUSION

A laboratory model of the No. 3 ESS has been constructed and although not all of the equipment is in final form, software debugging is underway.

A model of the 2B Processor has been added to one of the No. 2 ESS laboratory systems and checkout of emulated programs and system recovery is nearing completion. Remnant reed networks have also been added to the system laboratory and operational checkout is underway.

From the present state of development, it appears that the various objectives for both rural and suburban ESS applications will be met as described above.

Acknowledgments

These new developments depend critically on the effort of many organizations within the Bell System, but particularly the work done to develop the 1A technology and related integrated circuit technology for memories. These projects could also not have been carried out without the continued support and encouragement of Messrs. W. A. Depp, W. O. Fleckenstein and R. W. Ketchledge.

References

1. Bell System Technical Journal, October, 1969, Volume 48, No. 8.

2. International Switching Symposium Record, 1972, page 26, "1A Processor - A High Speed Processor for Switching Application," R. E. Staehler.

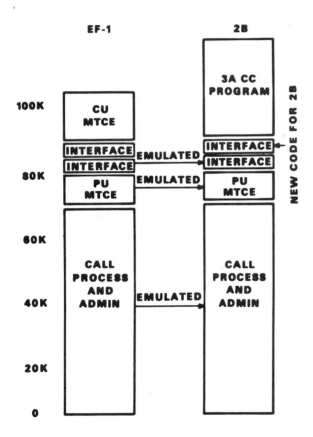

Fig.7 Programs for 2B ESS

Supplementary Bibliography for Paper 5

NO. 2B AND NO. 3 ESS

NO. 2B ESS: BIG BONUS FOR SMALL CENTRAL OFFICES
BELL LAB REC 54: 27, JAN 1976

DESIGN OF A MICROPROCESSOR CONTROL FOR A PROCESSOR (3ACC)
IN AN ELECTRONIC SWITCHING SYSTEM (ESS NO. 2B, ESS NO. 3)
T. F. STOREY
BELL SYSTEM TECHNICAL JOURNAL FEB. 1976 - P183-232

Paper 6

No. 4 Electronic Switching System (No. 4 ESS)

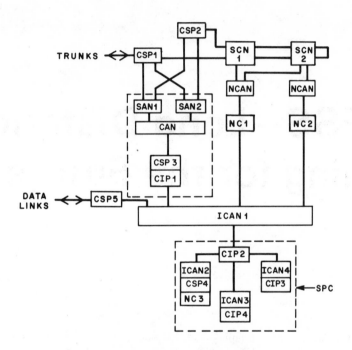

```
SCN1  = TIME SLOT INTERCHANGE
SCN2  = TIME MULTIPLEX SWITCH
CIP1  = SIGNAL PROCESSOR
CIP2  = CENTRAL CONTROL
CIP3  = PROGRAM STORE
CIP4  = AUXILIARY DATA STORE
CSP1  = TRUNK CIRCUIT (2-WAY)
CSP2  = SERVICE CIRCUIT
CSP3  = CALL STORE
CSP4  = CALL STORE
CSP5  = CCIS TERMINAL
ICAN1 = PERIPHERAL BUS
ICAN2 = CALL STORE BUS
ICAN3 = FILE STORE BUS
ICAN4 = PROGRAM STORE BUS
NC1   = TIME SLOT INTERCHANGE TIME SLOT MEMORY
NC2   = TIME MULTIPLEX SWITCH SLOT MEMORY
NC3   = NETWORK MAP
SAN1  = SCANNER
SAN2  = DISTRIBUTOR
SPC   = 1A PROCESSOR
```

Solid-state, time-shared switching gives No. 4 ESS both compactness and unprecedented capacity. Scheduled for commercial service in 1976, this new system for tandem and toll switching will allow the Bell System to gear for heavy traffic of the future—economically.

No. 4 ESS—Long Distance Switching for the Future

G. Douglas Johnson

IN NOVEMBER OF LAST YEAR, the first telephone call was completed through the new No. 4 ESS (Electronic Switching System). Although the call was between two adjacent telephones at Bell Labs' Indian Hill facility in Naperville, Illinois, it was set up through new Western Electric-built equipment, under stored-program control with new No. 4 ESS operational software, and was otherwise representative of a long distance call. With this call, No. 4 ESS entered the last stages of preparation for service as the latest and most powerful member of the Bell System's long line of stored-program-controlled switching systems, ranging from machines for local switching (No. 1 and No. 2 ESS) to machines for operator-assisted calls (TSPS No. 1 —see *A Decade of ESS*, RECORD, *December 1970*). Designed primarily as a successor to today's electromechanical 4A crossbar system, No. 4 ESS is a high-capacity, versatile toll and tandem switching machine for the long distance telecommunications network. No. 4 ESS will handle at least 350,000 long distance calls per hour—about three times as many as the electromechanical system.

Long distance telephone traffic in the Bell System will grow tremendously over the next two decades. From about 3 billion calls in 1970, the number is expected to increase to 9 billion in 1980 and to 25 billion by 1990. To direct all these calls to their destinations, toll switching equipment will have to grow proportionately—an unsettling prospect in an era of rapidly rising construction and maintenance costs.

To cope with this increase in toll message traffic, a powerful switching machine like No. 4 ESS is required. This is particularly true for many metropolitan centers. Without the relief of a large machine, New York, Chicago, and Los Angeles by 1985 would each need many more additional machines of 4A crossbar size, and many other cities would face the same problem to a smaller degree.

Toll service to these cities becomes increasingly inefficient as the number of switching machines increases. Traffic from the outside world must be examined more carefully and routed not just to the proper city, but to the specific toll office within the city having connections to the desired cus-

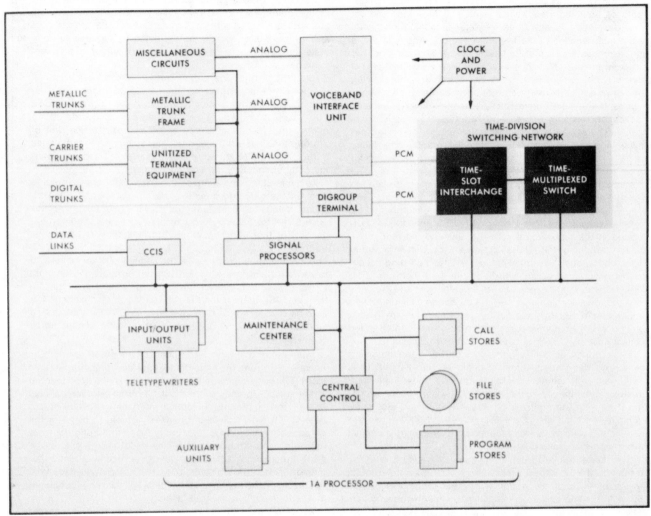

In No. 4 ESS, a time-division switching network (upper right) routes digital signals from incoming trunks (upper left) to the proper outgoing trunks. Signals on digital trunks, which enter the system through the digroup terminal, can be switched directly. Metallic and carrier trunks and miscellaneous circuits, however, carry analog signals, and these must be converted to pulse-code modulation (PCM) digital signals by the voiceband interface unit. All operations are directed and supervised by the 1A Processor (bottom), aided in routine tasks by signal processors (center). The equipment units are synchronized by a clock.

tomer's local office. This requires more trunk groups to the city, each group being used at less than maximum efficiency. If a distant office does not have a trunk group to the serving toll office, the call must be routed to another metropolitan toll office where it is reswitched over an interoffice trunk to the serving toll office and thence to the customer's office. All this leads to inefficient trunking and switching and materially increases the cost of metropolitan toll service. But since No. 4 ESS can handle more than three times the traffic of the 4A crossbar switching system, its nationwide introduction will materially alleviate the metropolitan multimachine problem.

The new system, like other electronic switching systems, is directed by a stored program which, acting through a processing unit, carries out all switching functions. No. 4 ESS (illustration,

AN IDEA WHOSE TIME HAS COME

No. 4 ESS had its origin in the 1950s, when the basic concepts of an integrated transmission and switching system were developed to anticipate the telecommunication needs of the last decades of the twentieth century. About 15 years ago, a research group at Bell Labs built a working model of an experimental solid-state exchange, quite similar to what is now No. 4 ESS. However, the devices and manufacturing processes available then were not advanced enough to make a large toll system commercially feasible. Now, technology has caught up with theory, and No. 4 ESS has become a reality. The recent availability of high-speed integrated circuits—and particularly small, fast, reliable solid-state memories—has provided the modern technological foundation for large-scale use of an old idea.

At the heart of No. 4 ESS (as in the earlier solid-state exchange) is a unique method of time-shared switching. The following is a description of how this switching method works.

All switching functions in the No. 4 ESS network are performed in the time-slot interchange unit and the time-multiplexed switching unit. These units work together in a hybrid time- and space-division switching arrangement under control of programs operating through the 1A Processor. (The time-slot interchange provides the time division, and the time-multiplexed switching unit provides the space division.) Using the number dialed by the caller, a trunk-hunt program locates an unoccupied outgoing trunk in a trunk group leading to the called customer. A path-hunt program examines the many possible paths (in space and time) between the incoming trunk and designated outgoing trunk, selects an idle path, and commands the network to connect the trunks. The commands—data specifying the actions required of each switching stage—are stored in a cyclically repeating time-slot memory and are read out at the system rate of 8000 times per second. A precise network clock coordinates this and all other timing operations.

The actual trunk-to-trunk connection consists of repetitive transfers of PCM-coded information from the incoming trunk to the outgoing trunk. A similar, inverse process is carried out at the same time to complete the two-way conversation. The PCM sampling interval of 1/8000 second is further subdivided into 128 time slots of slightly less than 1 microsecond each, during which a complete set of eight PCM digits—the number needed to encode one channel—is transferred from trunk to trunk. This operation continues for the duration of the call. Although the two customers are thus only intermittently connected, the quality of the PCM transmission between them is as good or better than it would be if they were continuously connected through today's long distance telephone network.

The No. 4 ESS time-shared network achieves its great power by fully exploiting the time between these intermittent connections. The diagram opposite, based on one-way transmission only, illustrates the principle of operation. (The inverse operation used for two-way transmission is similar.) PCM-coded data from a voiceband interface unit or a "digroup" terminal (for digital trunks) enters from the left. Eight-bit coded signals from each of the 120 channels appear sequentially and are stored in chronological order in the 120 cells of the input buffer memory—channel 1 in cell 1 during the first time slot, channel 2 in cell 2 during the second, and so forth. The path-hunt program loads the time-slot memory with information to make the required connections. Thus, at the beginning of a particular time slot, the time-slot memory specifies that a particular set of high-speed crosspoints in the time-multiplexed switch be closed. In addition, the time-slot memory controls the selection of the proper cells in the input buffer and the output buffer as required to complete the path between incoming and outgoing time-slot interchange (TSI) units.

Eight PCM bits (the signal from one channel) are then sequentially read out of the input buffer memory of the incoming TSI and read into the output buffer of the outgoing TSI. Finally, the output buffer is read out in an ordered sequence of 120 channels into a voiceband interface unit or digroup terminal. All the above operations are repeated once during each PCM frame, or 8000 times per second, intermittently connecting the two customers.

To understand the manner in which calls are completed through the network, consider the color symbols in the diagram opposite. Based on the number the customer has dialed, the trunk-hunt program has requested the interconnection of the following input (I) and output (O) channels: I-3 to O-119, I-122 to O-2, I-120 to O-240, and I-239 to O-123. The basic idea is to rearrange the sequence of channels and to reroute them in a way that will get an incoming channel to the proper outgoing channel. The path-hunt program determines that, during time slot 1 (dark color), channel I-120 is to be connected to O-240 and I-122 to O-2 and that, during time slot 2 (light color), channel I-3 is to be connected to O-119 and I-239 to O-123.

Input buffer memory cell 1 accepts the eight PCM bits from channel I-1 from the voiceband interface unit during time slot 1. Likewise, at the same time, cell 121 of the second input buffer memory accepts the eight bits from another channel (I-121) from a second voiceband interface unit. Also during time slot 1, the PCM code previously stored in cell 1 of the output buffer memory is read out of the output buffer memory and into the output voiceband interface unit. Similarly, the code stored in cell 121 is read out of the second output buffer memory and into the second output voiceband interface unit. In time slot 2 the next sequential cells (2, 122, etc.) are loaded and read in similar, ordered fashion.

As determined by the path-hunt program and as ordered by the time-slot memory, cell 120 of the input buffer memory is read out during time slot 1 (dark-color arrow). This PCM code had been read into cell 120 from the voiceband interface unit in the previous read-in cycle.

Now the channels can be routed to output buffer memories, with one more rearrangement in sequence. Cell 120 is connected via the first horizontal and second vertical crosspoint (dark circle) of the time-multiplexed switch and via the output buffer selector (dark arrow) of the second time-slot interchange to output cell 240. During this first time slot, eight PCM digits are read from cell 120 and into cell 240. At the 120th time slot of the frame, cell 240 will be read to the voiceband interface unit, effectively interconnecting channels I-120 and O-240 when the cells are read out in chronological sequence. Similarly, channels I-122 and O-2 are also connected in time slot 1, and channels I-3 and O-119 and I-239 and O-123 are connected in time slot 2.

By this complex process, No. 4 ESS connects and reconnects an incoming trunk to the proper outgoing trunk thousands of times per second—without degrading signal quality. Thousands of other calls share the same switching paths, resulting in very large capacity with low blocking probability.

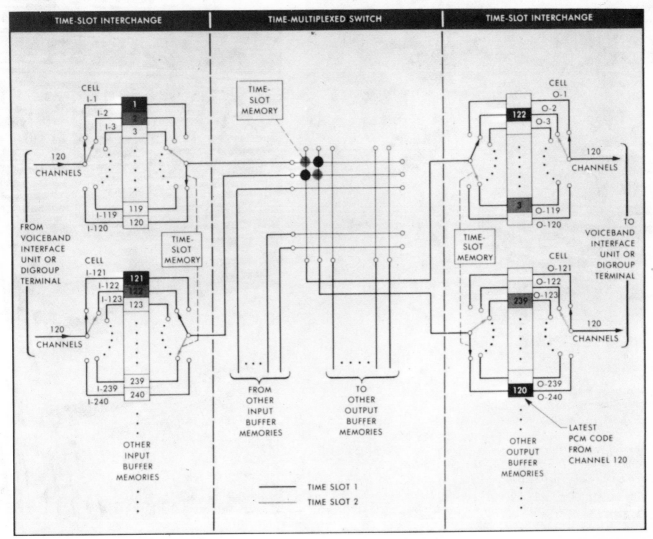

| | | |
| TIME-SLOT INTERCHANGE | TIME-MULTIPLEXED SWITCH | TIME-SLOT INTERCHANGE |

The time-slot interchanges rearrange the various channels in time, and the time-multiplexed switch rearranges them in space, with the net outcome that an incoming trunk is routed to the proper outgoing trunk. In the example here, incoming channels 120 and 122 are connected to outgoing channels 240 and 2, respectively, during the first time slot (dark color). During the second time slot (light color), channels I-3 and I-239 are connected to O-119 and O-123. Time-slot memory provides control.

page 39) employs the new 1A Processor to control the switching machine (see *No. 4 ESS Will Triple Toll Capacity*, RECORD, *September 1972*). With its advanced integrated circuits, this new processor is four to eight times faster, and is even more dependable and easier to maintain, than its electronic predecessors. The central control directs other units of the processor complex as well as peripheral units to process calls and perform other system functions. The 1A Processor employs high speed "writable" (electronically alterable) core memories for both program and call stores. In addition, the processor uses a high-capacity disk file having lower access speed. The writable stores and disk file contribute to the system's flexibility and economy. The processor also uses auxiliary units to control tape and data links, as well as a maintenance center and input/output units to control

A crystal, oscillating at a precisely controlled frequency, is the system "clock," synchronizing the equipment. The metal box above holds the crystal. Walter Zweig of Bell Labs, Indian Hill, Illinois, checks the clock's operation. Mark Pophal (right photo) monitors No. 4 ESS performance on a laboratory test console.

teletypewriters and cathode-ray tube displays.

No. 4 ESS is the first large machine in the Bell System to switch digital signals directly. It does this with its new time-division switching network, which handles up to 107,000 trunks and service circuits (see "An Idea Whose Time Has Come," page 228). Briefly, in time-division switching many calls are handled at once by a common switching element, the calls being separated from each other by very short time intervals. In space-division switching—the kind used exclusively in other toll machines—each call is handled by a separate switching element. Even with very heavily loaded trunks carrying traffic over 90 percent of the time, only one-half of one percent of the calls will fail to go through No. 4 ESS because of network blocking.

For the first time, a switching network is completely duplicated—a standby network keeps up to date on the status of calls being switched, and so is ready to take over the calls at any instant

if necessary. In addition, the switching network has a duplicate, independent path memory. These features give No. 4 ESS a degree of reliability not obtained in any other switching network.

Only digital signals can be handled in the No. 4 ESS network. Today, most of the signals in a toll office are not digital, but analog. Before they can be processed by No. 4 ESS, they must be sampled, quantized, and coded in pulse-code modulation (PCM) form. These functions are performed by the voiceband interface unit, which is similar to the D1, D2, and D3 channel banks (see *The D3 Channel Bank,* RECORD, *August 1972* and *The D1D Channel Bank: Modernizing the D1 Workhorse,* RECORD, *February 1973*). Each voiceband interface unit accepts 120 channels from analog trunks or special service circuits, samples each one 8000 times per second, encodes the samples into PCM format, and interleaves the 120-channel PCM-coded outputs onto a single coaxial cable connected to a timeslot interchange unit. After switching by the time-division switching network, the signals must be changed back to analog form for further transmission over analog trunks. Even with these two conversion steps, No. 4 ESS is expected to be more economical than present toll systems; and of course with digital trunks, where conversion is not required, it will be much more economical.

No. 4 ESS will serve these types of trunks:

(1) "Metallic" (noncarrier) trunks from nearby offices terminating in metallic-trunk circuits, each providing the necessary signaling interface, gain adjustment, and conversion from two-wire to four-wire circuits.

(2) Trunks from carrier systems terminating in unitized facility terminals (see *Getting It All Together with Unitized Terminals*, RECORD, *January 1973*), which combine the operations of carrier demodulation, signaling, echo suppression, and gain adjustment.

(3) Digital trunks, handled by the "digroup" terminal, which accepts the digital signals from five T1 carrier lines, each line carrying 24 channels, and multiplexes the signals into the same 120-channel PCM format that the voiceband interface unit produces from analog trunks. Thus, No. 4 ESS is able to switch digital signals directly. This feature has immediate and large-scale application for almost all trunks connecting toll offices to local offices and later application when long distance digital facilities such as waveguide are available.

Signal processors are associated with the metallic-trunk frames, unitized terminal equipment, and digroup terminals. These subordinate processing units relieve the main 1A Processor of much of the repetitive work associated with signaling. The signal processors receive and transmit dial pulses directly, and—in conjunction with separate multifrequency (MF) transmitter and receiver units—control MF interoffice signaling. By assuming these and other routine tasks, the signal processors enable the main processor to handle much more traffic.

The 1A Processor controls common channel interoffice signaling (CCIS) terminals (see *CCIS: A New Signaling System for Faster, More Flexible Telephone Service*, RECORD, *January 1973*). These terminals allow the processor to communicate, by data link, directly with the controlling processors in other No. 4 ESS offices and in similarly equipped 4A ETS offices (4A crossbar offices equipped with electronic translation). CCIS is a fast and efficient method of transferring signaling, network management, and other control information between stored-program-control switching machines. CCIS will lead to much shorter setup

The time-multiplexed switching frame—one of the most important parts of No. 4 ESS—occupies Paul Wiley's attention. He is conducting a troubleshooting operation on the system.

times for customers' calls, which will therefore be connected to their destinations faster.

No. 4 ESS also has switching and trunk maintenance centers, as well as a network management area. These have been carefully planned, and include sophisticated, processor-controlled displays which provide efficient interfaces between human and machine.

No. 4 ESS provides code conversion, alternate routing, centralized automatic message accounting (CAMA), and other standard toll features. With stored program control of all operations, it has flexibility and potential for future expansion of service features. Most call-handling procedures can be altered by modifying programs rather than by changing equipment.

So that No. 4 ESS can keep ahead of increasing traffic, "growth" procedures will be available as

At the time-slot interchange frame, John Lurtz checks equipment status via a teletypewriter (left photo). A salient feature of No. 4 ESS is the facilities it provides for communication between human and machine. An example is the control console (above), a mock-up version of which Ernest Gomez operates here.

required to add trunks, transmission equipment, and switching units. These procedures will be made easier by the duplicate network and central control and by the other units backed up with a replacement that can be switched into service. And because the network is substantially non-blocking, any trunk can be connected to any vacant network port without regard to the traffic influence of any other trunk. Thus, it will not be necessary to balance loads or rearrange existing network terminations as new trunks are added.

All No. 4 ESS equipment is arranged for an efficient modular layout. All parts of the network and terminal equipment handle trunks in groups of 12 or digroups of 24. Individual trunks and special service circuits can also be handled, although less efficiently. Standard floor plans are available for all equipment, maintenance, and operating areas.

This standardization will reduce the lead time from order to service because it will minimize the custom engineering that Western Electric and the Operating Company must perform. In addition, the installation time will be reduced over that for an equivalent crossbar system because No. 4 ESS has fewer frames and wires, employs precut connectorized cables, and undergoes more complete factory testing and more automated field testing.

No. 4 ESS will improve the use of personnel by minimizing much of the routine associated with record keeping, translation revisions (to accommodate changes in trunk codes), and other paperwork. This improvement has been achieved by automating much of the data handling and by employing interactive cathode-ray tube displays at the interface between human and machine. Furthermore, improved maintenance facilities permit much of the trunk testing to be done by one person, without coordinated action by two or more people. Operating Companies, therefore, will not need large staff increases to handle the greatly increased traffic of the future.

Space is no less significant a consideration. In metropolitan telephone buildings, space is becoming increasingly more valuable. No. 4 ESS, because of its modern integrated circuits and digital transmission facilities, in some cases requires only one-fifth the floor space of an equivalent 4A crossbar machine.

As indicated at the beginning of this article, the development of the time-division network is nearing completion. At Bell Labs' Indian Hill facility two large system laboratories (known as Delta and Echo) will be completed later this year and used for confirming the proper interworking of hardware and software. The first No. 4 ESS office (in Chicago) is scheduled to begin commercial service early in 1976.

Supplementary Bibliography for Paper 6

NO. 4 ESS

SYSTEM GENERAL

INTRODUCTION TO NO. 4 ESS
VAUGHAN HE
PROCEEDINGS OF INTERNATIONAL SWITCHING SYMPOSIUM MIT 1972
(E173-1597) P19-25

SYSTEM PLANNING FOR NO. 4 ESS
RITCHIE AE + SMITH WB
INTERNATIONAL SWITCHING SYMPOSIUM RECORD MUNICH 1974 (621.381537/159
P223

NO. 4 ESS WILL TRIPLE TOLL CAPACITY
BELL LABS RECORD 50: 264 (SEP 1972)

SYSTEM FEATURES AND SUBSYSTEMS

DEVELOPMENT OF FEATURES FOR NO. 4 ESS
TUOMENOKSA LS + VAUGHAN HE
INTERNATIONAL SWITCHING SYMPOSIUM RECORD MUNICH 1974
(621.381537/159) P415

THE CIRCUIT MAINTENANCE SYSTEM FOR THE NO. 4 ESS
DEL RIESGO CH
THE NATIONAL ELECTRONICS CONF VOL 29 1974 P33-34

NO. 4 ESS SIGNAL PROCESSOR
TENDICK FH
INTERNATIONAL CONF ON COMMUNICATIONS IEEE 1974 CONF RECORD 74
CHO-859-9-CSCB P417-1

NO. 4 ESS: SWITCHING NETWORK
JANIK J + SLANA MF
P41D-1 OF INTERNATIONAL CONF ON COMMUNICATIONS IEEE 1974
CONF REC 1974 CHO-859-9-CSCB

NO. 4 ESS: SYSTEM ASPECTS OF THE NETWORK
JOHNSON GD + CIESLAK TJ
P41A-1 OF INTERNATIONAL CONF COMMUN IEEE 1974 CONF REC 74
CHO-859-9-CSCB

NETWORK CLOCK FOR THE NO. 4 ESS TIME DIVISION NETWORK
HUTTENHOFF JH + SCHLEICHER WR
P41E-1 OF INT CONF COMMUN IEEE 1974 CONF REC 74 CHO-859-9-CSCB

NO. 4 ESS: VOICEBAND INTERFACE
DAMMAN CL + DAVIS JH
P41C-1 OF INT CONF COMMUN IEEE 1974 CON REC 74 CHO-859-9-CSCB

NO. 4 ESS: 1A TECHNOLOGY
HILSINGER HA + NEVILLE SM
P41B-1 OF INT CONF COMMUN IEEE 1974 CONF REC 74 CHO-859-9-CSCB

GETTING NO. 4 ESS ON LINE ON TIME
GEORGE F. WATSON
BELL LABORATORIES RECORD
VOL. 54 - NO. 4 - APRIL 1976 - P82

NO. 1A PROCESSOR

CONTROLLING LARGE ELECTRONIC SWITCHING SYSTEMS (1A PROCESSOR;
NO. 4 ESS). NEVILLE SM & ROYER RD.
BELL LAB REC 54: 30-33, FEB 1976.

1A PROCESSOR FILE STORE STYTEM
GUERCIO AM + HAGLUND RE
NATIONAL TELECOMMUNICATIONS CONFERENCE (NTC) RECORD
DEC. L-3, 1975 _- PP35-22 - IEEE CAT. NO. 75 CH 1015-7
CSCB VOL. 2

1A PROCESSOR AUXILIARY DATA SYSTEM
BREWSTER JH + KRANZMANN RF
NATIONAL TELECOMMUNICATIONS CONFERENCE (NTC) RECORD
DEC. 1-3, 1975 - PP35-17 - IEEE CAT. NO. 75 CH 1015-7
CSCB VOL. 2

1A PROCESSOR UTILITY SYSTEM
NORDQUIST WR
P324 OF NAT ELECTRON CONF PROC, 1975 (621.381/N27)

1A PROCESSOR CONTROL AND DISPLAY SYSTEM
STOHS NE + YANO PY
P330 OF NAT ELECTRON CONF PROC, 1975 (621.381/N27)

1A PROCESSOR - DEVELOPMENT AND STATUS
STAEHLER RE + GREENWOOD TS
P516 OF INT SWITCHING SYMP RECORD, MUNICH, 1974 (621.381537/I59)

1A PROCESSOR - A HIGH SPEED PROCESSOR FOR SWITCHING
APPLICATIONS
STAEHLER RE
P26-35 OF INT SWITCHING SYMP, MIT, 1972 (E173 I597)

Paper 7

Electronic Switching Center No. 1 (ESC-1)

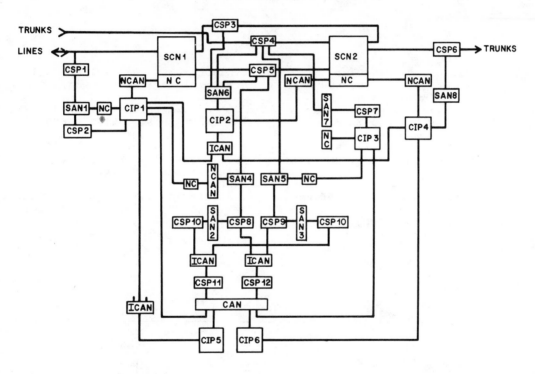

SCNI = LINE LINK NETWORK
SCN2 = TRUNK LINK NETWORK
CIPI = LINE MARKER
CIP2 = JUNCTOR CONTROL
CIP3 = TRUNK LINK NETWORK CONTROL
CIP4 = OUTGOING TRUNK MARKER
CIP5 = NUMBER TRANSLATOR
CIP6 = CODE TRANSLATOR
CSPI = LINE CIRCUIT
CSP2 = LINE SCANNER DETECTOR
CSP3 = RINGING CONTROL
CSP4 = TRUNK JUNCTOR
CSP5 = LOCAL JUNCTOR

CSP6 = OUTGOING TRUNK AND SERVICE CIRCUITS
CSP7 = INCOMING TRUNK SCANNER DETECTOR
CSP8 = LOCAL REGISTER
CSP9 = TRUNK REGISTER
CSPIO = SENDERS
CSPII = SENDER COMMON
CSPI2 = REGISTER COMMON
SANI = LINE SCANNER
SAN2 = (NOT NAMED)
SAN3 = (NOT NAMED)
SAN4 = SERVICE LINK NETWORK
SAN5 = TRUNK SERVICE LINK NETWORK
SAN6 = (NOT NAMED)
SAN7 = INCOMING TRUNK SCANNER
SAN8 = (NOT NAMED)

THE ESC-1—AN ELECTRONIC SWITCHING SYSTEM WITH DISTRIBUTED CONTROL

Adam A. Jorgensen

Stromberg-Carlson
Rochester, New York

IN THE COURSE OF PLANNING THE ELECTRONIC SWITCHING SYSTEM, NOW KNOWN AS STROMBERG-CARLSON'S ESC-1, IT WAS AN IMPORTANT CONSIDERATION TO FIND A SYSTEM ORGANIZATION THAT WOULD AVOID THE NECESSITY FOR A LARGE CONSTANT SIZE COMMON CONTROL THAT WOULD ALWAYS BE REQUIRED EVEN FOR THE SMALLER SIZE SYSTEM.

UNLESS A SOLUTION WAS FOUND WE COULD NOT EXPECT TO ATTAIN AN ECONOMICAL COMMON CONTROL SWITCHING MACHINE THAT WOULD BRING THE ADVANTAGES OF ELECTRONIC SWITCHING TO THE MARKET AREA OF THE SMALLER RURAL EXCHANGES IN SIZES UNDER 4000 LINES, BECAUSE A LARGE HIGHLY CENTRALIZED COMMON CONTROL WOULD LOAD THE COST PER LINE TOO HEAVILY IN SMALLER EXCHANGE SIZES.

IT WAS RECOGNIZED FROM THE BEGINNING THAT A DISTRIBUTED COMMON CONTROL ARRANGEMENT MIGHT NOT GIVE THE MAXIMUM EFFICIENCY IN THE LARGER EXCHANGE SIZES IN TERMS OF COST PER LINE. NOW, HOWEVER, AFTER SEVERAL SYSTEMS HAVE BEEN BUILT AND PLACED IN SERVICE WE ARE QUITE CONVINCED THAT THE PENALTY ON THE LARGER SYSTEMS, IF THERE IS ANY PENALTY AT ALL, IS VERY NOMINAL.

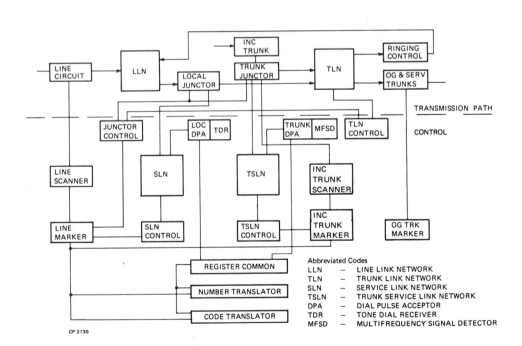

Abbreviated Codes
LLN — LINE LINK NETWORK
TLN — TRUNK LINK NETWORK
SLN — SERVICE LINK NETWORK
TSLN — TRUNK SERVICE LINK NETWORK
DPA — DIAL PULSE ACCEPTOR
TDR — TONE DIAL RECEIVER
MFSD — MULTIFREQUENCY SIGNAL DETECTOR

CP 2730

FIGURE I. ELECTRONIC SWITCHING, BLOCK DIAGRAM.

Reprinted from *1972 IEEE Int. Switching Symp. Rec.*, June 6-9, 1972, pp. 188-194.

SYSTEM DESCRIPTION

FIGURE 1 SHOWS THE FUNCTIONAL SYSTEM LAYOUTS IN BLOCK DIAGRAM FORM. THE FUNCTIONAL ELEMENTS OF THE ESC CAN, GENERALLY SPEAKING BE DIVIDED INTO FOUR BASIC AREAS: (1) SWITCHING NETWORK WHICH INCLUDES LINE CIRCUITS, LINE LINK NETWORK, TRUNK LINK NETWORK, JUNCTORS AND TRUNKS; (2) COMMON CONTROL EQUIPMENT WHICH INCLUDES CONTROLS, SCANNERS, MARKERS, REGISTERS AND TRANSLATORS; (3) TEST AND SUPERVISORY EQUIPMENT; AND (4) POWER EQUIPMENT AND DISTRIBUTION FRAMES.

(1) THE SWITCHING NETWORK ESTABLISHES A 2-WIRE PATH FOR ANALOG (VOICE) TRANSMISSION AND SIGNALING. IN ADDITION TO INTERCONNECTING LINES AND TRUNKS, THIS NETWORK INTERCONNECTS VARIOUS TYPES OF SERVICE TRUNKS.

THE CROSSPOINTS IN THE SWITCHING NETWORK USE GLASS REED SWITCHES WITH GOLD-PLATED CONTACTS. THE NETWORKS ARE BUILT UP FROM SWITCHING MODULES. THE MODULES ARE MANUFACTURED AS 3 BY 5, 4 BY 5 OR 5 BY 5 CROSSPOINT ASSEMBLIES.

EACH CROSSPOINT USES FOUR (4) REED SWITCHES, ONE EACH FOR CONNECTING TIP AND RING, ONE FOR CONNECTING THE SLEEVE LEAD AND ONE FOR KEEPING THE HOLD-WINDING ENERGIZED DURING THE CONNECTION.

BESIDES THE HOLD-WINDING, THE CROSSPOINT COIL HAS AN OPERATE WINDING. THE OPERATE WINDING IS WIRED IN SERIES WITH THE SO-CALLED MARK LEAD. THE MARK LEAD IS USED AS THE IDLE-BUSY NETWORK MEMORY AND FOR PATH FINDING PURPOSES. THE SLEEVE LEAD IS USED FOR HOLDING THE CROSSPOINT. A SLEEVE INDICATES BUSY WHEN IT IS GROUNDED AND IDLE WHEN IT IS AT NEGATIVE POTENTIAL.

PATHFINDING IS ACCOMPLISHED BY MEANS OF ELECTRONIC SCANNERS WHICH SEARCH FOR FREE PATHS THROUGH THE NETWORK USING THE MARK LEADS AND OPERATE WINDINGS OF THE CROSSPOINTS AS A BUSY/IDLE MAP OF THE NETWORK. THE SCANNERS ARE CONNECTED TO A CURRENT DETECTOR WHICH SENSES A FREE PATH. WHEN A FREE PATH IS FOUND, THE SCANNER STOPS AND APPLIES A STEADY DC POTENTIAL TO THE MARK LEAD WHICH ENERGIZES THE OPERATE WINDINGS OF THE SELECTED CROSS POINTS FOR THE ENTIRE PATH. AFTER THE OPERATE POTENTIAL HAS BEEN APPLIED FOR A SHORT TIME, APPROXIMATELY 2 MILLISECONDS, ALL SELECTED CROSSPOINT CONTACTS HAVE OPERATED. NEXT, A GROUND IS APPLIED TO THE SLEEVE FROM THE JUNCTOR OR TRUNK WHICHEVER APPLIES. THIS GROUND WILL MAINTAIN THE CONNECTION AS LONG AS THE CONNECTION STAYS UP.

THE OPERATION DESCRIBED ILLUSTRATES ONE CASE OF DISTRIBUTED CONTROL USED IN THIS SYSTEM. THE PATHFINDING AND THE PATH MARKING MECHANISM ARE INTEGRATED WITH THE MATRIX ELEMENTS. IN OTHER WORDS, THE MARKERS AND PATHFINDING EQUIPMENT GROWS AS THE MATRIX GROWS.

FIGURE 2 SHOWS IN A SIMPLE BLOCK DIAGRAM FORM THE TRANSMISSION SWITCHING NETWORK.

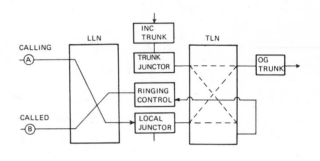

FIGURE 2. TRANSMISSION SWITCHING NETWORK.

IT CONSISTS OF THE TWO MAIN NETWORKS, THE LINE LINK NETWORK (LLN) AND THE TRUNK LINK NETWORK (TLN). THE TWO ARE INTERCONNECTED BY RELAY CIRCUITS WHICH PROVIDE LOOP SUPERVISION, SIGNALING AND INTERFACES WITH THE COMMON CONTROL.

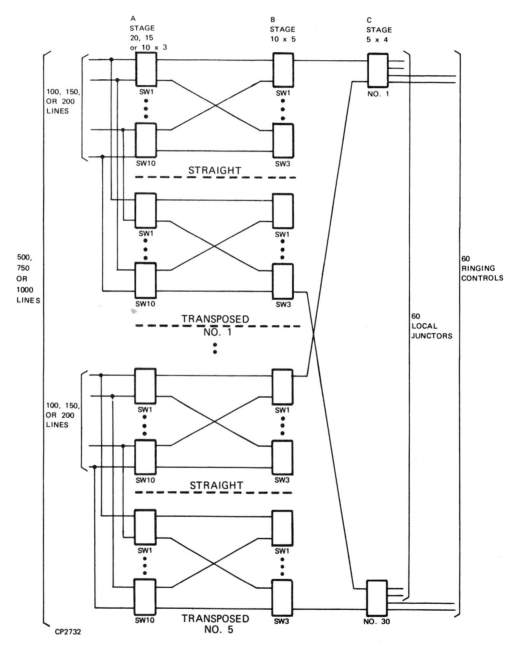

FIGURE 3. LINE LINK NETWORK (LLN).

CP2732

ISS 72

A MORE DETAILED DIAGRAM OF THE LINE LINK NETWORK IS SHOWN ON FIGURE 3. WITHOUT GOING INTO TOO MUCH DETAIL, IT IS SEEN THAT THE LINE LINK NETWORK IS A 3-STAGE NETWORK, ORGANIZED AS A SO-CALLED FAN-TYPE NETWORK, THAT IS, FROM EACH INPUT PORT THERE IS ONE, AND ONLY ONE, POSSIBLE PATH TO EVERY OUTPUT PORT. THE LINE LINK NETWORK CAN BE ARRANGED FOR VARIOUS DEGREES OF CONCENTRATION DEPENDING ON THE TRAFFIC REQUIRED BY THE NETWORK.

THE LINE LINK NETWORK ALSO UTILIZES A SO-CALLED TRANSPOSITION SCHEME, AS SHOWN ON FIGURE 3. WITH TRANSPOSITION EACH LINE IS SERVED BY TWO SEPARATE MATRIX GROUPS, NAMELY ONE "STRAIGHT" AND ONE "TRANSPOSED". THE TRANSPOSITION SCHEME PROVIDES FOR A HIGH DEGREE OF AVERAGING OF TRAFFIC FLUCTUATIONS WITHIN EACH BLOCK OF 100 LINES.

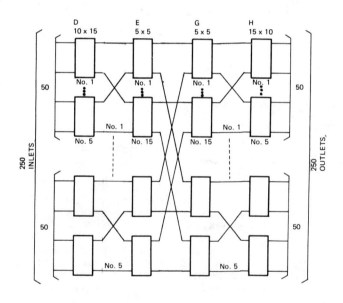

FIGURE 4. FOUR-STAGE TRUNK LINK NETWORK (TLN).

FIGURE 4 SHOWS A SECTION OF THE TRUNK LINK NETWORK.

THIS SECTION REPRESENTS THE SMALLEST TLN CONFIGURATION WITH 250 INLETS AND 250 OUTLETS. IT HAS FOUR STAGES AS SHOWN,

BUT CAN GROW TO 5000 INLETS AND 5000 OUTLETS BY INTERPOSING AN F-STAGE BETWEEN THE "E" AND "G" STAGES. ACTUALLY, THE F-STAGE IS SPLIT IN TWO, AN FA AND AN FB STAGE, SO THAT A FULLY DEVELOPED TLN HAS SIX (6) STAGES. AS A MATTER OF INTEREST THE TLN IS ARRANGED MECHANICALLY SO THAT IT CAN GROW BY PLUGGING TOGETHER FACTORY MADE UNITS WITH STANDARD PRE-FABRICATED PLUG-IN CABLES.

JUNCTORS SERVE TO EXTEND THE TRANSMISSION PATH FROM ONE SWITCHING NETWORK TO ANOTHER. THEY CONTAIN THE BATTERY FEED BRIDGES WHICH FEED THE CALLING AND CALLED PARTIES, AND MAINTAIN SUPERVISION OF THE TRANSMISSION LOOPS. AS A POINT OF INTEREST, THEY DO NOT EMPLOY A CONVENTIONAL IMPULSING RELAY, BUT A SATURABLE REACTOR CIRCUIT WHICH HAS OBVIOUS ADVANTAGES OVER AN IMPULSING RELAY. THE JUNCTORS ALSO SERVE AS THE CONNECTING LINK TO THE REGISTERS AND HENCE THE COMMON CONTROL. THE REGISTER ACCESS IS PROVIDED VIA A SPECIAL MATRIX. THE SERVICE LINK NETWORK WHICH WILL BE DESCRIBED LATER.

THE JUNCTORS FURTHER SERVE TO SEND BUSY TONE TO PARTIES THAT ENCOUNTER LINE BUSY OR EQUIPMENT BUSY.

RINGING CONTROL. INDIVIDUAL RINGING CONTROLS ARE PLACED IN THE TERMINATING PATHS FROM THE TRUNK LINK NETWORK BACK TO THE LINE LINK NETWORK. EACH PATH HAS ITS OWN RINGING CONTROL WITH ITS ASSOCIATED RING TRIP CIRCUIT. THE RINGING CONTROLS RECEIVE THE RINGING INSTRUCTIONS FROM THE NUMBER TRANSLATOR VIA A SYSTEM OF SIGNAL BUSSES.

LINE CIRCUITS. THE LINE CIRCUIT PROVIDES SIGNALS TO THE LINE SCANNER WHEN A SUBSCRIBER GOES OFF-HOOK. ON TERMINATING A CALL TO A LINE, THE LINE CIRCUIT PROVIDES THE BUSY/IDLE CONDITION INFORMATION TO THE COMMON CONTROL. ALL LINE CIRCUITS ARE OF THE LOCKOUT TYPE.

TRUNK CIRCUITS. THERE ARE FOUR (4) GENERAL CLASSES OF TRUNK CIRCUITS: INCOMING TRUNKS, OUTGOING TRUNKS, 2-WAY TRUNKS AND SERVICE TRUNKS. ALL BUT THE SERVICE TRUNKS CAN BE EITHER LOOP OR E & M TYPE.

THE SERVICE TRUNKS ARE USED FOR TAPE ANNOUNCERS, INTERCEPT, INFORMATION AND REPAIR, INSPECTORS RINGBACK, REVERTIVE CALL AND OTHERS.

COMMON CONTROL

The general organization of the Common Control is shown on Figure 5.

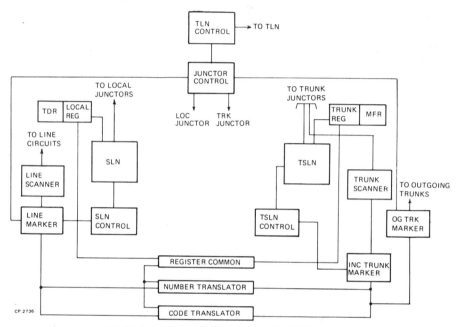

FIGURE 5. COMMON CONTROL, BLOCK DIAGRAM.

The Common Control connects to the transmission networks mainly at four points: (1) at the line scanner to the line circuits; (2) at the service link network (SLN) to the local junctors; (3) at the Trunk Service Link Network (TSLN) to the trunk junctors; and (4) at the Outgoing Trunk Marker to the Outgoing Trunks.

All Common Control Circuits or groups of Common Control Circuits are duplicated and interconnected by switchover circuits in case of failure of one or more Common Control Circuits. The switchover circuits and their associated monitor and control circuits are not shown on the block diagram.

Most of the Common Control Circuits are sectionalized in such a way that a system can grow in modular fashion by adding sections of common controls as the need arises.

Line Scanner. The Line Scanner continuously scans the line circuits for lines going off-hook.

The Line Scanner completes a scan of 1000 lines in less than 4 milliseconds. The Line Scanner operates in both the originating and in the terminating mode.

When a line going off-hook is found by the line scanner, it will stop. The position of the scanner indicates the equipment number of the line calling for service. This information is sent to the line marker which, in turn, starts control circuits to set up a path from a free local register, through the Service Link Network and the Line Link Network to the calling line. After the register is connected, the line scanner restarts and searches for other lines requesting service.

ISS 72

When a call has to be terminated, the Line Scanner is instructed by the Number Translator to stop at the Terminating Number. The Line Scanner will in turn, instruct the Line Marker to mark the terminating line, so that a path can be completed through the TLN, a Ringing Control, through the LLN to the terminating line.

In marking a line, the Line Marker places a negative 48 volt marking potential on the mark lead of the line.

The Incoming Trunk Scanner serves a function quite similar to that of the Line Scanner. It continuously scans a group of 300 trunks for service request. A trunk service request will be detected in less than 1.3 milliseconds. Similarly the Incoming Trunk Marker works with the Incoming Trunk Scanner to mark the mark lead for the Incoming Trunk requesting service.

The Incoming Trunk Marker also sets in motion the pathfinding mechanism which will connect a free Incoming Register with the Incoming Trunk via the Trunk Service Link Network.

The Outgoing Trunk Marker serves to mark a trunk group requested by an Outgoing Call. It receives its instructions from either the Code Translator or the Number Translator.

If the trunk group is busy, it will request an alternate Trunk Group Number from the Code Translator, or, if no alternate trunk group is avaible, it will instruct the Junctor to return equipment busy tone.

The two Service Link Networks (SLN and TSLN) serve to connect local junctors and incoming junctors to local registers and incoming registers respectively. They are 4-wire networks providing six switched connections between the registers and the junctors. The main difference between SLN and TSLN is that the SLN is a two stage network while the TSLN is a 3-stage network, the latter providing a higher grade of service for Incoming Trunks to Incoming Registers — than the grade of service afforded local calls.

Registers are organized in groups of twenty (20), with one Local Register Group serving from 500 to 1000 lines depending on traffic and one Incoming Register Group serving up to 300 trunks.

All registers consist of a relay circuit interface called the DPA and an electronic register storage and logic circuit.

Local registers have access to Tone Dial Receivers and Party Identification and Coin Detection circuits. Incoming Registers may have access to MF receivers.

All registers have access to senders, which, under control of the Code Translators provide all the various modes of sending required by a Common Control office. The senders will send the calling party's Directory Number (ANI) on DDD calls under control of the distant register, when required.

Register groups interface with register common circuits which, in turn, interface with the Number Translator and Code Translator.

The registers are connected with the translators on a time-slot basis via the Register Common circuits.

One Register Common can serve up to sixty (60) registers and a maximum of four (4) register commons can be handled by the Translators.

The use of time division between registers and translators affords a high degree of flexibility and economy in utilizing the intelligence stored in the translators.

The Number Translator performs two functions: On an Originating Call it translates the dialed directory number stored in the register into the equipment location number needed by the markers for terminating the call, on DDD calls it provides the directory number from the equipment number so that calling party's directory number can be sent to the distant DDD register.

In addition, the Number Translator provides classes of service for originating and terminating numbers. It will provide a maximum of 225 different classes of service.

The Number Translator utilizes the well-known dimond-ring principle. Large ferrite cores, each equipped with a pick-up coil are mounted on a large panel.

Variable jumpers are threaded through the cores in such asway as to provide the proper translation. There is one jumper for each equipment number and one jumper for each directory number. When a translation is needed, a current pulse is sent through the jumper. By transformer action, all cores traversed by the jumper will be activated and the pick-up coils on these cores will furnish the translation.

EACH CORE HAS TWO PICK-UP WINDINGS FOR REDUNDANCY. EACH OF THE TWO WINDINGS GO TO A SEPARATE TRANSLATOR CIRCUIT, ONE OF WHICH IS ON-LINE AND THE OTHER ONE IS ON STAND-BY.

THE NUMBER TRANSLATOR PROVIDES A MAXIMUM OF 10,000 EQUIPMENT NUMBERS AND 15,000 DIRECTORY NUMBERS, WHICH REPRESENTS THE ULTIMATE SIZE OF THE SYSTEM.

THE NUMBER TRANSLATOR ALSO PROVIDES RINGING CODE INFORMATION FOR THE RINGING CONTROLS AND REVERTING CALL CIRCUITS. IT PROVIDES INFORMATION FOR AUTOMATIC PRINT-OUT OF CALLING AND CALLED NUMBERS FOR MALICIOUS CALL TRACING, AND FOR PRINTOUT IF A CALL TIMES OUT OR ENCOUNTERS TROUBLE.

THE NUMBER TRANSLATOR HANDLES PBX NUMBER HUNTING AND PBX NIGHT SERVICE. IT WILL HANDLE CONSECUTIVE AS WELL AS NON-CONSECUTIVE PBX NUMBERS.

THE CODE TRANSLATOR TRANSLATES OFFICE CODES INTO ROUTING INFORMATION REQUIRED BY THE SENDERS IN ORDER TO REACH ANY DESTINATION REQUIRED BY ANY CALLING SUBSCRIBER OR TRUNK.

IT PROVIDES TRANSLATION FOR 1 TO 6 DIGIT CODES, ALTERNATE ROUTING WITH ONE PRIMARY TO THREE ALTERNATE ROUTES, ROUTING BY CLASS-OF-SERVICE, ROUTING BY CRITICAL TIME-OUT.

IT PROVIDES START OF CRITICAL TIMING, CALL RESTRICTION BY CLASS-OF-SERVICE, EMERGENCY AND OPERATOR CALLS FROM PAY-STATIONS WITHOUT DEPOSIT OF COIN.

IT PROVIDES ALL REQUIRED MODES OF SENDING AND SIGNALING AS REQUIRED BY DISTANT OFFICE REGISTERS.

THE CODE TRANSLATOR, LIKE THE NUMBER TRANSLATOR, USES THE DIMON-RING PRINCIPLE AND SERVES ALL REGISTERS ON A TIME-SHARED BASIS.

MAINTENANCE FACILITIES

THE ESC SYSTEM IS EQUIPPED WITH EXTENSIVE MAINTENANCE FACILITIES.

EACH CALL GOING THROUGH THE SYSTEM IS MONITORED AUTOMATICALLY FOR PROPER COMPLETION. WHENEVER A CALL ENCOUNTERS A TROUBLE CONDITION, AN AUTOMATIC PRINT-OUT IS PERFORMED. AN ELECTRIC TYPEWRITER PRINTS ALL DATA ASSOCIATED WITH THE CALL, SUCH AS THE CALLING NUMBER, THE TERMINATING NUMBER, THE IDENTIFYING NUMBERS OF THE CIRCUITS AND PATHS INVOLVED ETC., IN ADDITION TO A CODE FOR THE TYPE OF TROUBLE ENCOUNTERED. IT ALSO PRINTS THE TIME AND DATA FOR THE TROUBLE.

THE FAULT MONITOR SYSTEM ALSO ENGAGES THE SWITCH-OVER CIRCUITS, SO THAT, IF A FAULT CONDITION APPEARS TO BE IN A CERTAIN COMMON CONTROL GROUP, THE SYSTEM WILL AUTOMATICALLY SWITCH TO THE STANDBY CIRCUITS.

A MAINTENANCE CONSOLE PROVIDES A MAINTENANCE MAN WITH FACILITIES FOR SELECTING AND ROUTING ALL CIRCUITS IN THE OFFICE. THE MAINTENANCE CONSOLE ALSO DIS-PLAYS THE CONTENTS IN REGISTERS, COMMON CONTROL CIRCUITS, ETC., AND SERVES AS AN AID IN QUICKLY LOCATING A FAULTY CIRCUIT.

AN AUTOMATIC CALL GENERATOR IS PROVIDED WHICH CAN BE PROGRAMMED TO GENERATE A SERIES OF CALLS GOING THROUGH THE SYSTEM. THE AUTOMATIC CALL GENERATOR MONITORS THE COMPLETION OF THE CALL AND RECORDS, ON PEG COUNT METERS, THE NUMBER OF CALLS GENERATED, AND THE NUMBER OF CALLS NOT COMPLETED. A MAXIMUM OF FORTY (40) DIFFERENT CALLS CAN BE PROGRAMMED INTO THE AUTOMATIC CALL GENERATOR.

THE SYSTEM WAS FIELD-TRIALED IN HINCKLEY, OHIO, IN 1970, AND IS NOW IN FULL PRODUCTION.

Paper 8

North Electronically Controlled Crossbar Switching System No. 1 (NX-1E)

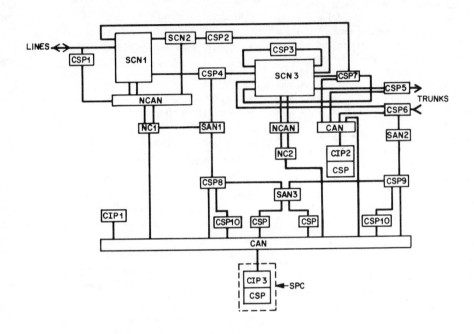

SCN1	= SUBSCRIBER STAGES A & B		CSP6	= INCOMING TRUNK
SCN2	= SUBSCRIBER STAGE C		CSP7	= SPECIAL FEATURE TRUNK
SCN3	= GROUP SELECTOR		CSP8	= REGISTER-SENDER ORIGINATING
CIP1	= DATA MEMORY AND CONTROLLER		CSP9	= REGISTER-SENDER INCOMING
CIP2	= TRUNK SUPERVISION CONTROLLER(S)		CSP10	= ELECTRONIC CODE RECEIVERS
CIP3	= CENTRAL PROCESSOR UNIT		NC1	= SUBSCRIBER LINE MARKER
CSP1	= LINE CIRCUIT		NC2	= GROUP SELECTOR MARKER
CSP2	= TERMINATING JUNCTOR .		SAN1	= SUBSCRIBER REGISTER LINK
CSP3	= TOLL TICKETING JUNCTOR (WRAP-AROUND)		SAN2	= TRUNK REGISTER LINK
CSP4	= ORIGINATING JUNCTOR		SAN3	= MULTIFREQUENCY RECEIVER LINK
CSP5	= OUTGOING TRUNK		SPC	= PROCESSOR

NX-1E, an Electronically Controlled Crossbar Switching System

ENN ARO, MEMBER, IEEE, T. K. CHENEY, JAMES R. MCMULLEN, MEMBER, IEEE, AND
CARL B. NENNERFELT, SENIOR MEMBER, IEEE

Abstract—A central office crossbar switching system with functionally separate electronic common control units is described. The common control subsystem is divided into routing control, trunk supervision control, and data storage functions. Routing control is performed by a stored program controlled electronic processor. Trunk supervision control is accomplished on an optional basis either by a common wired logic electronic control unit or by logic in individual trunk circuits which can have access to the routing control processor for trunk identifying purposes. Data storage is provided in electrically alterable ferrite core memory banks. All common control subsystems are redundant with automatic switchover in case of failure. Crossbar switches are used in the switching matrix. Marker logic and simple switching functions in trunk and receiver/sender circuits are designed with conventional relay techniques. The switching system incorporates new custom calling and Centrex features. It provides for improved administrative capabilities and can be used as an integral part to expand an existing electromechanical crossbar system in an evolutionary fashion.

INTRODUCTION

EACH NEW generation of switching equipment is designed to satisfy both the current user requirements and his anticipated future needs. This is accomplished by design features which allow for ease of making necessary equipment modifications in areas affected by changing requirements on system operation and performance.

The attainable degree of such built-in flexibility is limited by considerations of economy and state of the art in equipment implementation techniques. Consequently, as more new services, increased performance, and improved operating economics are demanded by the user, an obsolescence point will be gradually reached in the life of any switching system. This occurs when for economical or technical reasons it is no longer feasible to make all the required modifications in the system, although user requirements at the time of its introduction were more than adequately satisfied.

When electromechanical common control switching systems were introduced several decades ago, their capabilities significantly exceeded existing needs with respect to call handling and routing, switching matrix utilization, and operating economy. Even today these systems are fully adequate in many applications.

Paper 70TP63-COM, approved by the Communication Switching Committee of the IEEE Communication Technology Group for publication after presentation at the 1970 IEEE International Conference on Communications, San Francisco, Calif., June 8–10. Manuscript received April 7, 1970.

The authors are with North Electric Company, Galion, Ohio 44833.

The recent demand for new switching services has made mandatory a control and processing capability for many switching applications hereto available only in the most sophisticated and, needless to emphasize, rather expensive electronic systems. This development has been stimulated by new needs of the information industry on one hand and by the capabilities of modern common control systems coupled with electronic technology on the other.

Representative of novel switching services are the custom calling features: call forwarding and abbreviated dialing which require individual information storage and an on-line data modification capability on a per subscriber basis. Three-way conference, inquiry, and call waiting features in addition to data manipulation capability also need selective access to three-way calling facilities. Centralized and individually customized multi-private branch exchange(PBX) operation, expanded call routing, features accommodating international dialing, and various types of toll ticketing handling, switching of data (and video) traffic, automatic machine-to-machine communications, interworking with digital facilities, etc., are other examples of new demands on switching systems. In addition to powerful control capabilities to meet these requirements, the need for economical customization of individual central offices to match specific user demands and to provide the proper interface with the surrounding switching and transmission facilities is apparent.

The capability to design powerful logic systems which are required to meet the increasing requirements for sophistication in automatic switching control has been aptly demonstrated by the computer industry. Besides state of the art in technology, there are, however, several other equally significant factors to be considered in introducing a new generation of switching equipment. The communications switching industry, which has a major investment in manpower and equipment, is highly dependent on an orderly growth of an integrated co-operating continental (and global) network consisting of several equipment generations of a large variety of makes. It is providing to its users a vital service which must remain available and essentially uninterrupted during equipment malfunction, facility expansion, and overload conditions. These considerations were instrumental in establishing the objectives for the development of the NX-1E switching system which is described in this paper.

Reprinted from *IEEE Trans. Commun. Technol.*, vol. COM-18, pp. 734–739, Dec. 1970.

OBJECTIVES

The design concept was chosen to meet the following criteria.

1) Accommodate all current and presently anticipated facilities of class 4 or 5 central offices and centralized multi-PBXs.

2) Require a minimum of engineering for customizing the office for a specific application.

3) Protect the investment of operating companies in existing switching equipment by extending its useful life.

4) Facilitate orderly and gradual adaption of personnel, maintenance, and operation procedures to the new system.

5) Simplify and reduce the cost of system maintenance and administration.

6) Achieve a lower total system cost as compared to current systems.

7) Provide for economical expansion of installed systems.

8) Include flexibility for accommodating currently unanticipated system requirements.

9) Make provisions for taking advantage of future advances in technology for reducing system cost or improving performance without necessitating major redesign.

10) Enhance system reliability and maintainability over current equipment.

11) Take full advantage of in-house design know-how and production facilities while developing new capabilities as required.

To protect customer investment, provide continuity in system operation and maintenance procedures, and to use in-house capabilities most efficiently, the new system design was based on the philosophy of the NX-1D electromechanical common control crossbar system which has been in production at North Electric Company during the past fifteen years. Electronics was introduced into the system where feasible to increase the power of common control logic and take advantage of its speed, inherent reliability, and potential for cost savings. Software logic was used where applicable to obtain future flexibility, minimize custom engineering, simplify office administration, and provide maintenance diagnostics. Expansion economy and provisions for applying future technology to suitable parts of the system were achieved with proper functional modularity.

The remaining sections of this paper outline the application of these criteria to the NX-1E system design. A brief description of the NX-1D system is also given to illustrate the similarity and differences between the two systems.

NX-1D SYSTEM

The basic purpose of a switching system is to provide transmission paths between its terminals as directed by each individual user. Service requests from users are transmitted to the switching equipment in the form of appropriate command signals.

To accomplish its function, a switching system is comprised of two basic functional blocks: the switching matrix with its associated terminal circuits, and the control subsystem, which in a common control switching system is implemented as a distinct entity separate from the switching matrix elements. The control subsystem interprets service requests, analyses routing and supervision information, and generates the necessary control signals for operating the switching matrix or communicating with equipment such as subscriber instruments or other switching systems which are connected to the matrix terminals.

In the electromechanical NX-1D system (see Fig. 1) the matrix is composed of crossbar switches, arranged in three stage line selector arrays and in two or three stage group selector units. Incoming and outgoing trunk circuits terminate on the group selector, while subscriber lines are connected to the line group terminals. Intraoffice junctors (subscriber originating and terminating trunks) provide access to common control devices, and they constitute the linkage between the line and group selector stages.

The control subsystem in NX-1D is implemented with relay logic comprising registers and senders for originating and terminating address signaling, number group and translator units for determining call routing, markers for controlling the setting of line and group selector matrix crosspoints, and all necessary linkage for access to the proper control points. Control circuitry in the form of relay type line and trunk supervision logic and certain class of service indications is contained in individual line and trunk terminal equipment.

The control subsystem communicates with line and trunk circuits via register and sender access links which can connect the common control equipment to the transmission path of any line or trunk circuit. Internal communication of control signals to and from the markers is accomplished via the speech path utilizing a special multi-level dc signaling code. As register and sender control functions are implemented in the form of wired relay logic and all service classmark, number group and translator routing data are provided in the form of wired straps; engineering is required for system application, sometimes demanding hardware modification for a particular installation. This design approach makes necessary restrapping of wired system data for administration of daily service and routing changes in an operating NX-1D system. New features requiring machine controlled temporary changes in system data (such as call transfer, call waiting, abbreviated dialing, etc.) or capability for processing different length routing codes and storing more digits than the equipment was originally designed for are very difficult and rather expensive to implement.

In contrast, the switching matrix of NX-1D, due to its standardized modular design, requires no special engineering to meet capacity and performance criteria for individual central office installations. Furthermore,

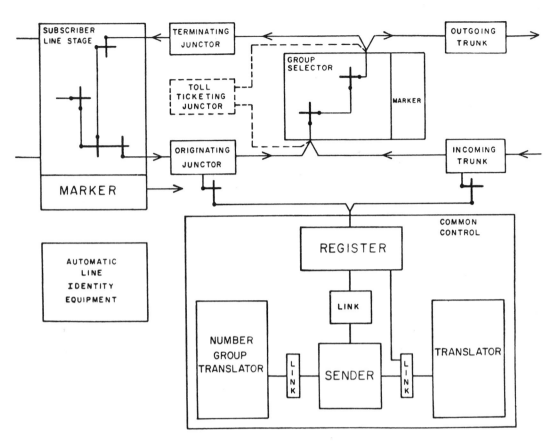

Fig. 1.   NX-1D system.

the crossbar switch is comparable from technical standpoint and superior in cost to other modern switching devices.

NX-1E System Concept

In establishing the design criteria for the new NX-1E central office (Fig. 2), it was decided to use the NX-1D matrix in the new system. This is desirable for providing internal compatibility between the two systems and constitutes a very satisfactory choice in terms of cost and operational characteristics.

New principles, however, were emphasized in the design of the NX-1E common control complex. The common control function of a switching system can be divided into three major subfunctions. They are as follows:

routing control—comprising register and sender functions;

supervision control—consisting of line and trunk supervision functions;

data base—memory—providing for storage of all system data (such as number group, translator, and classmark information) and other system parameters.

The common control equipment of NX-1E was accordingly consolidated into three distinct subsystems of the preceding types. The routing control subsystem is implemented in the form of an integrated circuit (IC) stored program processor (designated APZ 142) which performs all register and sender logic in software for a large number of physical receiver/sender (RS) units. The RS units are simple relay sets and perform all switching functions in connection with dial and code pulse sending and receiving. In comparison to the hardwired register-sender logic of the NX-1D, custom engineering of register and sender functions in NX-1E is reduced to relatively simple software modifications.

Since most new custom features are related to the routing control function, introduction of these is greatly simplified with software. Additionally, the flexibility gained through stored program operation makes possible improved and simplified maintenance and administrative functions. Adaptability to future routine and custom call handling requirements is another benefit gained with stored program control.

The data memory subsystem of NX-1E complements and enhances the operation of the routing control complex. It is implemented with electronic ferrite core READ/WRITE memories and contains all permanent and semipermanent system data.

A separate trunk supervision control unit (SCU) was originally visualized as part of the NX-1E system. Its

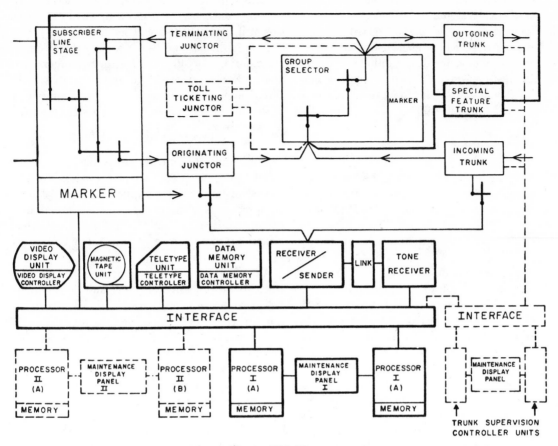

Fig. 2.   NX-1E system.

application would simplify central office trunk circuits and provide additional control capabilities for example in implementing three-way calling features through the use of three-port pooled intraoffice trunks which are wrapped around the group selector with the third port line terminal ended. A common unit of this type performs the supervision logic function in a time shared mode for a large number of central office and special features trunks. As the supervision sequences are well defined and do not vary between individual offices, the SCU was implemented with hardwired IC logic to provide a cost effective and reliable design.

An IC wired logic supervision control processor was designed and successfully tested in the laboratory for the trunk supervision function. In the final system architecture it was decided, however, to delay the introduction of the SCU in order to take advantage of developments in large scale integration and in hybrid technology.

For the initial NX-1E system supervision logic was retained in individual circuits similar to the NX-1D system. One of the main advantages of a centralized supervision logic unit was achieved by equipping means of identifying individual trunks to the routing control logic via simple interface circuits. Thus assignment of features to specific trunks and routing of calls to proper

three-way circuits for call waiting was made possible under control of the routing processor.

All control units are interconnected via a common bus system which also provides access to the RS units. Teletypewriters and magnetic tape units are provided on the bus for maintenance and administrative functions. All common control units are duplicated with automatic switchover between the redundant units, and the common bus system is also duplicated for reliability reasons.

The control units are modular and of simple inexpensive design with adequate processing capacity for small systems to provide for cost effective expansion of system capacity and for economical installations both in small and large initial system sizes. As the capacity of a particular type of control unit is exhausted, additional units can be added as required to properly service the given system configuration.

For the purpose of direct compatibility with existing NX-1D installations, the same internal control signaling paths and codes are used in both systems. Adapters connected to the common bus system provide access to operation data between the NX-1D and NX-1E system common control complexes in a hybrid installation. Compatibility between NX-1D and NX-1E is also simplified by retaining the NX-1D type markers which provide a suitable interface to the switching matrix and are controlled via the speech path by the same type of control signals in both systems.

ICs on plug-in cards are used in all electronic units except on the common bus, where special hybrid microcircuits and discrete components are employed. Manufacturing, testing, installation, and expansion are simplified by the modular design of the functional subunits, which are provided with plug-in cables.

Features and Capabilities

The NX-1E system can be configured either as a class 4, class 5, or a combination class 4 and 5 central office. It can also be installed as a centralized multi-PBX with or without central office capabilities. The system is equipped to provide both standard and custom calling features.

Due to the power and flexibility of stored program control in the routing subsystem, virtually any type numbering plan can be accommodated in the digit analysis and interpretation logic. This includes features such as international dialing, use of single or multi-digit access codes to special services, digit additions and deletions for interworking with direct control offices, use of various abbreviated calling numbers, recognizing and resolving of ambiguities between office and area or abbreviated dialing codes, etc. The power of digit analysis is further enhanced by the capability of providing originating and terminating service classmarks as required for trunk and line terminals to indicate on an individual terminal basis desired differences in call handling.

Since the classmarks are stored in an electrically alterable data-memory, temporary classmark and associated data changes can be made for specific line terminals by the routing control processor in order to provide additional flexibility in changing the call handling procedures as special custom features are exercised at the initiation or during the progress of a call. Such is the case, for example, when information is temporarily stored in the data memory on a per call basis to make possible routing of a third party to an established connection of a subscriber who is provided with the call waiting feature.

Equipment and associated program logic is implemented for tone or dial pulse signaling on both subscriber lines and trunks. Signaling means and control logic are provided for interworking with all U. S. toll service and ticketing systems currently in use. Automatic line (or terminal) identification is a standard feature of the system. Single and multiparty lines are handled with group classmarks or with individual classmarks on a per subscriber basis when calling line identification is possible.

New subscriber controlled custom calling features such as abbreviated dialing, call forwarding, three-way calling, and call waiting are available as optional services. PBX facilities include a variety of customized service packages of the Centrex type for business, hotel/motel, airport, hospital, and other specialized uses.

Maximum size of the NX-1E central office is 20 000 terminations or 40 000 directory numbers, the same as the NX-1D system. Internal compatibility permits direct expansion of existing NX-1D offices in the field with the "E" equipment to full system size.

Maintenance and Administration

The routing control processors are duplicated for redundancy purposes and perform automatic switchover in case of failure. This duplication of the common control equipment is terminated at the individual interface drivers and sensors in the interface unit, thus enabling either processor in a redundant pair access to each individual device.

As failures of the routing control subsystem affect only calls in the process of routing and do not disturb established connections, synchronization between on- and off-line processors is not provided in order to simplify switchover circuitry and take advantage of the idle off-line processor power for tasks not directly associated with call processing. Built-in hardware and software timers, parity checks, and simple diagnostic tests between the two processors in a pair are used to monitor the state of health of each processor in the pair.

A generous amount of hardware displays, exercisers, and indicator lamps are provided to simplify troubleshooting in case of equipment failure. These aids include a processor display with indicators for each register and data path in the machine, control panels for manually manipulating the processor system, exercisers for memory and interface circuitry, and activity indicators on vital circuit assemblies.

Software diagnostics together with selective printouts on teletypewriter of error data areas in affected programs are used to aid the maintenance personnel in troubleshooting. The maintenance philosophy is based on providing enough hardware and software aids for adequately guiding a trained maintenance technician in isolating the failed assembly. Repair is made by replacing the failed plug-in unit. Consideration has also been given for provision of built-in test facilities as an integral part of the system for testing plug-in assemblies with software programs which are stored in external memory on magnetic tape.

In each block of data memory consisting of four 16K-word self-contained core memories with individual power units and controller circuitry one memory module is provided as a spare. In case of memory module failure, the file control programs of the software executive system in the routing control processor will load the spare module with the data contained in the failed unit from a backup file on magnetic tape. This procedure is accomplished within a few seconds. If desired, complete duplication of the data memory modules with resident redundant system data can be provided.

Diagnostic maintenance programs, backup data for system files or programs, and office administration programs are stored on magnetic tape. These programs are loaded into an overlay area in the processor program memory upon initiation by a failure detection program or by manual action of the maintenance personnel from either the teletypewriter keyboard or the processor control panel.

Software programs are provided which perform functions associated with the daily administration of central office data, such as service connects/disconnects, directory number and classmark changes, routing changes, equipment additions, etc. These programs are operated from teletypewriter equipment in an interactive fashion, guiding the operator through the proper man–machine communication procedures on a step by step basis. Major blocks of system data can be changed by loading the new information in appropriate formats with magnetic tape or paper tape reader equipment.

The system program contains a monitor routine, which interprets codes received from the teletypewriter keyboard and initiates loading of the proper programs into the overlay area in the processor memory for performing the desired maintenance and administrative actions. In this manner an open-ended approach is achieved for adding new maintenance and administrative features to the system in the form of programs stored on magnetic tape as the need for these features arises.

To aid the programmer in software debugging, a hardware controlled video display unit in the form of a standard television monitor together with a special software processor is used. The software processor interprets commands from a keyboard for data display and processor actions, exercises these commands, and displays the results on the television screen either in octal or mnemonic form with appropriate legends.

Conclusion

In applying electronic stored program control to the routing function of a crossbar common control switching system, the call processing capabilities of the system are significantly improved. Program control together with an electrically alterable data memory simplifies system administration and maintenance, eliminating the need for physical rewiring of equipment in the field to accommodate service changes. Compatibility with existing electromechanical systems is achieved by common system architecture making possible additions of new equipment to existing electromechanical offices without the need of replacing installed equipment. Consequently, all the standard and currently anticipated new services can be provided economically with a minimum of custom engineering.

Acknowledgment

The authors wish to acknowledge the contributions of many individuals in North Electric engineering, manufacturing, and marketing organizations to the design and successful implementation of this system.

References

[1] T. K. Cheney, "A switching computer for communications," *Proc. 1969 IEEE Int. Conf. on Commun.*, pp 35-25–35-30.
[2] J. A. Watts, "NX-1E routing control complex," this issue, pp. 729–734.

Supplementary Bibliography for Paper 8

NX-1E

SUBSYSTEMS

```
NX-1E CALL PROCESSING SYSTEM
O'GRADY RP + WESOLOWSKI FT
P47-1 - 47-7 OF IEEE INT CONF COMMUN 1971 CONF REC (TI11C)

NX-1E MAINTENANCE AND ADMINISTRATION
OLSON FL + LOOS D
P47-8 - 47-13 OF IEEE INT CONF COMMUN 1971 CONF REC (NTI11C)

NX-1E ROUTING CONTROL COMPLEX
WATTS JA
IEEE TRANS COMMUN TECHNOLOGY 18:  729-33 (DEC 1970)
```

Paper 9

No. 1 Electronic Automatic Exchange (No. 1 EAX)

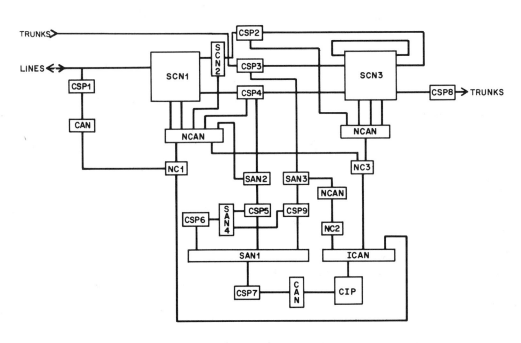

SCN1 = LINE MATRIX
SCN2 = LINE MATRIX-STAGE C
SCN3 = SELECTOR MATRIX
CIP = CENTRAL CONTROL
CSPI = LINE CIRCUIT
CSP2 = TERMINATING JUNCTOR
CSP3 = INCOMING TRUNK
CSP4 = ORIGINATING JUNCTOR
CSP5 = REGISTER JUNCTORS
CSP6 = SENDERS AND RECEIVERS

CSP7 = RS CORE MEMORY
CSP8 = OUTGOING TRUNK
NCI = ORIGINATING MARKER-LINES
NC2 = TERMINATING MARKER
NC3 = ORIGINATING MARKER-TRUNKS
SANI = MULTIPLEX
SAN2 = R STAGE
SAN3 = TRUNK REGISTER MATRIX
SAN4 = SENDER-RECEIVER MATRIX

NO. 1 EAX SYSTEM OBJECTIVES AND DESCRIPTION

D. P. Kroes

GTE Automatic Electric Laboratories

Northlake, Illinois

Introduction

The No. 1 EAX (Electronic Automatic Exchange) is a newly designed, commerically available, electronic common control telephone switching system. This paper traces the history of its design, describes the system, and demonstrates its application along with its major features. Telephone switching is accomplished in the No. 1 EAX by means of a two wire space divided, reed network, driven by a stored program electronic, common control.

The No. 1 EAX network includes three types of matrixes; namely, a Line Group, a Trunk Register Group, and a Selector Group. Each of these matrixes consist of correeds (electrically held reed crosspoints). The various trunk and junctor circuits use correeds and miniature card mounted relays.

The No. 1 EAX common control subsystems include an integrated circuit general purpose digital computer, and several integrated circuit peripheral processors; namely, an Originating Marker, a Register Sender, and a Terminating Marker. Memories included in the common control are ferrite core, magnetic drum, and magnetic tape.

History

At this time, in the independent telephone industry, the vast majority of the telephones are served by electromechanical switching systems. The preponderance are of the Strowger Step-by-Step (SxS) type. The Strowger switching system was first introduced by Automatic Electric Company at La Porte, Indiana in 1892. Of course, numerous modifications and improvements have been made over the years, but the mode of operation of the basic switch has remained the same.

In the early 1960's, the basic investigations of electronic common control end offices leading to a No. 1 EAX were begun. A laboratory experimental model was made operational at the end of 1962, to test feasibility. This design was tested and improved, and factory built equipment was placed into field test at Portage, Indiana in late 1965. The intent of the field trial was to verify the reliability and the design philosophy of the system and to determine what additional development would be required to prepare the system for normal commerical production. The field trial period extended for slightly over one year during which the system provided ordinary telephone service to 600 subscribers.

Upon completion of the field trial, the results of the tests and the future requirements of a commerical switching system were studied. A number of significant factors affecting the development and manufacture of an electronic switching system were rapidly changing:

— Integrated circuit and stored program technology were becoming practical, in terms of cost, speed, reliability, and applicability, to the telephone industry.

— Automatic techniques for development and manufacturing were becoming available, to reduce errors and cost.

— New features were being planned and made available and changes were being introduced to existing features.

The No. 1 EAX system was suitably modified and the resulting commercial system was cut into service in July 1972, at St. Petersburg, Florida, where it is now operational as an 8000 line switch, to partially replace an existing large SxS office and to absorb new growth. A second system was cut into service at Erie, Pennsylvania, in January 1973. Another system is being installed at Santa Ynez, California, and many others are in normal commercial production.

System Application

The No. 1 EAX is designed for use as a Class 5 (end office) as well as a combined Class 4 and 5 (toll and end Office). It can be applied using external AMA (automatic message accounting) equipment or with the addition of optional built-in CAMA (centralized AMA) or LAMA (local AMA) equipment. The Class 5 features can range from those associated with ordinary telephone service to those that take full advantage of a stored program controlled switching system.

Figure 1 shows a No. 1 EAX applied as a Class 5 (end office). It will serve a wide range of classes of service, including residential, business, keysystems, PBX's, PABX's, coin telephones, as well as more specialized classes such as official number, non-dial, mobile telephone, WATS, INWATS, etc. The figure shows a typical trunking diagram for the system. DDD may be provided via built-in LAMA or by trunking to CAMA, where desired. EDDD may be trunked to a TSPS (Traffic Service Position System), where available.

Figure 2 shows a No. 1 EAX applied as a combined Class 4 and 5 (toll and end office). In addition to the services provided as discussed for the Class 5, it provides service for tributary offices, and for switching to and from the intertoll network. Ordinarily the combined Class 4 and 5 would be expected to be provided with built-in AMA. DDD from the tributary offices could be ticketed by LAMA, a separate CAMA system, or by use of built-in CAMA, as desired.

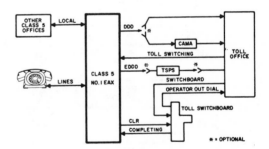

Figure 1. A Class 5 Office.

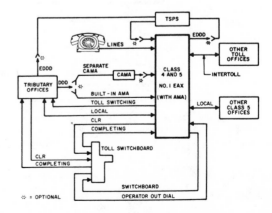

Figure 2. A Combined Class 4 and 5 Office.

Reprinted from *1973 IEEE Int. Conf. Commun. Rec.*, vol. I, June 11-13, 1973, pp. 10/1-10/5.

System Description

The block diagram of the No. 1 EAX hardware is shown in Figure 3. The system hardware can be divided into two major groupings:

(1) The Network Equipment, including three types of switching matrixes and the associated connect and access circuitry. These matrixes are called the Line Group, the Selector Group, and the Trunk Register Group.

(2) The Common Control Equipment, including the Originating and Terminating Markers, the Register Sender, the Data Processor and its associated memories and input-output devices, and the Maintenance and Control Center.

The Line Group

The Line Group is a switching matrix that provides two way switching to and from 1000 lines. Line and cutoff devices are provided for each inlet.

An originating call passes through two stages (A&B), to connect the line calling for service to one of up to 140 originating junctors. A connection is also established from the selected originating junctor to one of up to 20 register junctors through one stage (R), to provide for service circuit functions. The register junctor connection is released after completion of service from the Register Sender.

A terminating call passes through three stages (C,B,&A) to connect one of up to 120 terminating junctors to the called line. Terminating junctors provide a supervisory battery feed bridge, as well as ringing equipment for a terminating call.

The Trunk Register Group

The Trunk Register Group is a switching matrix that provides a two stage (A&B) connection from 200 incoming trunk circuits to up to 40 register junctors, to provide service circuit functions. The register junctor connection is released after completion of service from the Register Sender.

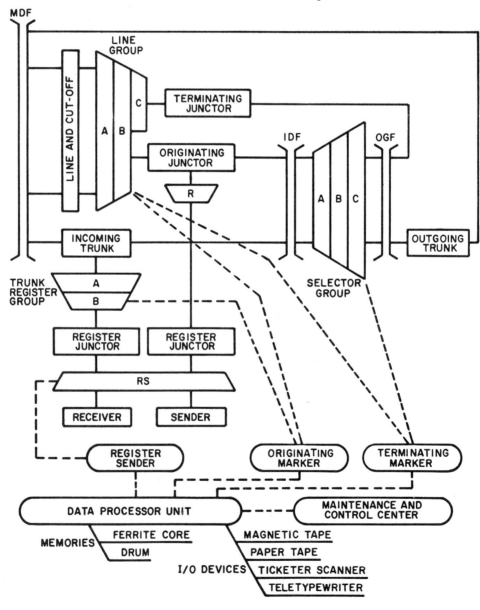

Figure 3. No. 1 EAX Block Diagram.

Associated with the Trunk Register Group are all of the incoming trunk circuits. The incoming trunk circuits provide supervision equipment and are a point of entry to this office from other offices. Various types are required depending upon supervision, signaling, and application.

The Selector Group

The Selector Group is a switching matrix that provides for mixing and distributing traffic from originating junctors and incoming trunk circuits on its inlets, to terminating junctors and outgoing trunk circuits on its outlets. The matrix is arranged in three stages (A,B,&C) with 400 inlets and either 800 or 1600 (optional) outlets.

Associated with the Selector Group are all of the outgoing trunk circuits. The outgoing trunk circuits provide supervision equipment and are a point of exit from this office to other offices. Various types are required, depending upon supervision, signaling, and application.

Also associated with the Selector Group are two frames. An Intermediate Distributing Frame is used for distributing traffic to its inlets. An Outlet Grading Frame is used for grading traffic to its outlets.

The Originating Marker

The Originating Marker is an integrated circuit, wired logic, processor that provides service to originating and incoming calls. It provides for autonomous scanning of various Line Groups and Trunk Register Groups for calls for service.

When a call for service is detected, the Originating Marker associates itself with the matrix through connect and access circuitry, selects an idle path through the matrix, establishes a connection from the inlet calling for service to a register junctor, and sends data to the Data Processor, to identify the inlet being served and the junctor(s) selected.

The Register Sender

The Register Sender is an integrated circuit wired logic processor with ferrite core storage. Its logic circuitry and memory are operated on a time shared basis, to perform various service circuit functions for up to 192 simultaneous calls.

Inputs to the Register Sender are via (up to 192) register junctors. They are arranged to return dial tone or start dial and to receive dial pulsing. They can be used to return line busy tone or reorder tone, if required. On outgoing calls they are arranged to accept start dial and to send dial pulsing.

When tone receiving or sending is involved, an appropriate receiver or sender may be attached through a one stage (RS) matrix. Up to 120 TCMF receivers, 32 2/6 MF receivers, 24 ONI receivers, and/or 32 2/6 MF senders may be provided.

The Terminating Marker

The Terminating Marker is an integrated circuit wired logic processor that provides for establishing paths for outgoing and terminating calls. Paths are set up in the Selector Group for an outgoing call and in both the Selector Group and Line Group for a terminating call.

When a call is to be completed, the Terminating Marker accepts data from the Data Processor to identify an inlet and the desired trunk group or line, associates itself with the required matrix(es) through connect and access circuitry, selects an idle path through the matrix, establishes a connection to the desired trunk or line, and sends data to the Data Processor to identify the specific terminating junctor or trunk selected.

The Data Processor

The Data Processor is an integrated circuit general purpose computer consisting of the following:

- a central processing unit including a facility for hardware interrupts

- a ferrite core main memory with supplementary storage via magnetic drums

- Input/output devices, including paper tape equipment, magnetic tape equipment, teletypewriter equipment, a scanner for ticketing, and a communications register for data communication to the markers.

The primary functions of the Data Processor during a telephone call are to accept information from the Originating Marker about an origination, to prepare the Register Sender for receiving, to translate the information received by the Register Sender, to send path instructions to the Terminating Marker, to prepare the Register Sender for sending (outgoing calls), and to secure a record for toll calls.

The Maintenance and Control Center

The Maintenance and Control Center serves as a centralized facility for the interface of the man with the machine. Its functions include the following:

- monitoring the operation of the system and its subsystems and the initiating of configuration controls.

- presenting maintenance output information and accepting requests for test call routines and test programs

- providing usage and event metering for traffic and providing the display and control required for switch and network management

- providing for testing the lines, trunks, junctors, and service circuits in the office.

Software

The No. 1 EAX software is a generic set of functionally organized programs. The programs that make up the stored program are the Operating System, Telephone Application programs, Diagnostic programs, and Office Administration programs.

The Operating System provides an operating software environment for the execution of other programs. It provides for centralized scheduling of all tasks to be performed by the Data Processor and also provides for common input/output and timing functions.

The Telephone Application programs provide the central logic and data processing required to provide the basic services and features of a telephone switching machine.

The Diagnostic programs provide for maintaining a working system in the face of errors and faults in the network and common control equipment. Most errors and faults cause a maintenance interrupt that results in isolation, reconfiguration, localization, and trouble reporting. Diagnostic programs are also available for routining line, trunk, junctor, and service circuit equipment.

The Office Administration programs provide for keeping the data base up to date and for making both minor and major changes to the stored program.

System Features

No. 1 EAX can be characterized as a full featured electronic common control system. Initially, the system is being applied to provide Class 5 (end office) service. Additional design efforts are well in progress to add Class 4 (toll office) service along with system improvement and cost reduction. The system is scheduled to be cut into service as a combined class 4 and 5 in 1974.

As stated earlier, the No. 1 EAX is expected to be used for conversion from electromechanical switching to electronic common control switching. Application studies have pointed up a large number of features of great significance to a telephone operating company considering such a conversion.

Manufacturing, Installation, and Testing

The benefits of No. 1 EAX begin at the manufacturing level. A design geared to automated production introduces real economy in production costs. The use of standardized modular equipment reduces the lead time to delivery, since equipment is not tailored to each specific site. This has its greatest advantage where office growth is unpredictable. A design for rapid field assembly, using plug-in switchgear, reduces installation time and cost. Field testing is enhanced by the use of programmed installation tests using the Data Processor which has complete access to control the system and to set up the tests.

Line Assignment

The No. 1 EAX allows the machine inlet, in most cases, to be chosen independent of the directory number and class of service. Subscribers can ordinarily be connected to the machine simply on the basis of the amount of traffic they are expected to generate. Directory numbers can readily be changed, when desired, such as when faced with an annoyance call problem. Subscriber features and services can be added and deleted, usually without physical rewiring. Load balancing of the traffic constitutes about the only reason for physical rearrangement of a machine inlet, once established.

The stored program common control design of No. 1 EAX will cause the activity on the main distributing frame to be dramatically reduced. In fact, where single party service is provided via dedicated plant, subscriber movement can usually be handled entirely by program changes.

Since directory numbers are unrelated to the machine inlet, directory numbers need not be wasted when machine inlets are left spare or when a group of lines are addressed with a single directory number, such as when serving a PABX. Directory number utilization is dramatically improved when Terminal-per-Line equipment is replaced. The resulting conservation of directory numbers allows more effective use of the ever more scarce office codes.

Subscriber Features

The common control design of No. 1 EAX makes a wider variety of subscriber features available on an economic basis, through the application of centralized common pool equipment. These features can usually be applied to a given subscriber simply on the basis of modifying his data storage.

The stored program design of No. 1 EAX makes available new types of features that are dependent upon memory storage for variable or repetitive processing. This opens the door to many individually programmable revenue producing features.

The particular features applied to a given subscriber are easier to change in a system of this type, and a record of all features in effect for a given subscriber is always readily available from memory and is automatically kept up to date.

Trunk Assignment

The No. 1 EAX allows trunks to be assigned to machine inlets, independent of the office codes and type of service. They can generally be connected to the machine simply on the basis of the level and pattern of the traffic they are expected to generate. Load balancing is greatly facilitated.

Since all signaling on calls to or from trunks is fully received and stored before network paths are selected, translation can be used rather than directly driving switch ranks from the dialed code to select routing patterns. The result is a great amount of flexibility of code choice, conservation of the scarcer office codes, and a reduction of blocking in the switch.

Centralized Signaling

The No. 1 EAX provides for centralized signaling in its Register Sender. This centralization of signaling equipment makes it economical to provide for longer subscriber loops. This extension of subscriber loops allows for the extension of wire center physical limits and/or the use of finer gauge cable. One new office may replace several older offices.

The use of centralized signaling equipment enhances the practicability of tone signaling such as the TCMF and 2/6 MF types. The use of special formats for CAMA, TSPS, are facilitated, as are formats to Directory Assistance Message Accounting and Automatic Intercept Centers, etc.

The common control of the No. 1 EAX provides for detection of a wide variety of permanent conditions from the time a subscriber begins a call until all parties have released. Called party timed disconnect is more easily provided.

Routing and Availability

The No. 1 EAX completely regenerates all pulsing and this reduces the amount of pulse correctors required with trunks, as well as reducing the amount of adjusting and testing required to assure satisfactory performance of switches and trunks.

The design of the No. 1 EAX, using a Register Sender concept, allows complete freedom of routing and code. The routing is very flexible, easily changed by program, facilitates high usage routes and alternate routing, while tending to conserve codes.

Since calls are established under common control the switch eliminates pocketed calls, that is, calls blocked in the switch when other routes are available.

The network for this system allows trunks to be loaded to full availability tables giving economies over systems with limited availability.

Maintenance and Monitoring

The No. 1 EAX provides for internal maintenance routines to be in effect coincident with all call processing steps, to detect errors and faults and present the result to the maintenance man. Centralized test equipment, along with storage for each equipped line and trunk, allows for built-in routining through the switch itself.

The complete registration and sending on each call allows for the simplified provision of ticketing for toll calls as well as for local calls, if required. The toll equipment can also be used to provide tickets for study purposes on the basis of programming.

The common control design allows for built-in traffic metering. Congestion in the switch can be detected and reported during call processing. The centralized control allows for the exercise of switch management controls and the provision of switch management displays.

Future

The stored program common control design of the No. 1 EAX offers a switching machine which is more easily kept in tune with future requirements than the types of machines it replaces. The operation of the machine can more often be modified by program change and improvement without affecting the hardware. When hardware is affected, the quantities are often reduced due to the common control design.

Capacity

The No. 1 EAX system has been designed so that, normally, a set of network equipment can be provided in any type of office that will fully load the Data Processor to its call processing limits, and rarely will the office be limited by the traffic handled by the network. The No. 1 EAX limits are as follows:

- 79,000 busy hour call attempts of a normal call mix during an average busy hour condition.

- over 200,000 ccs as measured at the main distributing frame.

- 64,000 directory numbers with up to 16 office codes.

- one set of common control equipment; namely, one Data Processor, one Maintenance and Control Center, one (to two) Register Senders, one (to four) Originating Markers, and one (to three) Terminating Markers

- Up to 30 Selector Groups (arranged with up to 10 Selector Groups multipled to form a section or up to seven separate sections) (up to 21 ccs per inlet)

- up to 45 Line Groups (up to 4800 ccs per Line Group)

- up to 60 Trunk Register Groups

The use of sectionalized Selector Groups (up to seven sections) allows for dedication of sections of the network to local traffic, toll traffic, incoming traffic, outgoing traffic, originating traffic, terminating traffic, and/or tandem traffic, as required, for efficiently equipping a large or special purpose office, while allowing all traffic to be kept in a single section (one central network) for efficiency in a smaller office.

Conclusions

The No. 1 EAX is a modern system that meets the requirements for a medium to large end office, separately or when combined with a toll office function.

The use of a stored program control for all decisions in a common control machine allows the machine to provide many features as designed and to later be expanded in features and services to encompass the ones that are certain to evolve in the future. The use of certain wired logic processors to perform repetitive unchangeable tasks allows the system to handle a very large processing load.

The No. 1 EAX is presently cutover at two field sites and is being made available in normal commercial production.

Supplementary Bibliography for Paper 9

NO 1. EAX

MAGNETIC TAPE TRANSPORT FOR NO. 1 EAX, TSPS, AND CAMA SYSTEMS.
GARTNER TH + HEFFNER ST + KRYLOW KE
AUTOMAT ELEC TECH J 13:294-307 (APR 1973)

REPORT ON THE NO. 1 EAX (ELECTRONIC AUTOMATIC EXCHANGE)
INSTALLATION AT ST. PETERSBURG, FLORIDA.
PROKUSKI RG + ST GERMAIN DP
AUTOMAT ELEC TECH J 13:270-9 (APR 1973)

NO. 1 EAX DIAGNOSTIC SOFTWARE.
WOLFF RW
P10-31TO10-35 OF INT CONF COMMUN 1973, V1 (T/I11C)   100761

NO. 1 EAX MAINTAINABILITY.
KEEHN PJ + WOLFF RW
P10-28TO10-30 OF INT CONF COMMUN 1973, V1 (T/I11C)   100761

NO. 1 EAX CALL PROCESSING AND METERING SOFTWARE.
WOODKA EA + GRYBOWSKI GT
P10-22TO10-27 OF INT CONF COMMUN 1973, V1 (T/I11C)   100761

NO. 1 EAX OPERATING SYSTEM SOFTWARE.
KALAT CA
P10-18TO10-21 OF INT CONF COMMUN 1973, V1 (T/I11C)   100761

NO. 1 EAX COMMON CONTROL
WEBER FA
P10-12TO10-17 OF INT CONF COMMUN 1973, V1 (T/I11C)   100761

APPLICATION TO NO. 1 EAX (ELECTRONIC AUTOMATIC EXCHANGE).
GRYCZ JE + HON SF + KEMPSKI AR
AUTOMAT ELEC TECH J 14: 127-34 (JUL 1974)

NO. 1 EAX-ICC 1973 (ELECTRONIC AUTOMATIC EXCHANGE).
KNUEPFER WJ
AUTOMAT ELEC TECH J 13: 378-85 (OCT 1973)

NO. 1 EAX.
KNUEPFER WJ
AUTOMAT ELEC TECH J 13(8): 378 (OCT 1973)

NO. 1 EAX DESCRIPTION AND PERFORMANCE STATISTICS.
DALY EB + ZELINSKI PA
P525 OF INT SWITCHING SYMP RECORD, MUNICH, 1974 (621.381537/I59)

NO. 1 EAX - MICROPROCESSOR-CONTROLLED UNIVERSAL MESSAGE SYSTEM
C. KENNETH BUEDEL AND ROBERT W. WOLFF
GTE AUTOMATIC ELECTRIC TECHNICAL JOURNAL - JAN. 1976 -
VOL. 15 - NO. 1 - P2

AUTOMATIC ROUTINING OF SPACE-DIVIDED APPARATUS IN
NO. 1 EAX
VANDERLEI KW
NATIONAL TELECOMMUNICATIONS CONFERENCE (NTC) RECORD
DEC. 1-3, 1975 PP5-8 - IEEE CAT. NO. 75 CH 1015-7 CSCB VOL. 1

———————————————

Paper 10

Electronic Tandem System No. 4 (ETS 4)

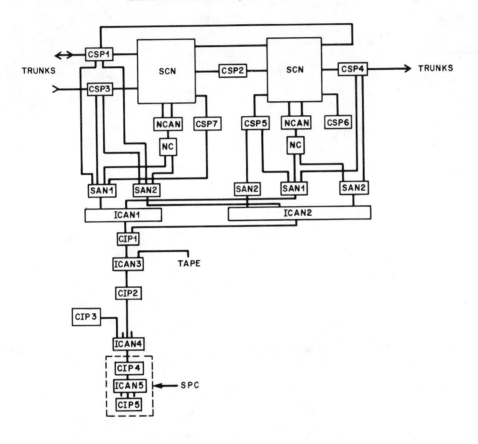

SCN1 = INCOMING SWITCH GROUP	CSP6 = INTERCEPT TRUNK
SCN2 = OUTGOING SWITCH GROUP	CSP7 = MF RECEIVER
CIP1 = TRANSLATOR UNIT	ICAN1 = RT BUS
CIP2 = TRANSFER CONTROL UNIT	ICAN2 = SMR BUS
CIP3 = DATA STORE UNITS	ICAN3 = TRANSFER BUS
CIP4 = CENTRAL PROCESSOR	ICAN4 = DATA TRANSFER AND
CIP5 = PROGRAM STORE UNITS	TRANSFER MULTIPLEXERS
CSP1 = TWO WAY TRUNK	ICAN5 = PROGRAM STORE BUS
CSP2 = TONE SENDERS	NC = CODE SWITCH CONTROLLER
CSP3 = INCOMING TRUNK	NCAN RELAY DECODING TREE
CSP4 = OUTGOING TRUNK	SAN1 = RELAY TEST UNITS (RT)
CSP5 = MF SENDER	SAN2 = RELAY OPERATING UNITS (SMR)
	SPC = CONTROL SUB SYSTEM

ETS-4 SYSTEM OVERVIEW

J. J. Dankowski, G. F. Dooley, and S. Y. Persson

North Electric Company
Paul H. Henson Research Center
Columbus, Ohio 43220

ABSTRACT

This paper presents a brief overview of the ETS-4 4-Wire Tandem Switching System. This serves as background information for four companion papers which highlight specific aspects of ETS-4 operation, performance, and evaluation. ETS-4 is a multiprocessor-controlled switching machine capable of handling high traffic loads. The system is designed for economical modular growth from modest to very large sizes in Class 4, 3, or 2 applications within the North American switched network hierarchy. System data and call processing logic are executed in the centralized processor complex, which controls service circuits, trunk interfaces, maintenance equipment, traffic administration facilities, and the full-availability 4-stage switching network implemented with code switches.

The software execution strategy employed within the multiprocessor complex, used for call processing and related system functions, is of particular interest. Principal call processing data records and software tasks are also central to the implementation of load and routing control functions, which are important for deployment of the ETS-4 system in the DDD toll network. Multiprocessor software operation and the implementation of load and routing control functions are further discussed in two of the companion papers.

Verification of system functions and evaluation of the load-handling performance for a system of the size and capacity of ETS-4, prior to its cutover into actual service, offer challenging problems. The approaches chosen and experiences gained while evaluating the ETS-4 system are presented in two papers of this series treating system verification and load testing. An additional paper of this series describes a powerful tool in the form of a processor driven office tester, which was designed to support the ETS-4 system testing and performance evaluation tasks.

INTRODUCTION

ETS-4 is a 4-wire, stored-program controlled switching system designed for application in the North American DDD toll network. As such, ETS-4 provides high-capacity switching capabilities for use in a Class 4 or higher toll center (see Figure 1).

The system design evolved from the AKE-13 System, which was developed in Sweden by the L. M. Ericsson Company and first put into service in Rotterdam, Netherlands in 1971. A number of those systems now serve the toll switching function in various parts of the world. Although the North Electric Company ETS-4 was based on the AKE-13 design concept, architecture, and dimensional structure, it has been extensively redesigned to meet the requirements of the North American network operation, and to take maximum advantage of U.S. components technology and North Electric manufacturing techniques. While redesigning the system to meet the North American DDD toll network standards, extensive facilities were added to provide network maintenance and network management capabilities.

Stored-program control is implemented in a multi-processor system, allowing modular expansion from a single processor-based control group up to seven control groups. Each control group consists of synchronous-paired central processing units, program store units, data store units, and multiplexors, all of which are implemented with high-speed integrated circuit logic and ferrite core memories.

The 4-stage switching matrix comprises 2-stage switch groups implemented with the compact, mechanically latching code switch. Two-stage incoming switch groups provide 800 inlets. These switch groups are connected via links to identical 2-stage outgoing switch groups that provide 800 outlets. The matrix is expandable in increments of 800 inlets or outlets up to a maximum size of 47 incoming switch groups and 47 outgoing switch groups. This expansion accommodates in excess of 60,000 trunks depending on the ratio of 2-way to one-way trunks.

The fully expanded ETS-4 system, having seven control groups and 94 switch groups, can handle incoming traffic in excess of 720,000 CCS (with a matching loss of less than 0.002) at a busy hour load of 340,000 attempts.

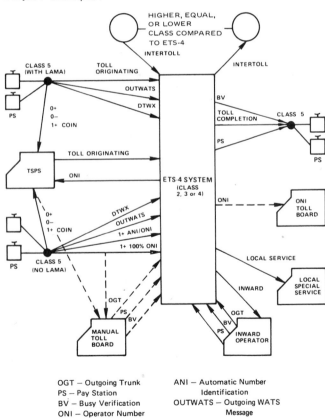

OGT – Outgoing Trunk
PS – Pay Station
BV – Busy Verification
ONI – Operator Number Identification
DTWX – TeletypeWriter Exchange

ANI – Automatic Number Identification
OUTWATS – Outgoing WATS Message
TSPS – Traffic Service Position System
LAMA – Local Automatic Message Accounting

Fig. 1. Typical Toll Network Environment of ETS-4

Reprinted from *1975 IEEE Int. Conf. Commun. Rec.*, vol. I, June 16–18, 1975, pp. 14/1–14/6.

ETS-4 provides capabilities for centralized automatic message accounting (1+, noncoin); on-line administration of trunk, route, and translation data; recording of traffic data; network management and load control facilities; trunk test facilities; system, trunk, and device maintenance reporting; and automatic transmission measuring facilities.

GENERAL SYSTEM DESCRIPTION

Hardware

As shown in Figure 2, ETS-4 contains a control subsystem, a transfer subsystem, a switching subsystem, and an input/output subsystem.

Control Subsystem. The control subsystem performs major logic functions, and controls all input/output and switching operations by executing the stored-program logic. Figure 3 shows the major components of the control subsystem, which comprises up to seven control groups and a reference data store channel (data store channel 7). Each control group consists of a processor, a data store channel, and a transfer channel. The processor contains a pair of parallel, synchronous Central Processing Units (CPU-A and CPU-B), a Supervisory Unit (SVU), and a pair of Program Stores (PS-A and PS-B). Each program store (A and B) comprises three Program Store Units (PSU-0, PSU-1, and PSU-2), each containing 65,536 17-bit words (16 data bits plus parity) for a total program store size of 196,608 words. The CPUs are instruction-synchronous and contain matching circuits to compare the results of each operation during program execution, as well as parity checks and timeout monitoring of external operations toward program store, data channels, and transfer channels. The configuration of the control subsystem elements (CPU, PSU, buses, DSU, etc.) is determined by working states (EXecutive, Stand-By, BLocked, etc.). For example, a normal configuration is CPU-B=EX, CPU-A=SB, PS-B=EX, PS-A=SB,

etc.; however, CPU-B can access PS-A and vice-versa.

The SVU supervises operation of the two CPUs and intervenes if an alarm is registered. The SVU also handles interconnect signals from the other processors and stores working state information, pertaining to all processor groups, in the control subsystem. The SVU is a hard-wired processor, which, upon an alarm condition, initiates recovery routines and supervises

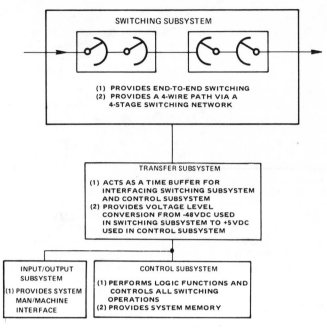

Fig. 2. ETS-4 Simplified Block Diagram

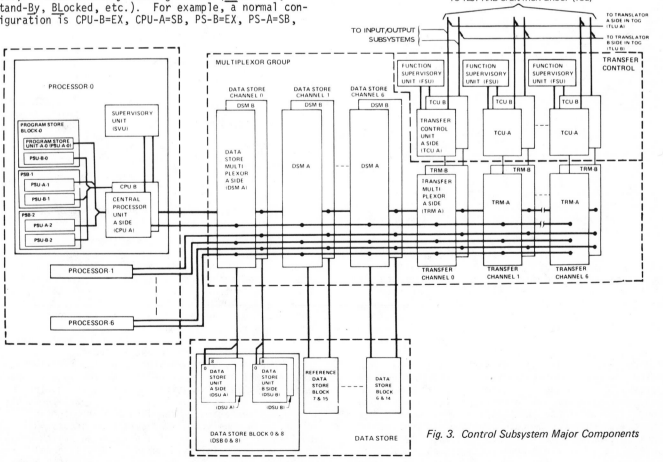

Fig. 3. Control Subsystem Major Components

system reconfiguration and recovery actions in the CPUs. The SVU also synchronizes the CPU pair. Although the SVU is an unduplicated unit, it contains a considerable amount of redundant logic to ensure that an SVU fault will not adversely affect the performance of a functioning CPU associated with that SVU.

The data store channel comprises the Data Store Multiplexors (DSM-A and DSM-B) and two data stores (A and B). The data store consists of a main data store unit and an extension data store unit, each having 65,536 17-bit words. For example, in data store channel 0, DSU-0 is the main unit and DSU-8 is the extension unit. Thus, each data store channel contains 131,072 words, fully duplicated on the A and B sides. The data store multiplexor provides selection and queuing from a CPU in any processor channel to access data store. The multiplexor is, in effect, a high-speed switching matrix that connects the address and data peripheral output buses from a CPU to a data store for the duration of a memory access cycle. The multiplexor is asynchronous with respect to the processors and allows access from the CPUs in whatever order the access requests arrive. If there is a simultaneous bid from two or more CPUs during a 100-nanosecond scan interval, the DSM will service requests from the lowest numbered channel to the highest numbered channel before beginning a new scan interval. A cross-over from a CPU-A to a DSU-B is handled via electronic interconnection gates between DSM-A and DSM-B.

The transfer channel comprises the Transfer Multiplexors (TRM-A and TRM-B), the Transfer Control Units (TCU-A and TCU-B), and a Function Supervision Unit (FSU). The transfer multiplexors are similar to the previously described data store multiplexors. The TCUs serve as an interface between the TRM and the transfer subsystem, and the TCUs transfer and supervise address and data information between the CPU and the connected unit. The outputs of TCU toward the transfer subsystem are balanced ac Transfer Buses (TRB-A and TRB-B); each TCU has four TRBs. In channel 0, two of these buses connect to the transfer subsystem and two are used as follows.

- Transfer Bus-Working State (TRB-WS) connects to all SVUs and multiplexors to transfer working state information between the working state registers in these units and the CPUs.

- Transfer Bus-Input/Output (TRB-I/O) connects to the input/output subsystem and transfers all information to and from the input/output devices.

In the remaining channels, 1 through 6, all four TRBs can be connected to the transfer subsystem. The function supervision unit monitors the operation of TCU-A and TCU-B and, if a malfunction is detected, signals the SVU which initiates corrective action.

The control subsystem forms a powerful multiprocessor system with a large volume of high-speed, random access memory (196,608 words of program store and up to 1,048,576 words of data store) and a high-speed interface to the transfer subsystem. The processors in any control group can access the data stores or transfer control units in any control group and in the reference data store channel. The CPUs in each channel can execute many special purpose data manipulation instructions such as compare and test instructions and field scan instructions, as well as arithmetic, logic, and read/store instructions toward transfer channels, data stores, and their own program

store within a multilevel, priority interrupt structure.

Transfer Subsystem. The transfer subsystem and its relationship to the other subsystems is shown in Figure 4. The transfer subsystem comprises Test and Operation Groups (TOG) that contain the individual sense and control points for communicating with devices external to the processing system. The transfer subsystem thus provides a buffer interface between the control subsystem and the switching subsystem. Each TOG is interconnected to the control subsystem via Transfer Buses (TRB-A and TRB-B). The TOG consists of two redundant Translation Units (TLU-A and TLU-B), a number of Relay Test units (RT points), and relay operation units (SMR points). Each RT point is a sense element through which the processor can detect a relay state; e.g., high impedance or low impedance. Each SMR point is an isolated-contact, mercury-wetted reed relay that the processor can latch closed or open. The RT points are built up in matrices of 72 words by 16 bits and the SMR points are grouped into matrices of 16 words by 16 bits. The RT matrices are packaged in groups of four matrices per RT unit and the SMR matrices are packaged in groups of eight matrices per SMR unit. A fully equipped TOG comprises at least one RT unit and five RT or SMR units. Thus an evenly distributed TOG contains two RT units and four SMR units, which provides 9216 RT points and 8192 SMR points. Up to three TOGs can be accessed from one redundant TRB pair. This allows a maximum of 55,296 RT points and 49,152 SMR points in control group 0 and 110,592 RT points and 98,304 SMR points in control groups 1 through 6. This far exceeds the number of RT and SMR points required by the maximum number of trunks, code switch controllers, and other processing devices in any channel.

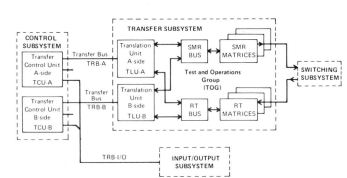

Fig. 4. Transfer Subsystem Interface and Functional Block Diagram

Switching Subsystem. Figure 5 shows the switching subsystem and its interface with the control subsystem, via the transfer subsystem. The 4-wire communication path used to connect an incoming trunk to an outgoing trunk is provided by the switching subsystem. It comprises the switching matrix, trunks (incoming, outgoing, and 2-way), multifrequency (MF) senders and receivers, tone senders, intercept trunks, and recorded announcement machines. The basic building blocks of the switching matrix are code switches (see Figure 6), which are organized into incoming and outgoing switch groups. The code switch is a compact, mechanically latching switching array, which, for the ETS-4 application, is built in a 10-inlet, 41-outlet, 4-wire configuration. Each incoming or outgoing switch group consists of two switching stages (GSA and GSB). The GSA stage of the incoming switch group accommodates 800 inlets, linked via 800 internal links to the GSB stage. The GSB stage provides 1640 links out, which connect to MF receivers and tone senders and to the GSB stages of the outgoing switch groups. The GSA and GSB stages of the outgoing switch groups provide for connection of the inter-switch group links to the 800 outlets of each outgoing switch group. Of the 1640 link positions per switch group, 140 are reserved for MF receivers, tone senders, and MF senders. The remaining 1500 link positions interconnect incoming and outgoing switch groups. Figure 7 depicts the linkage within the matrix. The matrix provides full availability between any inlet and any outlet, and is expandable to 47 incoming switch groups and 47 outgoing switch groups. With an offered traffic of 21.6 CCS (hundred call seconds) per inlet, the matching loss through the matrix is less than 0.002 up to the full expansion of 37,600 inlets and 37,600 outlets.

Operation and control of matrix code switches are performed by software through code switch controllers (VMR and VMR-C). The VMR portion of the controller is a relay-decoding tree that allows access to one of 20 code switches, and controls one of 10 verticals and one of 41 horizontals (through operation of six horizontal codebars of the code switch). The VMR-C portion of the controller performs all timing, sequencing, and error checking functions associated with code switch operation.

The trunks within the switching subsystem can be divided into three basic categories: incoming one-way, outgoing one-way, and 2-way. All trunk signaling logic, timing, and control are performed by software; thus, the physical trunk circuit is relatively simple.

A physical trunk circuit for E&M supervision can be programmed in software for incoming, outgoing, or 2-way operation; multifrequency (MF) or dial pulse (DP) signaling; ticketing or nonticketing operation; etc.

Senders and receivers are provided for MF signaling and are also controlled by software. All dial pulse sending and receiving are controlled, through software, directly from the trunk itself.

The Recorded Announcement Machine (RAR) accommodates dual recording drums with eight channels each. One channel contains reorder tone, which feeds the tone senders. The remaining seven channels contain audible ringback and six recorded messages, which are connected to the Intercept Trunks (ITR), to provide various intercept messages for incoming calls that cannot be completed.

Input/Output Subsystem. The input/output subsystem provides the major communication link between the control subsystem and personnel performing loading, administration, or maintenance functions on the system. This communication is performed as follows:

- Via teleprinter in an interactive mode when commands or data are being entered or requested

- Via teleprinters or high-speed line printers in a receive mode when data or error messages are being transmitted

- Via magnetic tape units when programs or data are being loaded or when data (toll ticketing or traffic recording) is being output.

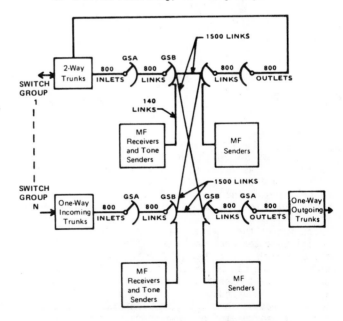

Fig. 5. Switching Subsystem - Major Components

Fig. 7. ETS-4 System Simplified Switching Subsystem Linkage

Fig. 6. Code Switch

A simplified block diagram of the input/output subsystem is shown in Figure 8. Access to or from the control subsystem is provided via the Transfer Bus (TRB) and two buffers. Output data is transferred from the control subsystem into the buffer, which is then read and decoded by an input/output minicomputer. Two minicomputers control all peripheral devices (teleprinters, line printers, and magnetic tape units) under the direction of the control subsystem. Devices may be assigned to either of the two minicomputers. Functional assignment and use of the devices are controlled by software in the control subsystem.

output devices and performs centralized data protection and queue administration. The diagnostic software group executes detailed tests against the central processing units, data store units, program store units, and transfer control units when initiated by maintenance personnel. The goal of these diagnostic tests is to trace a fault to a replaceable element such as a printed wiring assembly.

Application software, under administration of the operation software, performs all the telephony logic associated with the transfer and switching subsystems. Application software comprises the following six major groups.

● Call Handling Software, which provides the logic for operation of all trunk types (one-way incoming, one-way outgoing, 2-way, intercept, ticketing, and operator number identification), multifrequency senders and receivers, and tone senders. It further performs all translation logic for call routing; the software for on-line modification and checking of translation data; and coordinates all interactions within the software blocks associated with call handling, both within a processing channel and between processing channels.

● Matrix and Recovery Software, which provides the logic for selection of devices and paths through the matrix, operation and monitoring of code switches, and blocking of devices (i.e., trunks, senders, receivers, etc.) in the switching subsystem, either automatically because of some malfunction or by operator-initiated command. Finally, this software provides the logic for recovery of the switching subsystem if the system restarts because of a malfunction in the control or transfer subsystem.

Fig. 8. Input/Output Subsystem Simplified Block Diagram

Software

Software in ETS-4 can be divided into two major categories. As shown in Figure 9, these are operation software and application software. A more detailed description of the system software structure is presented in a related paper written by E. A. Lissakers et al[1]. Operation software monitors and maintains operation of the control and transfer subsystems, and administers the work performed in these subsystems to foster execution of the application software. Operation software can be subdivided into four major groups: basic operation group, maintenance and recovery group, input/output group, and diagnostics. The basic operating software group contains a system monitor that assigns the work to those resources of the multiprocessor system which are available at any moment, and to a job monitor that administers the dispatching of programs indicated by the system monitor. These operations are supervised within the multilevel priority interrupt system. The basic operating software group also loads both fixed and movable programs. The maintenance and recovery software group provides systematic checks of the control and transfer subsystems, fault localization, unit blocking, system reconfiguration after a fault has been detected, and testing of units before and after they are repaired and placed back into operation. The input/output software group handles all interwork with the peripheral input/

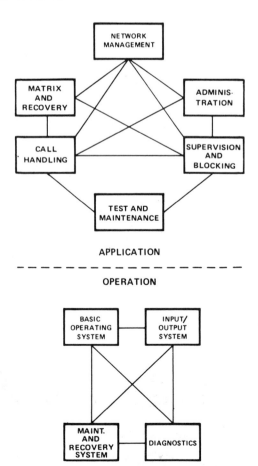

Fig. 9. ETS-4 System Software Structure

- Supervision and Blocking Software, which comprises a collection of programs for: supervision of blocking, congestion, errors, and seizure of devices in the switching subsystem; fuse, tone generator, and TOG monitoring; and indications of various alarm conditions. This software also includes blocking check programs that provide blocking state status of the devices in response to internal or operator-initiated requests.

- Network Management Software, which includes programs that initiate automatic dynamic overload controls during periods of processor overload, or that activate various network controls to alter traffic patterns in the toll network in accordance with a variety of preplans. A more detailed presentation of load and network controls is presented in a paper written by G. W. Hassell et al[2].

- Administration Software, which includes programs for collecting and recording long-term and short-term traffic measurement data on devices and routes and for recording call attachment delays (CAD); program routines for on-line modification of route and device assignment data; and programs for translation between machine language, or data representations, and external operator representations for command inputs to the switching subsystem and message printouts.

- Test and Maintenance Software, which includes programs for operating maintenance and test equipment such as the Automatic Transmission Measurement System (ATMS), the Toll Test Desks (TTD), test lines, the Circuit Tester (CIT) which makes performance measurements of all MF senders and receivers and tone senders, and the Link Tester (LINK-T) which routinely performs voltage and resistance measurements on randomly selected 4-stage matrix paths to incoming or outgoing trunks. Additionally, programs are provided for internal tracing of an established path, through the matrix, from a specified incoming or outgoing trunk or an MF sender or receiver; establishing specified matrix paths; operating relays; test-marking devices; deactivating a specific device timeout; etc.

These six major software groups encompass all of the telephony operations in a modern toll office and provide efficient call processing, routing, ticketing, maintenance, and administration within a modular, multiprocessor-controlled system.

The total software system comprises approximately 296,000 instructions, of which 141,000 are full-time resident in program store, 43,000 constitute movable programs that can be loaded in program store for execution, and 112,000 are resident or movable in the minicomputer subsystems that provide input/output or processor maintenance function control in the ETS-4 multiprocessor complex.

SUMMARY

The majority of the toll switching functions are performed in the ETS-4 software, thus allowing an evolutionary approach to the changing demands of the DDD network. The system processes toll originating, intertoll, and toll completing traffic, and is capable of providing CAMA ticketing of 1+ calls with automatic or operator number identification. Billing data is prepared in single-entry format on magnetic tape.

The switching matrix provides full availability between incoming and outgoing terminations, with a matching loss less than 0.002, at an average loading of 0.6 erlangs (21.6 CCS) per incoming termination. As discussed in a paper written by A. Kuczura et al[3], the individual control group capacity is more than adequate to handle in excess of 80,000 call attempts per hour. Translation and domain screening capabilities provide routing to primary and up to five alternate routes based on translation of from one to six received digits, including provision for OUTWATS, INWATS (with principal city translation), and TWX types of calls. Administration of the system data base relating to translation, routing information, trunk types, and trunk assignments is accomplished through keyboard input from teleprinters.

The ETS-4 traffic recording facilities provide a means for accurate traffic measurements and supervision in a network with extensive alternate routing. Measurement, supervision, and control of traffic flow are performed by software, thus eliminating the need for added hardware monitoring equipment. Traffic data may be output in hardcopy format on teleprinters or on magnetic tape for off-line analysis and data reduction. The system provides long-term recording for office and network planning and short-term recording for daily administration. Data is collected on usage (in CCS); congestion (overflow in %); number of attempts on trunk groups, MF senders, MF receivers, and tone senders; as well as on traffic distribution for separation of revenue purposes. Additionally, attempts per Circuit per Hour (ACH) and Completions per Circuit per Hour (CCH) can be calculated by the system.

The ETS-4 system incorporates a number of maintenance aids such as a Circuit Tester (CIT) for automatic routine testing of MF senders, MF receivers, and tone senders; a Link Tester (LINKT) for matrix maintenance; error message printouts for fuse supervision, device monitoring, and system performance monitoring; and a minicomputer-based processor maintenance center for status reporting and diagnostics of the control subsystem.

The ETS-4 system was extensively tested as discussed in a paper written by H. J. Moses et al[4] to verify all of its performance requirements and load capabilities. After successful testing, ETS-4 was introduced into the DDD toll network (early in 1975) and has since processed many millions of toll telephone calls.

REFERENCES

(1) E. A. Lissakers and D. P. Oestreich, "Multiprocessor Control of ETS-4," presented at ICC'75, San Francisco, California, June 16-18, 1975.

(2) G. W. Hassell and R. D. Packard, "Load and Network Control in ETS-4," presented at ICC'75, San Francisco, California, June 16-18, 1975.

(3) A. Kuczura and S. Y. Persson, "ETS-4 Processing Capacity and Load Testing," presented at ICC'75, San Francisco, California, June 16-18, 1975.

(4) H. J. Moses and D. L. Wagers, "ETS-4 System Verification Testing," presented at ICC'75, San Francisco, California, June 16-18, 1975.

Supplementary Bibliography for Paper 10

ETS-4

SYSTEM GENERAL

INDEPENDENT'S FIRST ELECTRONIC TOLL TANDEM CUTS (ETS-4)
SMITH R
TEL ENG MANAGE 79: 42 (JULY 1, 1975)

ETS-4 MAINTENANCE
WAGERS DL
P52 of NAT ELECTRONIC PROCEEDINGS 1975 (621.381/N27)

STRUCTURE AND CHARACTERISTICS OF THE ETS-4 TOLL AND TANDEM
SWITCHING SYSTEM
ARO E + LONG SJ
P129-134 OF INT SWITCHING SYMPOSIUM 1972 MIT (E173-1597)

STRUCTURE AND CHARACTERISTICS OF THE ETS-4 TOLL AND TANDEM
SWITCHING SYSTEM
ARO E + LONG SJ
P129-134 OF INT SWITCHING SYMPOSIUM, MIT,L972 (E173 1597)

ADDITION OF A DIGITAL NETWORK TO AN ANALOG TANDEM SWITCH
(ETS4).
SKAPERDA N + FELLINGER F
P224 OF INT SWITCHING SYMP RECORD, MUNICH, 1974 (621.381537/I59)

STS, A SOFTWARE TEST SYSTEM FOR THE ETS-4 STORED PROGRAM
CONTROLLED
SWITCHING SYSTEM.
LACIVITA J + MERRITT R + ROBINSON P
PP 135-8 OF INT SWITCHING SYMP, MIT, 1972 (E173 I597)

ETS-4 SYSTEM OVERVIEW
DANKOWSKI J. J. + DOOLEY G. F. + PERSSON S. Y.
P 14-1-6 OF INT CONF ON GOMMS, SAN FRAN, 1975 (75CH 0971-
2 CSCB) VOL. I

MULTIPROCESSOR CONTROL OF ETS-4
LISSAKERS E A + OESTREICH D P
P 14-7-11 of INT CONF ON COMMS, SAN FRAN, 1975 (75CH 0971-
2 CSCB) VOL I

LOAD AND NETWORK CONTROL IN ETS-4
HASSELL GILBERT + PACKARD R DUANE
P 14-12-17 OF INT CONF ON COMMS, SAN FRAN, 1975 (75 CH 0971-
2 CSCB) VOL I

PROCESSOR-CONTROLLED OFFICE TESTING SYSTEM
ARO E + LISSAKERS E A + SOUTHARD G D
P 14-18-22 OF INT CONF ON COMMS, SAN FRAN, 1975 (75 CH 0971-
2 CSCB) VOL I

ETS-4 SYSTEM VERIFICATION TESTING
MOSES HOWARD J + WAGERS DAVID L
P 14-23-27 OF INT CONF ON COMMS, SAN FRAN, 1975 (75 CH 0971-2 CSCB) VOL I

ETS-4 PROCESSING CAPACITY AND LOAD TESTING
KUCZURA A + PERSSON S Y
P 14-28-33 OF INT CONF ON COMMS, SAN FRAN, L975 (75 CH 0971-2 CSCB) VOL I

ETS-4 AUTOMATIC TRANSMISSION MEASUREMENT SYSTEM
BULL J + LONCHAR R
NATIONAL TELECOMMUNICATIONS CONFERENCE (NTC)
DEC. 1-3, 1975 - PP5-30 - IEEE CAT. NO. 75 CH 1015-7
CSCB VOL. 1

Paper 11

Total Communication System No. 5 (TCS 5)

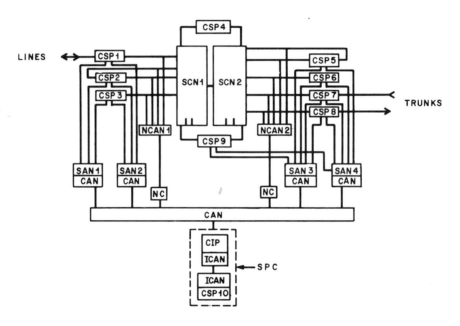

SCN 1 = LINE BLOCKS
SCN 2 = TRUNK BLOCKS
CAN = TELEPHONE INTERFACE
CIP = CENTRAL PROCESSOR
CSP 1 = LINE CIRCUIT
CSP 2 = TANDEM JUNCTOR
CSP 3 = SENDER
CSP 4 = AUXILIARY TRUNK
CSP 5 = JUNCTOR
CSP 6 = TEL-TOUCH RECEIVER

CSP 7 = INCOMING TRUNK
CSP 8 = OUTGOING TRUNK
CSP 9 = TRANSFER JUNCTOR
CSP10 = CALL STORE
NCAN1 = LINE MARKER DRIVER
NCAN2 = TRUNK MARKER DRIVER
SAN 1 = LINE SCANNER
SAN 2 = RING CONNECTOR
SAN 3 = TRUNK SCANNER
SAN 4 = TRUNK CONNECTOR
SPC = CENTRAL CONTROL UNIT

TCS System Organization and Objectives

Increasing demand in the US for a communications system with new facilities has led ITT to develop the TCS system. This is a stored program control system using two ITT 1650 miniprocessors working in the call load sharing mode which provides high reliability and excellent overload capabilities. The switching network uses pnpn diodes as crosspoints, rather than more conventional electromechanical types. By carefully choosing components, techniques, and manufacturing procedures, many of which are already used in ITT's TE-400 A and META-CONTA* L exchanges, it has been possible to organize the TCS system so that it is competitive below 800 lines, with extension up to 6 000 lines.

J. REINES
E. G. PLATT
M. C. BYCKOWSKI
ITT Telecommunications Electronic Switching Center, Des Plaines, Illinois, USA

Introduction

The telecommunications industry in the United States has afforded increased opportunities to independent telephone equipment manufacturers over the last few years. This has occurred due to the ability to interconnect to the public network, and to changes in purchasing policies by major holding companies. Servicing these opportunities was the main objective of the TCS development.

The above market developments occurred at a time when ITT's efforts in solid state networks were yielding a commercially successful product. (There are approximately 100 000 lines of the TE-400 A PABX in service [1]). At the same time Bell, ITT, and other manufacturers had introduced stored program switching systems which became economic typically above 2 000 lines.

With the increased competition, there were demands by customers, primarily in the private communications field, for new features which could best be implemented using a stored program system. Such a stored program system, however, had to be economic considerably below 2 000 lines. In fact, a system competitive below 800 lines was set as the goal after detailed marketing analysis. (The TE-400 A family of systems covers a range of 50 to 800 lines.) The system was to be expandable to 2 400 lines at 7·5 ccs (0·208 erlangs) both-way traffic per line. Expansion above 2 400 lines was desirable, but not at the cost of increasing the lower economic limit.

An end marked solid state network working under the control of two ITT 1650 miniprocessors has resulted in a system that meets the low end objective and can be expanded to 6 000 lines.

This paper covers detailed objectives, TCS system organization including hardware and software, redundancy and reliability arrangements, and traffic handling procedures and capacity. It also serves as an introduction to detailed companion papers on electronic design, transmission, call processing programs, maintenance and administration programs, simulation techniques, and equipment practice and manufacturability.

Objectives

Flexibility of Application

A paramount objective of TCS was to provide a large number of facilities in the private communica-

tions field. The flexibility of stored program control made it desirable also to use the same hardware configuration for other applications. This flexibility should enable features which have not been thought of today to be easily implemented.

The first TCS application is a private automatic branch exchange (PABX), followed by a centrex CU (customer unit) application and a rural public exchange. Flexibility for voice/data features and centrex CO (central office) was to be built in initially.

Maintenance and Administration

As TCS applications are largely for unattended exchanges, wherever practical it must be possible to monitor office and traffic performance remotely. Tests and administrative procedures are to be initiated by local or remote teletypewriters. Outside plant tests should be as good or better than those possible with electromechanical crosspoint systems.

Early experience with stored program switching systems has shown that the majority of system failures are associated with interactions between software and external events or transient hardware faults. For this reason it was important to design a system that was particularly immune to this type of fault.

Other maintenance goals included simple on-site troubleshooting and repair, automatic localization to a small part of the system, and small replacement units. In addition, maintenance should have the least possible impact on the system's prime function of processing calls. Of course, normal maintenance should not shut down the system.

In the office administration area, economic and simple arrangements for traffic reporting, translation changes, and office growth were important goals.

Technical Performance and Capacity

In a system with the wide coverage planned for TCS, it is important that the equipment meets all the technical objectives commonly accepted for new switching systems. In particular, the transmission objectives for new switching systems proposed by the manufacturers' subcommittee of the United States Independent Telephone Association were adopted for TCS. To further extend the potential application of the system, a secondary objective was to meet the transmission stan-

---

* A trademark of ITT System

Reprinted with permission from *Elec. Commun.*, vol. 48, no. 4, pp. 365-374, 1973.

dards for future private switching systems of selected telecommunications authorities outside the United States.

In the area of reliability, a system out-of-service objective of less than 2 hours in 40 years was established. Repair frequency should be as good or better than the TE-400 A performance of 1 printed board return for repair every 10 months per 100 lines.

The minimum capacity set for the system was 2 400 lines with 15 000 busy hour calls and 18 000 ccs (500 erlangs). Blocking probability goals were 0·01 for trunk to line calls and 0·02 for line to line calls. Additional capacity was highly desirable provided that it did not affect the low economic end of the system.

Economic

Two main criteria were used in establishing economic objectives. First, the equipment per line costs, for the lowest economic size, should be less than for existing electronic stored program switching systems of 2 000 to 4 000 lines. In addition, the installed price of the equipment should be competitive with other electronic or electromechanical common control switching systems covering a similar size range.

Second, the system should become competitive considerably below the size at which existing stored program switching systems do, and should fit in the product offering of ITT Electronic Switching Center. The TE-400 A [1] electronic switching systems are expandable to 800 lines and the US offering of the Metaconta L version [2] covers a range starting at 2 000 to 4 000 lines up to 64 000 lines. Hence, the minimum economic range objective was 800 lines to 2 400 lines.

A secondary, but extremely important, economic

objective was that the system should have the flexibility to evolve and take cost advantage of the technological developments continuously occurring in the components field.

Other Objectives

Many other objectives were set for the TCS development, including minimum possible space requirements. As much as possible of the conventional installation cycle should be performed at the factory to reduce installation costs and improve quality control. Other goals are commonality in components, techniques, and manufacturing operations with TE-400 A and Metaconta L systems, and minimization of customer application engineering and maintenance training requirements.

System Organization

General Design Plan

The objective of achieving a system which was economic below 800 lines required approaches which in a highly centralized, stored program system, would minimize get started costs. This was accomplished through persistent attention to this objective in all phases of the design. However, decisions in three main areas had a significant effect on the realization of this objective. These areas are the network, the processor and its use, and the system reliability (redundancy) approach.

Network

Details on the electrical design of the network are given in the companion paper by White and others [3]. The technique is based on, and uses the same devices as, the network of the TE-400 A. Experience with the 100 000 TE-400 A lines now in the field confirms early predictions on its performance and reliability. The cost of the *pnpn* diodes has reached a level at which they are attractive compared with other crosspoints, and this cost is likely to continue to drop as volume increases and as solid state manufacturing processes improve.

The network consists of 4 switching stages, with single wire transmission referenced to ground. Signals are coupled to outside plant through isolation transformers. Figure 1 shows the network diagram. A line to trunk call traverses the 4 stages from the line side inlet to the trunk side outlet. Local junctors are connected to two ports of the network, as shown in Figure 4, and the calling and called subscribers' calls traverse the 4 switching stages to reach the local junctor. These arrangements make the network carrying capacity independent of the mix of local and external traffic. Figure 1 shows the full availability characteristic of the network, that is, any inlet can reach any outlet.

Because of the *pnpn* diodes and the control, which is discussed below, the network is extremely compact and thus economic in packaging costs. One line block (Figure 1) is constructed on one printed board (8·7 inches × 10 inches). It need only be equipped when the

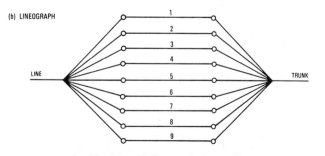

Figure 1 - TCS network diagram.
(a) Matrix consisting of from 1 to 4 matrix units
(b) Lineograph for any size network.

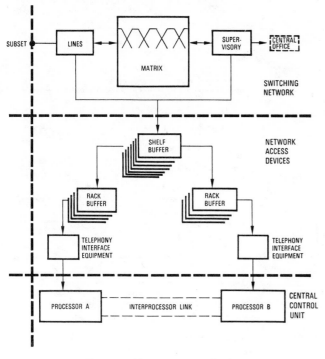

Figure 2 - TCS system organization.

lines associated with it are equipped. The same equipping characteristics are true of the tertiary and quaternary printed boards. Network equipment is thus installed only as lines and trunks are equipped, thereby reducing the get started cost. The compactness of the network is illustrated by the fact that the third switching stage (tertiary) for a fully equipped 6 000-line system requires only 60 printed boards located in two of the 7 shelves of the control rack. Two additional shelves are used for processor input, output, and maintenance circuits. The remaining space is used for the processors and their memory.

The control of the network is end marked. This means that the application of a positive potential from the line and a negative potential from the trunk causes the network to search, select, and operate one of the available paths between the line and the trunk. The trunk then holds the path using a current source that provides the holding current for the *pnpn* diodes. This connecting operation lasts 4 ms.

The impact of this simple procedure and the electronic network on get started costs is important. To appreciate this importance, consider how this function is handled with more conventional approaches. First a network map is maintained in the memory of both processors and a program analyzes and selects the crosspoints of a desired path. The processor then passes appropriate commands to a marker circuit which in turn accesses and operates the desired crosspoints, and finally interrupts the processor to report on its mission. Alternatively, the network could be scanned for free paths, and when selected the marker operates them. This alternative requires crosspoints with scan points. Additional costs over the end marked approach in-

clude the marker equipment, the memory associated with the administration and command of the markers and the more expensive crosspoints or the memory required to map and analyze the network, audit, and compare the maps in both processors, and reconfigure the maps in case of faults. In addition, real-time, which could be used to trade-off for hardware, is consumed. These costs are compared with the command codes and simple marking circuits in line and trunk type circuits using the end marking approach.

A traditional shortcoming of end marked networks has been the inability to detect faulty crosspoints. The reliability of solid state crosspoints is such that this shortcoming is not important for small networks. However, as the network grows, the capability to detect crosspoint faults must be introduced. The method for implementing it in TCS is particularly simple because of the lineograph of the network and the stored program. Figure 1b shows that the network has 9 paths between any inlet and any outlet. A simple circuit in the tertiary printed board under program command, can cause any 8 out of the 9 paths to appear blocked. A test call between an inlet and an outlet would qualify 4 diodes. A failure would trigger several test calls between a fixed inlet and variable outlets and vice versa. Correlation of the results of these test calls isolates the fault down to a printed board. The maintenance program required to perform this function resides off-line in on-demand, back-up storage and is loaded into the main memory for execution during low traffic periods. Complete checkout of the network is programmed approximately once a month, this being considerably more frequently than required by MTBF calculations.

Two other important attributes of the network are worth mentioning. First, since the voltages through the network path drop upon firing and the holding current is selected to support only one diode in each state, no double connection is possible. Second, should it be desirable to change the network topology for traffic reasons, this can be done without affecting the rest of the equipment.

Control Unit

Having determined that the flexibility objectives required a processor for system control, it was important to minimize its impact on initial costs. The ITT 1650 processor was chosen because it is manufactured in large volumes and thus, TCS can profit by the associated economics. Word length is 16 bits and its 78 instruction set includes byte and bit addressing. Its interrupt structure allows 64 levels of interrupts, not all of which are used in TCS. Five interrupt levels are used internally by the processor and 12 by TCS telephony related hardware circuits. Eight general purpose registers are available to the programmer. Memory capacity is 65 536 words available in 4 096 or 8 192 words per printed board. In addition, expansion to 131 072 words is possible by mapping 65 536 words in pages into the main memory. The program can be protected through memory protect. Three options are available with cycle times of 800 ns, 960 ns, and 1 440 ns.

With the important emphasis on get started cost, real-time is sacrificed in favor of minimizing fixed hardware. Thus, as in the case of markers, the need for an independent scanner or input/output unit has been avoided.

Using a very compact routine, the processor addresses, commands, and interrogates the telephony circuits via the telephony interface equipment, the rack buffer, and the shelf buffer (Figure 2). This procedure required 19 processor cycles per group of 16 telephony circuits accessed. In a fully loaded TCS with one processor out of service, the other processor uses approximately 25 percent of its real-time in the TIE (telephony interface equipment or telephony input/output) mode. The reasonably small real-time investment for this function is possible because of the small number of cycles required to access the telephony equipment. This in turn is possible because of the small physical size of the exchange. The distance from the telephony interface equipment (which is housed with the processor in the control rack) and the most distant shelf buffer (which is housed in one shelf with the accessed telephony circuits) is less than 150 feet.

A typical sequence starts with the processor executing an output instruction which transfers an address and a command to the telephony interface equipment which, in turn, sends the information to the rack buffer input bus via its line drivers. The addressed rack buffer (which resides one per telephony rack for each processor) receives it and transmits it to the shelf buffer. The shelf buffer receives the signal and commands the addressed circuit(s). The process is then inverted with the telephony circuit status being transmitted back to the telephony interface equipment. This process lasts 6 μs. During this time the processor obtains from its memory the previous status of the telephony circuit and is ready to input the new status to determine whether a change has occurred and take appropriate action.

In the TIE mode, in one input/output cycle the processor scans 16 line circuits for originations or 16 supervisory circuits (trunks, TEL-TOUCH* registers, et cetera) for request for service. This scanning is structured so that even when one processor is out of service, every line is scanned for origination once every 160 ms, and every supervisory circuit once every 20 ms for request for service. In the case of the supervisory circuits, the request for service may mean that an incoming call is arriving, that a dial pulse has been received, or that a new signal condition has been received by the supervisory circuit. Lines in-dialing and Tel-Touch registers are scanned every 20 ms. Other input/output functions of the processor in the TIE mode include commands to mark and release the matrix, to send (regenerated) a dial pulse by a trunk, gate ringing phase to party line circuit, send coin collect signal to coin box, and change status of attendant** console. They also include general

* A trademark of ITT System
** US term for operator

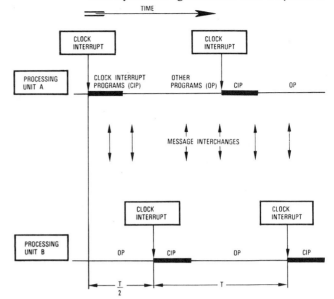

Figure 3 - Call load sharing technique in which each processor normally handles only 50 percent of the input load.

commands to, and status checks of the telephony circuits. In addition, check commands and status are built in thus permitting verification of the correct operation of the telephony bus at regular intervals.

The telephony interface equipment contains an exclusion function. This function precludes simultaneous access of the telephony equipment by both processors. This limitation is necessary to avoid conflicts in command. Because the processors normally stagger the access of the telephony circuits every 10 ms, no undue congestion is encountered. The size of the exchange and the speed of network connections permits one network connection to be set up at a time.

System Dependability

To meet the objective of a maximum of 2 hours system down in 40 years, it is necessary to have redundancy in the common control equipment. There are a number of ways of providing this redundancy. However, experience has shown that the majority of system faults are transient program faults. These occur when an infrequent (therefore not found in debugging) external event interreacts with a flaw in the program to cause a program crash. If both processors are executing synchronous programs and seeing the same input events, a system crash results. The call load sharing mode developed by ITT for its Metaconta systems [2, 4] eliminates this problem by ensuring that both processors handle different input loads and work on different programs at any one time. Call load sharing has been adopted for TCS.

The call load sharing technique can be understood with the aid of Figure 3. In this technique each processor normally handles 50 percent of the input load. (Each processor scans line equipment positions at one half the total number of lines apart ensuring essentially a 50 percent call processing load per unit). When a processor handles a service request for a call, it handles the whole processing of the call. After each action on a call the processor updates the other via the interprocessor link. To maintain the highest possible independence when processor unit A is scanning (clock interrupt programs), processor unit B handles other programs. Each processor receives a clock interrupt every 20 ms but 10 ms apart from the interrupt for the other processing unit. Thus, the load input is said to be 180 degrees out of phase.

In the event of a processing unit failure, the good machine takes over the full load. This includes calls being handled by the faulty processor which had reached a stable state (conversation or ringing phases). The faulty processing unit is then subjected to a series of audits and diagnostic routines available from a system reload device. If there is a hard fault, a teletypewriter report is issued identifying the location of the fault and appropriate alarms are generated. If no fault is detected because the fault was transient (software or hardware), the processing unit goes through a reload and a recovery cycle, and starts handling traffic again: a teletype message will report reason for reload.

In adopting call load sharing for TCS, several additional criteria were considered. The approach is simple and requires a minimum of redundant equipment. Fallback is straightforward and reconfiguration only involves running a program in the sane computer that changes a bit in all call records to the "this processor is handling this call" state. Redundant equipment is routinely exercised since each processing unit normally handles 50 percent of the load. System load carrying capacity is specified as if one processor was out of service (simplex configuration), so in normal operation, this technique provides a high peak overload capacity.

Availability of the reload device, with its low cost storage, is helpful in minimizing the initial cost. Deferrable maintenance and administration programs, which would normally reside in the main processor storage, can now be brought into the processor memory on-demand.

Telephony Equipment

Typical telephony circuits are shown along with the network in Figure 4. Each telephony circuit contains a network marking circuit for each network connection. Those connected to the supervisory side provide a current source to hold network paths. Circuits connected with outside plant have a transformer for isolation and balance. As this transformer appears in every line and every trunk it must be small and inexpensive. Transmission distortion introduced by these transformers and other ohmic and reactive elements in the speech path, are compensated by a highly stable amplifier. This circuit is best described as a solid state hybrid amplifier. It is discussed in detail in the companion paper by Stewart [5]. This amplifier enables the system to meet all the TCS insertion loss and return loss objectives.

A deliberate attempt was made to centralize the logic within the processor. With few exceptions, the

telephony circuits change status as a result of a command which in turn is caused by a reaction of the processor to a request for service or a new call.

One unusual approach is that all DC supervisory and dialing signals are extended via the scanning distribution into the processor. The supervision correlation between lines and supervisory circuits is handled in the call records in software.

The speed of connection and disconnection of the network, and feeding of the subscriber loop from the line circuit, permit extensive use of the resetting technique. Resetting consists of switching the calling and called parties during different call phases. This technique has proven to be particularly effective in saving costs in the trunk circuits. As indicated earlier, accidental or planned double connections are not possible and switch loop, override, and similar call procedures are inserted in series rather than in parallel as in other systems.

A typical PABX incoming call is shown in Figure 5. In Step 1, a trunk request for service is scanned by the processor and identified as an incoming call. The processor selects an attendant loop then sends a command to mark the trunk network appearance. After 2 ms the processor sends a command to the selected attendant loop to mark its line network appearance and after a further 2 ms checks that the connection has been established. The attendant is alerted and the speech path cut-through. In Step 2, the attendant has dialed the called subscriber and is connected to announce the call. In Step 3, the attendant releases, the attendant loop is released, the network is reset, and the line circuit and trunk are connected. Under normal circumstances, this is the end of this call. However, there is a blocking probability of 0·01 in Step 3, and connection of the line circuit to the trunk may not be possible. Since the call has reached a stable conversational state it is im-

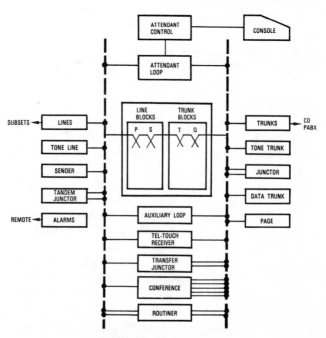

Figure 4 - Network block diagram.
CO - central office.

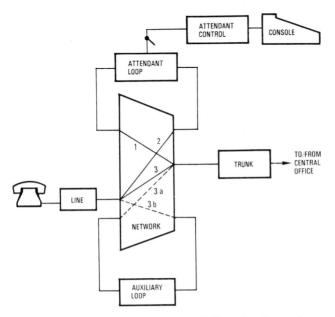

Figure 5 - Treatment of an incoming call illustrating the resetting technique and the virtual nonblocking characteristics of the network.

Relays are used in certain parts of the interface with outside plant or where a metallic connection is mandatory. All relays are sealed or have dust covers. There are fewer than 2 relays per line in a typical TCS exchange.

Long life derating rules are applied throughout to ensure the long life objectives for the system.

Installation and Growth

To meet the challenging objective of competing with electromechanical common control equipment as regards the installed price of the initial installation, it was necessary to minimize installation costs. Typically other systems with up to 6 000 lines are not system tested in the factory. However, the physical size (Figure 6) of TCS made this objective feasible. To implement this objective, self-standing cabinets were designed to contain the equipment. These are called racks and are dimensioned to fit through normal elevator and office doors. Height is 78 inches, width 45 inches, and depth 24 inches. Each rack can house 7 shelves of printed boards. All connections between shelves and racks are by plug-in cables. Connections to the main distributing frame are also by plug-in cables. Addi-

portant to reduce further this effective blocking probability. This is accomplished by changing the connection from fixed point to fixed point (fixed trunk and fixed line) into a fixed to variable point connection. An auxiliary loop, located in the network to minimize traffic correlation, is selected by the processor and connections 3a and 3b are tried. Should the procedure still fail due to blocking, a further attempt is made with a different auxiliary loop. For the largest TCS exchange, the equipping of 12 auxiliary loops (6 printed boards) yields an effective blocking probability of approximately 10^{-5}. The term "virtually nonblocking" is used for this type of connection.

It should be noted that selection of a telephony circuit is accomplished by a program running in the idle circuit selection interrupt level. An exclusion circuit restricts this level to one processor at a time.

Technology

An important criterion in the selection of components for TCS was commonality with TE-400 A as this takes advantage of volume production, simplifies manufacturing, and minimizes retraining of ITT and customer maintenance personnel. Monolithic integrated circuits are used throughout. The processor uses transistor transistor logic (TTL) with medium scale integration. The memory is of the magnetic core type. The rest of the equipment employs diode transistor logic ·(DTL). The high modularity of the design enables new technologies to be incorporated as they become viable.

Where integrated circuits are not practical, silicon planar epitaxial discrete devices are specified. Four types of transistors cover over 99 percent of the transistor volume. Carbon or metal film resistors are used for long term stability.

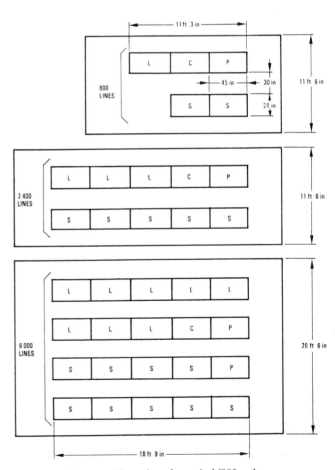

Figure 6 - Floor plan of a typical TCS exchange.
L - line cabinet (800 lines)
C - control cabinet
P - power supply cabinet
S - supervisory and trunks cabinet.
Each cabinet measures 78 × 45 × 24 inches (1980 × 1142 × 610 mm).
Average floor loading is 100 lb/sq ft and the console 20 lb.
Ceiling clearance is 9 ft.

TCS System Organization and Objectives

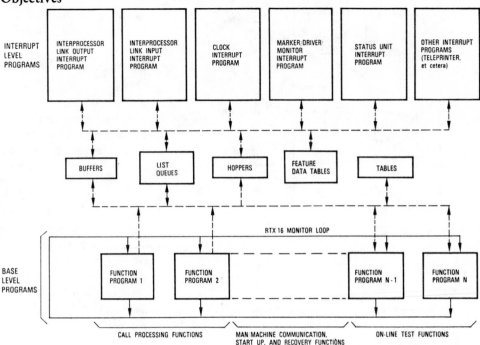

Figure 7 - Real-time program organization.

tional details on the equipment practice and its achievements with respect to cost and maintainability can be found in the companion paper by Drigot and others [6].

The test plan is to assemble and test the complete TCS exchange in the factory. These tests use on-line and on-demand maintenance programs, and include "smart load boxes" capable of subjecting the system to the rated load. Upon completion of factory tests, the interrack cables and the tips and rings cables are disconnected and the racks and cables crated for shipment. At the site the equipment is uncrated, cables connected, and power brought in.

Equipment performance is verified using the same on-demand tests conducted in the factory. Shipment damage is repaired and the exchange is ready to go into operation.

Growth is simply based on plugging in printed boards or cables. The latter are necessary when a new shelf or rack is added. New shelves are attached to the rack by 4 bolts. Of course, the parametric data of the program have to be changed. Minor changes may be made through the teletypewriter, but for more extensive changes it may be more appropriate to update the reload device. The ability of the two processors to store different data, facilitates this procedure.

Programming

Program Size

The first application of TCS is a 2 000-line PABX. For this application the processor resident program and data tables occupy less than 57 344 words of 16-bit length. A large number of applications will be covered with 65 536 words, and memory expansion to 131 072 words will cover all the presently conceived applications of TCS. In addition, a number of pro-

grams reside in the reload device. These programs are called on-demand by the core resident program, or through manual intervention using the teletypewriter. The on-demand programs are used for deferrable maintenance and administration functions. Of course, an image of the on-line program and data tables also resides in the reload device.

Call Processing Programs

The TCS program is organized in a conventional resource oriented manner (Figure 7). It is interrupt driven by clock signals of 2 ms and 20 ms periodicity. The 20 ms signal causes an interrupt to the clock level for accurate time dependent supervision and outpulsing. The 2 ms signal is used for matrix marking timing.

Call records are maintained in transient call buffers. These are data words which contain variable information about each call. Information contained in this variable area identifies all the equipment associated with the call, in addition to the existing stable state of the call. Dialed digits and outpulsing information are maintained in a register buffer associated with the transient call buffers.

Extensive use of table driven programs facilitates modularity and the implementation of new features. Of particular interest are the static call skeletons. These skeletons are data tables which define all types of system calls and could be treated as the finite states of the switching system. Telephony type call diagrams, such as those shown in Figure 8, define the stable states of all call types in the system and the sequence conditions in going from one state to another. When these skeletons are represented as data tables in memory they provide a single and complete transformation from a telephony system call description diagram to program actions.

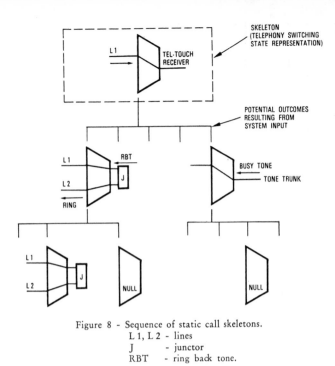

Figure 8 - Sequence of static call skeletons.
L 1, L 2 - lines
J   - junctor
RBT   - ring back tone.

software are covered in detail in the companion paper by Garney and others [7].

Maintenance and Administration Programs

Reliability is of the utmost importance in switching systems. In line with the objectives described earlier it was important to devise a dependable, but simple and inexpensive maintenance procedure.

The approach used was to divide the system into a common control group and a telephony group. The first group includes the processor, memory, control, and exclusion circuits. The second group includes multiple circuits such as lines, trunks, and junctors. A failure in the common control group affects a large number of subscribers, whereas a failure in the telephony group affects only a few subscribers. The TCS maintenance philosophy is therefore that, when any element of a common control group is suspected (involved in one problem), the appropriate side of the common control group should be removed from the normal processing flow and tested. Prompt removal limits the number of calls affected by a fault. In the telephony group, the equipment must be at least statistically shown to be suspect (involved in more than one problem), and then it alone is removed, provided that its removal does not have a detrimental effect on the overall system operation.

Functional modularity of the hardware allows the software to combine the usual isolation and localization functions into a single go/no-go verification function. The result of this verification determines whether or not the function of the system is operating correctly. Most system functions reside on a single plug-in printed board, and in no case on more than 4 boards.

As far as possible, the maintenance routines follow the normal call processing flow. Simple hooks have been introduced to facilitate this action. For example, a bit that allows a piece of equipment to be tagged "maintenance busy" is included in memory along with the equipment information. When equipment in the telephony group is found to be faulty and condemned, its maintenance busy bit is set. The equipment is then unavailable for normal call flow, but available for on-demand maintenance routines.

Many periodic program audits are performed by the maintenance programs, including such tests as watchdog time-out, data range reasonableness checks, statistical analysis, check sum verification, and memory protect.

As a further test on total system operation, a simple test circuit originates calls in the system every 4 minutes. Lack of detection of dial tone triggers a number of actions aimed at alerting the system to the trouble and repairing it.

Office routining includes the normal outside plant tests required of public exchanges. The circuits that provide this capability also permit tests inward towards the switching system. These tests are useful in verifying the line circuit operation from the test desk.

On-demand tests, recent changes, and traffic admin-

Data table information consists of 4 parts. Part 1 indicates the lists with which each type of telephony equipment is associated. Part 2 indicates the equipment that is connected through the network in this skeleton, and the state of each equipment. Part 3 indicates the resultant action which should be taken when a scanning program detects that a piece of equipment has changed its previous state. Finally, Part 4 contains additional data, which are used in making decisions about classes of service, and special case programs which in special situations may be used to process a transition from one state to another.

A simplified version of how the skeleton tables are used is illustrated in Figure 9. The transient call buffer points to a skeleton (number 14) and provides the relative equipment number of the types of equipment described in the skeleton. When the transient call buffer receives information indicating that L3 has disconnected, a common program unpacks skeleton 14 and the transient call buffer. The common program references L3-D and determines that the next skeleton is number 7. This is also unpacked and compared with 14 to determine which connections and state are common and which need to be changed. Appropriate matrix mark and unmark commands are entered into appropriate queues. The transient call buffer is updated with the new skeleton number (7) and relative equipment numbers, and is then packed.

The procedure for the creation and use of static call skeletons is systematic and simple. Thus, the addition of new call features is straightforward and minimizes the introduction of faults into existing software.

Of particular interest is the potential this technique has to simplify and automate consistency checks and software application engineering. The static call skeletons and other important aspects of the call processing

TCS System Organization and Objectives

istration are facilitated by teletypewriter messages. Recent changes are also possible by regeneration and reload of the reload device. Traffic reporting facilities in TCS include extensive data gathering capabilities. Reporting of the data is either on a timed basis or on-demand.

The companion article by Besman and others [8], covers TCS maintenance and administration in depth.

Simulation

Environmental simulation in TCS is covered in detail in the companion paper by Foucault and others [9]. The environmental simulator is based on a similar device invented for the Metaconta system [10]. It consists

of the two system processors, an interface, and a simulation processor. The simulation processor contains a program that provides inputs to the system processors through the environmental interface. These inputs simulate actions by the system hardware, including simulated input events. The simulation processor controls the clock of the system processors thus causing all the simulation events to appear as in real-time. In addition, it has access to the system processors' memory.

The simulation program accepts call patterns as input parameters. These call patterns are presented as regular calls to the operational program in the system processors, and normal operation of the program is verified by the simulation processor. The simulation programs include a number of traces and other aids that are useful in debugging the program. In addition to being able to run a large number of call patterns, it is possible to simulate system faults, traffic patterns, and traffic loads.

The environmental simulator is an extremely powerful tool for software development, and it is also useful during the system production cycle for checking new features in new software packages.

Technical Performance and Capacity

Transmission

Very early attention to this area yielded an excellent solution to the insertion loss introduced by ohmic and reactive components in the speech path. A highly stable solid state hybrid amplifier, mentioned earlier, compensates for these elements. The resultant insertion loss at 1 000 Hz, for example, is 0.5 ± 0.15 dB for the line to trunk connection. Crosstalk coupling was minimized by care in transformer spacing and reasonable wiring precautions. Worst case figures have indicated a crosstalk figure of 80 dB at the midband frequency.

As discussed in the paper by Stewart [5], calculations and laboratory analysis confirm that TCS meets the transmission objectives for future systems of the United States Independent Telephone Association. Similar efforts also confirmed that it satisfies the transmission standards for private communications systems of selected authorities outside the United States.

Reliability

Theoretical calculations indicate a system mean time between failures (MTBF) of 40 years with a mean time to repair (MTTR) of 5 hours. If an MTTR of 2 hours is achieved, the MTBF is 100 years.

Actual results on the frequency of repair of the TCS are expected to be as in the TE-400 A (see earlier section "Objectives: Technical Performance and Capacity") in view of commonality in components, design practices, manufacturing techniques, and test techniques.

Capacity

The system minimum capacity objective of 2 400 lines and 18 000 ccs (500 erlangs) has been met. In addition, the system can grow to 6 000 lines and 21 000 ccs (586 erlangs).

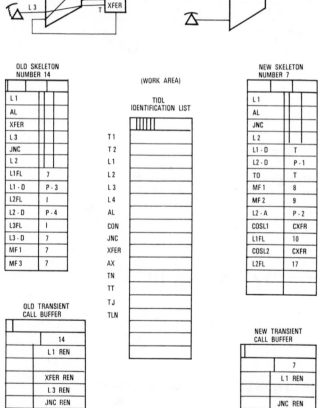

Figure 9 - Feature tables and marking driving monitor showing how the skeleton tables are used.

L 1	- line 1	TN	- tone trunk
AL	- attendant loop	COS L 1	- class of service — line 1
XFER	- transfer junctor		
JNC	- junctor	CXFR	- class of service transfer
L 1 FL	- line 1 — flash		
L 1-D	- line 1 — disconnect	P-1	- program 1
MF 1	- marking failure of connection 1	L 2-A	- line 2 — answer
		T	- timed disconnect program
REN	- relative equipment number		
		TIDL	- unpacked transient call buffer
T 1	- trunk 1		
AX	- auxiliary loop	TJ	- tandem junctor
CON	- conference	TT	- Tel-Touch register
TLN	- tone line	TO	- time-out

Present estimates indicate that TCS can be engineered to 23 000 busy hour call completions. In arriving at the above capacity the number of calls that the processor can carry during an hour at 95 percent occupancy (peak capacity) was estimated. This result is reduced to account for false starts (which are estimated at 30 percent of originating calls). This peak capacity is further reduced to allow 10 percent for traffic peaks, thus arriving at the engineerable load capacity of 23 000 busy hour calls. In arriving at this capacity it was only necessary to allow 10 percent for traffic peaks. This is possible because of the very large overload call carrying capacity inherent in the call load sharing redundancy approach.

Peak processor capacity calculations are based on cycle counts in the program, environmental simulator results, and comparisons with existing systems.

Status

The first TCS exchange is due to be cutover during the first quarter of 1974. This exchange is currently being debugged in the factory at the Electronic Switching Center of ITT in Des Plaines, Illinois. Other important debugging tools being used in the systems laboratory include two engineering test models and an environmental simulator. Three additional exchanges are planned for 1974 shipment. These include hotel, centrex CU, and public exchange applications. Bid results against competitive systems indicate that TCS is meeting its economic objectives.

Acknowledgments

The development of TCS contains contributions from many people at the Electronic Switching Center

and ITT. Also D. Fisher and B. Fontaine of ITTE were instrumental, respectively, in the traffic dimensioning of the network and the introduction to call load sharing.

During a development project of this nature there are many occasions on which management support and confidence is necessary and forthcoming. For this we are very grateful to all the ITT management who have been involved with the TCS project at one time or another.

References

[1] J. Reines and S. E. White: ITT TE-400 A Full Electronic PABX: *IEEE International Conference on Communications*, San Francisco, 8—10 June 1970. New York, Institute of Electrical and Electronics Engineers, 1970, pp 3—6 — 3—14.

[2] S. Kobus, J. A. de Miguel, and A. Regnier: Metaconta L Stored Program Control of Latching Crosspoint Matrices: *Electrical Communication*, 1971, volume 46, no 4, pp 235—245.

[3] S. E. White, N. Jovic, H. L. Williams, T. A. Akers, J. M. Corrado, and W. Vehe: TCS Electronic Design: *Electrical Communication*, 1973, volume 48, no 4, pp 375—389 (this issue).

[4] S. Kobus, A. Kruithof, and L. Viellevoye, Central Control Philosophy for the Metaconta I. Switching System: *Electrical Communication*, 1972, volume 47, no 3, pp 159—163.

[5] A. Stewart: TCS Transmission Aspects: *Electrical Communication*, 1973, volume 48, no 4, pp 390—396. (this issue).

[6] W. J. Drigot, R. W. DeBolt, Y. C. Lee, and R. P. Dicius: TCS Equipment Practice: *Electrical Communication*, 1973, volume 48, no 4, pp 429—435 (this issue).

[7] D. J. Garney, R. W. Arnold, B. Cohen, and A. M. D'Amore: TCS Call Processing Software: *Electrical Communication*, 1973, volume 48, no 4, pp 397—410 (this issue).

[8] A. I. Besman, G. W. Couturier, G. Light, and T. P. Johnson: TCS Maintenance and Office Administration: *Electrical Communication*, 1973, volume 48, no 4, pp 411—423 (this issue).

[9] C. C. Foucault, D. J. Cerny, and L. Ponce de Léon: TCS Environment Simulation: *Electrical Communication*, 1973, volume 48, no 4, pp 424—428 (this issue).

[10] B. Fontaine: Real-Time Environment Simulation: *Electrical Communication*, 1971, volume 46, no 3, pp 188—190.

Bibliography

[1] J. Reines: Solid-State Crosspoints Boost PABX Performance: *Telephony*, 6 December 1971, volume 181, no 23, pp 46—47, 50—52.

[2] K. L. Liston: Kelex Electronic Switching System: *Colloque International de Commutation Electronique*, Paris, 28 March—2 April 1966. Paris, Editions Chiron, 1966, pp 178—188.

Supplementary Bibliography for Paper 11

TCS 5

FIRST TELCO CUTOVER OF FULLY ELECTRONIC SP STORED PROGRAM
PABX (TCS2)
ZOFFINGER GH + NEILSEN ER
TEL ENG MANAGE 78: 60 (MAY 1, 1974)

PUERTO RICO TEL MARKS ON ELECTRONIC "FIRST" WITH NAVAL
STATION PABX (TCS2)
ZOFFINGER GH + NEILSEN ER
TELEPHONY 186: 96 (APR 15, 1974)

TCS SYSTEM SOFTWARE PRODUCTION
COOPER S + GARNEY D + GLASS M + KOLLER W + ZYNSZAJN V
P307 OF NAT ELECTRON CONF PROC 1975 (621.381/N27)

Paper 12

Canadian No. 1 Electronic Automatic Exchange Production Level No. 2 (C1-EAX-PL2)

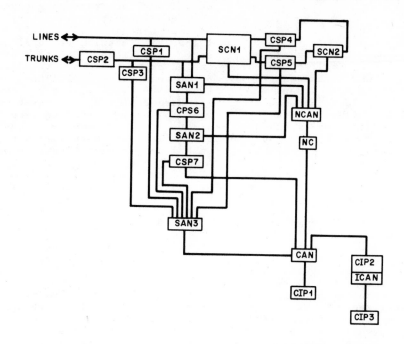

SCN1 = STAGES A AND C
SCN2 = STAGE B
CAN = DATA BUS
CIP1 = PROGRAM MEMORY
CIP2 = DATA MEMORY CONTROL
CIP3 = RING CORE MEMORY
CSP1 = LINE CIRCUIT
CSP2 = TRUNK ADAPTER
CSP3 = LINE CIRCUIT

CSP4 = TERMINATING LINK
CSP5 = ORIGINATING LINK
CSP6 = REGISTER JUNTOR
CSP7 = REGISTERS AND SENDERS
ICAN = DATA MEMORY SELECTOR
NC = MARKER OUTPUT AND CONTROL
NCAN = MARKER CONNECT MATRIX
SAN1 = STAGE AR
SAN2 = STAGE R
SAN3 = STATUS DETECTOR CONTROL
        AND DRIVER

C-1 EAX - SYSTEM EXPANSION

R.W. Duthie
GTE Automatic Electric (Canada) Ltd.
Brockville, Ontario K6V 5W8

Abstract

This paper introduces a new common control system organization for the C-1 EAX which permits its capacity to be doubled to 4800 lines and trunks. The new common control has a highly modular structure and utilizes integrated circuits and semiconductor memories. An evolutionary development, the new common control, permits further growth in systems already in-service.

Introduction

C-1 EAX is a stored program switching system designed to meet the needs of smaller central offices. The system has been in volume production since 1970 and there are currently some 56 systems and 57,000 lines in commercial service in Canada, the United States and Israel. Field experience has been excellent and has proven the system concepts were sound. All common control switching systems have two fundamental problems: their capacity is limited and the cost of the common control tends to limit the minimum size at which the system can be proven in economically. The C-1 EAX is not exempted from these two problems. A third problem, which is common to all electronic switching systems, is that the rapid advances in electronic component technology, usually make the devices selected at the outset of design, "obsolete" by the time the system is ready for operation in the field. The C-1 EAX component technology was selected in 1964 and utilized discrete germanium transistors. During the 6 year period of development, technology had advanced through silicon discrete, to small scale integrated circuits, and even large scale integration using MOS was becoming fairly common.

Late in 1970, studies showed that all three problems could be satisfactorily resolved through the design of a new common control for the C-1 EAX, employing low cost integrated circuits and having a greater capacity. The new common control would be a direct replacement for the existing control system and would have identical interfaces to the switching network, so that no changes would be required in the network equipment.

The task of developing this new common control was completed in only two years, with the first system cut-over in December 1972 as a 600 line PAX serving our Brockville factory. Commercial system cutovers will begin in October 1973.

Throughout this paper, we will refer to the new common control as the Production Level 2 (PL-2) control, and the original control, as the Production Level 1 (PL-1) control.

Network Expansion

Expansion of the network area was accomplished very simply by doubling the size of the central B matrix of the 3 stage network, as is shown in Figure 1. The B matrix now provides for a maximum of 48 line groups, each serving 100 lines. Provision for additional registers and senders was accomplished by allowing two R matrices per 2400 line section. This allows full availability to a maximum of 44 registers and 20 senders.

It was not necessary to change the packaging of the B & R matrix cabinets, since a single cabinet contained 12 (12X24) B matrices, and 1 (32X72) R matrix, or sufficient network to serve 1200 lines. Cabinets are externally cabled so that 2 cabinets serve 2400 lines, 6 cabinets serve 3600 lines, and 8 cabinets serve 4800 lines. Thus no new circuit or hardware design was necessary and most important the network has the same low getting started cost for small offices. Traffic capacities, of course, remain unchanged since each line group continues to be served by 12 AB links and 12 BC links.

Depending, on the traffic mix, the call handling capacity of the PL-1 system could be limited by the single marker provided. While a single marker was adequate for 2400 lines it could not handle the increased load expected from 4800 lines. Thus at least two markers capable of pulling two paths simultaneously are now required.

We did not wish to make any wiring changes in the network cabinets which would not be compatible with either common control, so we decided to look at the network from a marking point of view as being divided into six zones A1,A2,C1,C2,R1 and R2 as shown in Fig. 2. A single marker pulls a complete connection, for example, from zone A1 to zone C1. A simultaneous connection can be established by the second marker from A2 to C2. However, certain simultaneous connections cannot be allowed or a double connection will occur. For example if marker 1 pulls an A1 to C1 connection, marker 2 cannot pull an A2 to C1 connection at the same time. Such "collisions" are prevented by the system software.

The PL-1 control provided duplicate markers but only one could operate at a time, the second being a "standby". The PL-2 control now uses the "standby" as an active marker, so that loss of a marker will only degrade service. Thus the cost of markers is not increased. However, in some high calling rate offices, loss of one marker would cause serious degradation of traffic, so a third marker can be provided capable of assuming the load of either of the other two. In actual fact, the load is distributed by software evenly over all three markers.

The call handling capacity of this scheme is very slightly more than twice the capacity of the PL-1 single marker, and met all of our objectives for system expansion. The most

Reprinted from *1973 IEEE Int. Conf. Commun. Rec.*, vol. II, June 11-13, 1973, pp. 29/1-29/6.

important considerations were to avoid any changes to the network, and to avoid penalizing the small office with the cost of a more elaborate marking system required for growth above 2400 lines.

Common Control Organization

The Production Level 1 common control for C-1 EAX represents a carefully selected compromise between hardware and software. It tends to use hardware for all simple but time consuming tasks such as digit collection and digit sending, and uses software for all complex, short term tasks, such as network path selection and digit translation. The call stores are distributed throughout the peripherals such as registers and senders. A read-only memory is used for program storage and data base storage. There is no interrupt capability in the Central Processor, but rather a program controlled polling of devices.

The most outstanding change made is in the architecture of the common control. The PL-1 system had multiple busses interconnecting all the various subsystems, whereas the PL-2 system has a single (duplicated for reliability) minicomputer type databus allowing a highly modular and flexible system architecture. (This area is treated in detail in a companion paper in these proceedings). Each subsystem is formed by one or two modules, one of which is connected to the databus. A block diagram is shown as Figure 3. Control modules are connected to the databus and interface modules connect control modules to the network.

A brief description of each major subsystem follows:

Central Processing Unit - CPU. This is a 20 bit, 16 accumulator parallel processor which can directly address 64 K words of program memory, and indirectly address up to 15 additional pages of 64K words each. The order set is patterned after the PL-1 CPU, but as a result of detailed program analysis includes several additional instructions which reduce program length and execution times. The average time to execute an instruction is 6 μ sec as compared to 40 μ sec for the PL-1 CPU.

Program Memory. The program memory employs a reprogrammable read-only MOS device, described in detail below. A maximum of 16K words (20 bits/word) is provided per module in 2K word increments. Only 6K words are required in a typical application. In PL-1 a ring core or Dimond memory was used for program storage.

Data Memory. The data memory uses the same ring core memory as PL-1 because of the ease with which daily updates can be made. While large in size with respect to semiconductor memories, no equivalent device is available which offers all its advantages, its relatively low cost, and its proven performance. A maximum capacity of 16,800 words is available in 700 word increments. This capacity allows for up to 9100 directory numbers, up to 16 office codes, 18 class of service bits per line, and adequate space for

trunk tables, PBX hunting groups etc. Physically, there are 3 module types, a Data Memory Control, containing the databus interface, input and output logic, a Data Memory Selector, an interface module with the drive and sense circuits and the Ring Core Memory modules themselves.

Status Detector. The status detector is used to sense the busy/idle/call-for-service states of relay contacts in the network. In the PL-1 control this function was combined with the ring core memory. This tended to limit the speed of the memory and a number of problems in the field occured when false potentials such as ringing voltages were accidentally connected to the status leads causing component failure in the memory drive circuits. It was therefore considered highly desireable in PL-2 to completely separate the status detecting function from the memory function. Similar techniques are used, however, thus minimizing changes in network circuits, and protection against false potentials is provided in the PL-2 control. Two modules are provided, a Status Detector Control, (SDC) and an interface module to the network, the Status Detector Drivers. (SDD).

Marker. A single marker consists of a Marker Control module (MKC), which contains storage decoding, and timing logic, and a network interface module, the Marker Output (MOP), which contains reed relay drivers, and connect circuits. A maximum of 3 are provided.

Registers & Senders. Registers and Senders are provided in two module types. A Register Sender Control module (RSC) which contains all storage (call stores), digit counting logic, sender decoding logic, timing logic, and tone decoding logic, for 4 registers and 2 senders. A maximum of 11 modules can be ordered providing 44 registers and 20 senders, the limitation being in the network. Network interfaces are provided by Register Line Circuits, and Sender Line Circuits, which mount in interface modules. Signalling systems offered include dial pulse, CCITT R1, R2, #5, and DTMF.

Console Control - CNC. This module contains the configuration controller which determines which Databus is on-line, a 24 hour time of day clock, teletype printer interface, random number generator, peg count buffers, and various test console interfaces. It is the only unduplicated module in the system.

Maintenance software includes fault detection and recovery, and manually initiated test routines. A centralized maintenance console is used for fault location. This philosophy has been proven in the many systems in service to be entirely appropriate and highly successful for the intended applications of the C-1 EAX. We had, therefore, no desire to change this philosophy and while the PL-2 common control introduces improvements it in no way represents a substantial departure from the concepts of the PL-1 control.

MOS Program Memory

The program memory employs a floating gate avalanche injection metal oxide semiconductor device. This is a reprogrammable read-only memory. Each device consists of 2048 memory bits in a single 24 pin package.

The device is supplied by the manufacturer with each bit set to a "one". Any bit may be set to a "zero" by addressing it and pulsing the bit location with a 750 ma current. However, once set to a "zero", it cannot be altered by any means except by exposure of the semiconductor surface to high intensity ultraviolet light. Accordingly, a quartz lid is used to seal the packages rather than the usual metal or epozy lids. Exposure of the chip to ultraviolet resets all bits to "one". In operation as a read-only memory, it has a cycle time of 3.5 µsec.

Erasure of a card requires 20 minutes in a specially designed ultraviolet light box. After erasure the card is plugged into a module called a Memory Card Loader (MCL) for programming. This MCL contains the power supplies and high current drive circuits necessary for loading the memory. The program to be loaded is punched on paper tape and read into a minicomputer's memory. The minicomputer is connected to the Databus, and the CPU transfers the data from the minicomputer memory to the Memory Card Loader, which in turn loads the MOS memory card. Approximately 30 minutes is required to load 2048 words.

The loaded card is then inserted in the program memory module, read and compared with the data in the minicomputer to verify that each bit has been properly set.

This memory has many characteristics in common with the card changeable twister memory. It has all of the desireable characteristics of being read-only, non-destructive read-out, etc, but in addition it has a bit density which in terms of bits per card is much higher, thus eliminating the need for mechanical card handlers.

Packaging

No changes were made in the network packaging so this area will not be discussed. All common control hardware is mounted on 12" X 13" double sided, plated-through-hole printed cards. The PL-1 system utilized a building block approach to card design, where a relatively small number of card types, each containing from 4 to 8 logic elements were mounted on a small card 5" X 6" and then wired together externally to form individual subsystems. This approach is impractical for integrated circuits in the control modules so a functional board philosophy was adopted where a complete subsystem is mounted on a single card, or group of cards.

A total of 32 different board types are required for the control area. These contain from 17 to 68 integrated circuit packages with an average of 46 packages per card. The minimum conductor width allowed on a card is 0.025 inches and no conductors are allowed between the pads for the IC devices. While these design rules made board layout difficult, the end result was a very low cost per IC for packaging. Power and ground conductors are very carefully planned in board layout

and a considerable number of decoupling capacitors are provided to reduce the high frequency impedance of the power conductors.

To prevent card warpage and bending in insertion, a steel plate is attached to the back side of each card. This "stiffener" acts as a ground plane and shield, protects the card during handling, and provides a certain amount of thermal capacity which can assist in cooling the equipment during air conditioner failures.

All cooling is provided by convection, with the cards mounted at 1" centres. A maximum of 10 watts per card is allowed at a room ambient of 110 F. At the outset it was believed that the high power densities that are encountered with IC's would require the use of blowers. However, extensive studies showed that the space saved by having blowers was largely offset by the space required to house the blowers. Furthermore the cost of the blowers and their power convertors, and the additional maintenance required are significant disadvantages.

Power is supplied to each module from a 48 volt feeder, and one or more DC-DC convertors are supplied with each module. Interconnections from the module to the Databus are provided by a special connector assembly which mounts on the backplane. The Databus uses flat ribbon cable, and is the only wiring which runs from file to file on the rear of the frames. Plug ended cables interconnect control modules to interface modules and these enter a control module at the front and connect to a cable card which in-turn plugs into the backplane. Thus a module is completely plug-in and can be easily added or even replaced in the field in a working system.

A typical control module consists of two cable cards, a bus interface unit card, 6 functional cards, and a 48V to 5V DC-DC convertor card. This uses 11 of the 16 slots available. Modular packaging is not particularly efficient in its use of space with only 68 % of the available slots occupied in a typical office. However, it is believed the advantages far outweigh this one disadvantage.

A maximum of 5 files can be mounted on a frame 8 feet high, with no equipment more than 7' above the floor. Single sided 20" wide racks are used, for all control modules. Interface modules mount on 27.5" wide racks, identical to the standard racks used for GTE Automatic Electric's family of electronic switching systems.

Conversion of PL-1 to PL-2

An important feature of the Production Level 2 common control is its ability to replace in a working exchange the Production Level 1 common control. This allows exchanges already in service to double their ultimate capacity if this should ever be necessary. In one or two cases already, growth has far exceeded the original estimate and a conversion is now being planned.

In general the procedure is to install the new control and the network addition as a separate exchange and complete all system testing in an off line environment.

The relays provided in the PL-2 network interface cards to remove faulty subsystems from service are then used to isolate the PL-2 control, and then the network addition is cabled to the existing network, in the same manner as any network addition is made. The common control leads are cabled to the existing network, and carefully terminated one wire at a time. (about 500 wires in total), on the live network.

Just prior to cutover, the PL-1 A system is locked on line and the B system interface cards unplugged. Cutover is accomplished by simultaneously causing the PL-1 system to transfer to its now non-existent B common control, and operating the PL-2 common control connect relays. An important part of all procedures is that it is always possible to get back to the original configuration quickly should any problem develop.

Conclusions

The development of the PL-2 common control for the C-1 EAX to expand capacity and reduce costs represents the first evolutionary step in the life of this system. This step was completed in only 2 years compared with the 6 years necessary to develop the original system. It illustrates how readily advanced technologies can be applied to an existing electronic switching system providing significant new improvements yet protecting the investment in training and facilities already made.

References

1. "C-1 EAX Electronic Automatic Exchange for 2400 Lines and Trunks" by R.W. Duthie, Switching Techniques for Telecommunication Networks, IEE Conference Publication No 52

2. "Field Experience with C-1 EAX" by G. Verbaas and R.W. Duthie, IEEE Transactions on Communication Technology, April 1970 Volume COM-18 Number 2

3. "C-1 EAX - Modular Common Control" by R.A. Borbas and J.P. Dufton," Proceedings of the International Conference on Communications 1973, Seattle, Washington.

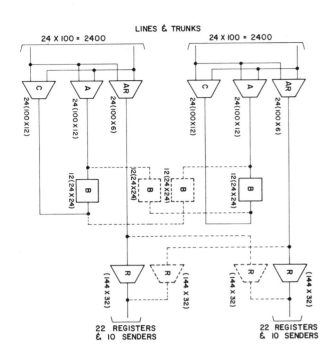

LINES & TRUNKS

24 X 100 = 2400   24 X 100 = 2400

22 REGISTERS & 10 SENDERS   22 REGISTERS & 10 SENDERS

FIG.1   NETWORK EXPANSION
B Matrices shown with dotted lines provide
interconnection paths between two 2400 line
network units.   R Matrices shown with dotted
lines provide full availability to all registers and senders from any line and trunk.

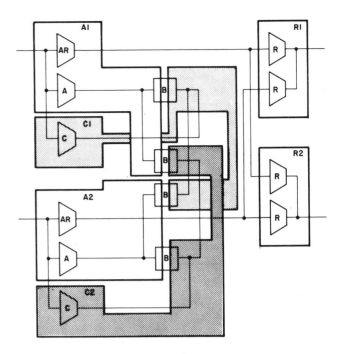

LINE TO LINE CONNECTIONS
   AI-CI, AI-C2, A2-C2, A2-CI
LINE TO REGISTER CONNECTIONS
   AI-RI, AI-R2, A2-R2, A2-RI
SIMULTANEOUS CONNECTIONS ALLOWED
   AI-RI WITH A2-CI, AI-C2 WITH A2-CI, ETC.
SIMULTANEOUS CONNECTIONS NOT ALLOWED
   AI-RI WITH AI-C2, A2-C2 WITH A2-CI, ETC.

FIG.2   SIX MARKER ZONES

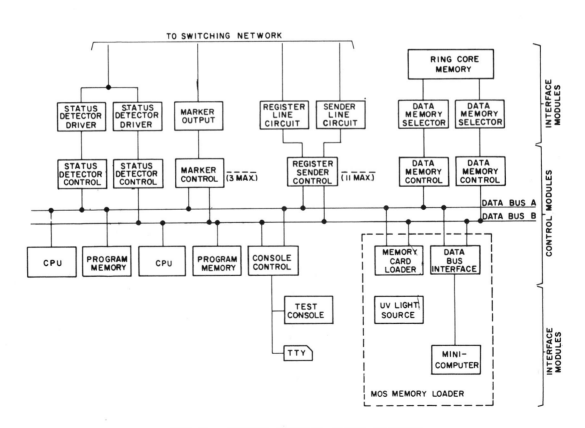

FIG.3   COMMON CONTROL BLOCK DIAGRAM
MOS Memory Loading facilities are used at the factory to load programs and are not normally
provided with the system.

94

FIG.4   C-1 EAX (PL-2) COMMON CONTROL
Interface frames and console shown on left.
CPU modules have test panels.   16K program
memory module has cover removed.

FIG.5   SYSTEM MEMORIES
Single printed card contains 2048 words of
program memory, three ring core memory modules
contain 2800 words of data base.

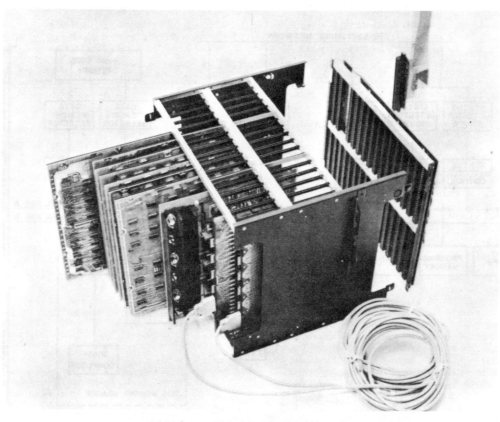

FIG.6   TYPICAL CONTROL MODULE
From left, bus interface card, 6 functional cards, power supply, cable
cards, file, backplane assembly, and databus cable assembly.

Supplementary Bibliography for Paper 12

C1-EAX

C1-EAX SOFTWARE AND REAL-TIME CONSIDERATIONS IN A SMALL
STORED PROGRAM SWITCHING MACHINE
AUGUSTUS JH + DUFTON JP + DUTHIE RW
P577-84 OF INT SWITCHING SYMPOSIUM MIT 1972 (E173-1597)

EAX-C1 (ELECTRONIC AUTOMATIC EXCHANGE) FOR THE SMALL
CENTRAL OFFICE
DUTHIE RW
AUTOMATIC ELEC TECH J 10 276-85 (JUL 1967)

C1-EAX EXPANDED
AUTOMATIC ELECTRIC TECHNICAL JOURNAL 13(8): 408 (OCT 1973)

Paper 13

Local Stored Program System No. 1 (SP1)

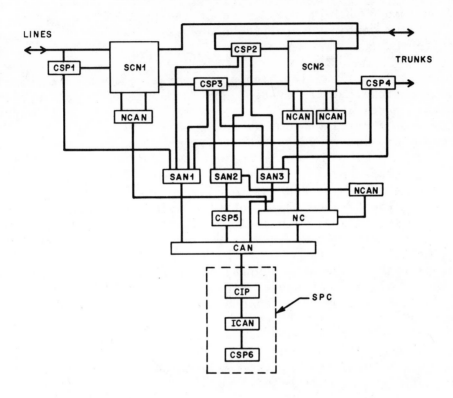

SCN1	= LINE NETWORK	CSP5	= SERVICE CIRCUIT
SCN2	= ROUTE NETWORK	CSP6	= CALL STORE
CAN	= INTERFACE BUS	NC	= MARKER
CIP	= CENTRAL PROCESSOR UNIT	NCAN	= MARKER CONNECTOR
CSP1	= LINE CIRCUIT	SAN1	= SCANNER
CSP2	= INCOMING TRUNK	SAN2	= SERVICE LINK NETWORK
CSP3	= ORIGINATING JUNCTOR	SAN3	= DISTRIBUTER
CSP4	= OUTGOING TRUNK	SPC	= CENTRAL CONTROL

THE SP-1 ELECTRONIC SWITCHING SYSTEM

H.L. Webster

I. <u>INTRODUCTION</u>. The Northern Electric SP-1 Electronic Switching System is a common control system, yet it also employs distributed control. It is an electronic system yet it makes liberal use of electromechanical devices. These statements may appear to be paradoxical but in reality they describe the sound philosophy behind the design of the system. That philosophy is to use an optimum combination of techniques and technology — to get the best out of both.

The result is a flexible, high performance system, much superior to comparable electromechanical systems now in existence, yet competitive in cost. In this paper I propose to give examples of the hybrid nature of the SP-1 System, but first I would like to establish where SP-1 fits into the broad category of electronic switching systems.

SP-1 is a stored program controlled system. This is the common control aspect of the machine and is its most outstanding feature. In computer parlance, the SP-1 central control complex is a time sharing, multi-programmed machine of third generation technology. But this is where the similarity to commercial computers ends. Because of the unusually demanding nature of its task — to provide continuous control without interruption for scores of years — the SP-1 central control has to demonstrate a reliability unheard of in the computer field. In SP-1 this is achieved through specially designed components, redundancy, and a very sophisticated diagnostic and maintenance system. Moreover, since cost is a very significant factor in a competitive telephone switching system, the amount of equipment has to be held to a minimum consistent with reliability. In SP-1 this is achieved by a very efficient software system designed to maximize the utilization of logic circuitry and memory.

II. <u>DESIGN OBJECTIVES</u>.

<u>Size</u>:   (1) initial installations   2000 to 10,000 lines
           (2) nominal maximum   20,000 lines
           (3) physical capacity   37,800 lines

<u>Switching Capacity</u>:   36,000 calls ABSBH (Average Busy Season Busy Hour)
                      100,000 CCS (2800 Erlangs)

<u>Grade of Service</u>:   total overflow   4%   max.
                  dial tone delay > 3 sec. 1.5% max.
                  originating matching loss 1%   max.
                  incoming matching loss   2%   max.

<u>Reliability</u>:   less than 2 hours downtime in 40 years (total system).

H.L. Webster is Director of Switching Development with
   Northern Electric Laboratories, Canada

Reprinted with permission from *IEE Conf. Publ. 52, Switching Tech. Telecommun. Networks*, Apr. 21-25, 1959, pp. 240-245.

Floor Space: approximately half that of existing crossbar systems.

Maintenance and Administration: simple maintenance procedures and low operating and administration costs through such features as:

    (1) Automatic trouble indication and diagnosis.
    (2) Plug-in electronic boards.
    (3) Flexible line and trunk assignment.
    (4) Changes to line and trunk data by teletypewriter.
    (5) Traffic data record on tape or teletype.
    (6) Automatic call tracing.
    (7) Improved handling of permanent signals.

Service Features:

Standard: Individual, two-party, multi-party, coin, message-rate, revertive calling, rotary dial or DIGITONE dialing. DP and MF signalling, tandem operation. Automatic message accounting on magnetic tape. Immediate ringing, automatic number identification.

Optional: Centrex, Speed Calling, Call Forwarding, Call Waiting, 3-way calling.

Other: Flexibility to add new features easily and economically.

Cost: Competitive with existing common control systems.

III. DESIGN APPROACH. The design objectives just described suggest a few key words — flexibility, simplicity and economy. These were the basic guidelines in our system studies and led to the following conclusions concerning the design of the system:

    (1) Overall control of the system would be by stored program. This would give a high degree of flexibility.

    (2) The network would be crossbar with sleeve lead control. For economy and compactness the new MINIBAR switch would be used. The sleeve lead would result in significant savings in memory and real-time capacity by providing network status and by permitting distributed control under the direction of the stored program.

    (3) Maximum use would be made of integrated circuits in the central control complex. This would simplify logic design, diagnostics and maintenance and would improve reliability.

    (4) The central control complex would be duplicated for reliability. The normal operation would be match-mode and either unit would be capable of carrying on without degradation of service.

    (5) There would be a comprehensive diagnostic program to simplify maintenance.

Many other design decisions have been made during the progress of the development as detailed requirements have been settled and as alternative courses of action have evolved.

IV. <u>GENERAL DESCRIPTION</u>. The SP-1 System can be described in terms of three subsystems: the Switching Network, the Peripheral Equipment, and the Central Control. Fig. 1 shows the make-up and relationship of these subsystems.

(1) <u>The Switching Network</u>. The basic switching element is the MINIBAR switch. This is a 200 point 6-wire switch (10 x 20 array) used in groups of 5 or 10 switches to form the building blocks of the switching networks. There are three basic networks in the System — the Line Network, the Route Network, and the Service Network.

    (a) The Line Network (LN), consisting of up to 63 Line Link Frames (LLF), interconnects lines and PBX trunks with originating and terminating junctors over 3-wire paths. Each LLF has two switching stages, a line switch stage of 20 or 30 switches with a capacity of 400 or 600 lines, and a junctor switch stage of 10 switches with a capacity of 60, 80, 100 or 120 junctors. Originating and terminating junctors are normally, but not necessarily, provided in equal quantities.

    (b) The Route Network consists of originating route link frames and terminating route link frames arranged in pairs. Each frame has two stages of switching, a total of four for the complete network. A system may use up to 24 pairs of route link frames, each with a capacity of 200 inputs and 200 outputs.

    The inputs to the originating route link network are originating junctors and incoming trunks. The outputs consist of outgoing trunks, terminating junctors and tone trunks.

    (c) The Service Network provides access from originating junctors and incoming trunks to service circuits such as digit receivers, ringing, and coin-control. The basic service link frame is a 3-stage network with a capacity of 200 inputs and 100 outputs. Supplementary frames may be added to increase the input capacity to either 400 or 600. Up to eight service link frames can be used in a single installation.

    (d) Trunk Circuits and Junctors. The trunk circuits in the SP-1 System are simple compared to conventional trunk circuits. Functions such as pulsing and ringing are performed by service circuits; controlling and timing are performed by Central Control.

    Originating junctors serve as the talking bridge and main control point for supervisory signals on intraoffice and outgoing calls. They perform the functions of intraoffice trunks and in many cases, act as outgoing trunks.

    Terminating junctors are simple 3-wire connections from the terminating Route Network back to the Line Network. Supervisory control is provided by the originating junctor or incoming trunk.

(2) <u>Peripheral Equipment</u> consists of markers, network controllers, signal distributors, scanners, service circuits and the bus system.

    (a) Markers and Network Controllers. The marker sets up metallic paths through the switching network by operating select and hold magnets on the MINIBAR switches. It is assisted in this function by network controllers associated with each network frame. The marker receives its instructions from Central Control over the bus system and gains access to the specified network frames through a marker connector. Once the switches have been operated, the marker tests the path for electrical continuity, foreign potentials and crosses. If a fault condition is detected, the connection is dropped and Central Control instructs the marker to try again over a different path, and concurrently starts a diagnostic routine.

(b) A signal distributor operates or releases electrically latching relays in trunks, service circuits, markers and originating junctors under the direction of the Central Control. Essentially, it is a buffer between the high speed Central Control and the relatively slow relays. The signal distributor and the marker are good examples of distributed control in the SP-1 System.

(c) The scanners provide the input information for detecting service requests and supervising calls in progress by sampling or scanning lines, trunks, and various diagnostic points at discrete intervals, as directed by the Central Control. A scanner consists of a duplicated controller and a single matrix of 1024 ferrod sensors arranged in 64 rows of 16.

(d) Bus System and Interface. A balanced AC Bus System, driven by the input-output control of the central processor, provides the means of communication to and from peripheral units. The Bus System is duplicated and contains a peripheral bus, an enable bus, a scan return bus, an "All Seems Well" bus and a maintenance bus.

The interface contains receiving circuitry for the peripheral units. Peripheral units such as markers and signal distributors receive orders from the peripheral bus and the enable bus via bus receivers into silicon controlled rectifiers (SCR's). The SCR's provide the means for storing the high speed orders and the amplification required to operate relays.

(3) (a) *The Central Control is a binary digital machine consisting of a Central Processing Unit (CPU), a Program Store and a Call Store. The CPU controls the actions of all other units in the system by executing, one at a time, instructions from the programs in the Program Store. It also analyzes troubles in the system under the direction of maintenance and diagnostic programs. The Program Store contains all instructions and data required to process calls and to administer the office. The Call Store is the "scratch pad" memory which handles all the temporary information required during the processing of calls.

(b) Software. This paper has dealt mainly with the hardware aspects of the SP-1 System, but it is quite obvious that a stored program switching system can only be as good as its software. The

*Described in an accompanying paper by W.J. Ives.

SP-1 software system is good because it is simple in concept. Its modular organization requires a minimum of memory for such a comprehensive program, and makes efficient use of real time. It also lends itself readily to extension and change. Dr. Hall's paper will describe the software system in detail.

(c) The Maintenance Center provides the interface between the switching system and the operating personnel, and, as such, is the administration center of the office.

CONCLUSION. As previously stated, the SP-1 Electronic Switching System is a flexible, high performance system which employs to best advantage the features of common control and distributed control, of electronic devices and electromechanical devices. Because of the flexibility of its stored program control, SP-1 will readily adapt itself to the service demands of the future.

BIBLIOGRAPHY.

(1) D.H. McNaughton, SP-1 Electronic Switching System, NEC, Chicago, Dec.68.
(2) Buchan & Reid, SP-1 Central Control Complex, NEC Chicago, Dec. 68.
(3) Jezioranski & Mlacak, SP-1 Switching Network & Peripheral Equipment, Chicago, Dec. 68.
(4) L.C. Beaumont, SP-1 Structure and Maintenance, NEC, Chicago, Dec. 68.
(5) Hall & Gagnier, SP-1 Call Processing Software, NEC, Chicago, Dec. 68.
(6) Telesis, Northern Electric Publication, SP-1 System, to be pub. Jan. 69.

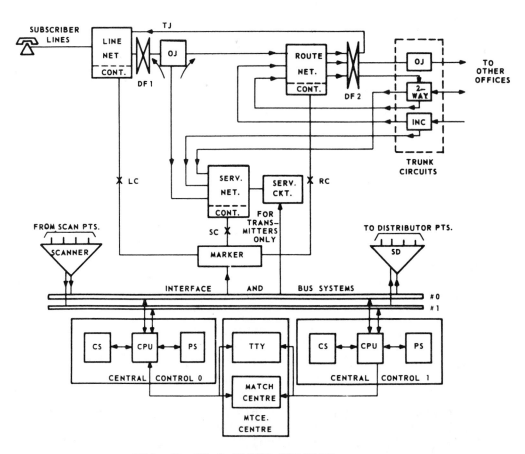

FIG. 1 SP-1 BLOCK DIAGRAM

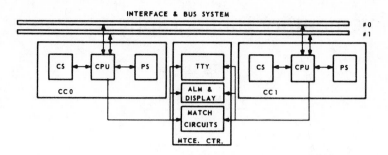

FIG. 1.   CENTRAL CONTROL COMPLEX

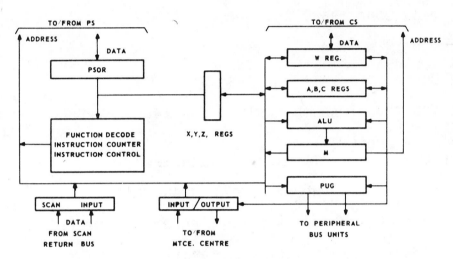

FIG. 2.   CENTRAL PROCESSING UNIT

FIG. 3   LOGIC CIRCUIT BOARD

Supplementary Bibliography for Paper 13

SP-1

SYSTEM GENERAL

SYSTEM OBJECTIVES AND DESCRIPTION FOR SP-1 ELECTRONIC
SWITCHING SYSTEM
MCNAUGHTON DH
NAT ELECTRON CONF 1968, 24TH PROC P612-17 (E4/N27)

SP-1 SYSTEM IN ACTION
BLAIS R + BOMBA JS + WALLIS JN
NORTH ELEC TELESIS 1 (4) .134-8 (JAN. 1969)

SERVICE AND TECHNICAL OBJECTIVES FOR THE SP-1 ELECTRONIC
SWITCHING SYSTEM
KENNEDY JC + PEDDE O
NORTH ELEC TELESIS 1 (4) 114-19 (JAN 1969)

COMPONENTS AND HARDWARE

SMALLER, FASTER MEMORIES FOR SP-1 ELECTRONIC SWITCHING SYSTEMS
NOTLEY G + REID J
TELESIS 3 (8): 226-31 (JUL/AUG 1974)

CENTRAL CONTROL COMPLEX FOR SP-1 ELECTRONIC SWITCHING SYSTEM
BUCHAN JS + REID JN
NAT ELECTRON CONF 1968 24TH PROC P628-33 (E4/N27)

SWITCHING NETWORK AND PERIPHERAL EQUIPMENT FOR SP-1 ELECTRONIC
SWITCHING SYSTEM
JEZIORANSKI JS + MLACAK JG
NAT ELECTRON CONF 1968 24TH PROC P18-23 (E4/N27)

SP-1 ELECTRONIC SWITCHING SYSTEM - HARDWARE
IVES WJ
IEE CONF SWITCHING TECHNIQUES FOR TELECOMMUN NETWORKS
APR 1969 CONF PUB NO. 52 P250-2

STRUCTURE AND MAINTENANCE OF THE SP-1 ELECTRONIC SWITCHING
SYSTEM CONTROL COMPUTER
BEAUMONT LC
NAT ELECTRON CONF 1968 24TH PROC P624-7 (E4/N27)

HARDWARE FOR THE SP-1 SWITCHING SYSTEM
HARDWICK GR + IVES WJ
NORTH ELEC TELESIS 1 (4) 120-5 (JAN 1969)

THE SP-1 ESS PERIPHERAL MAINTENANCE SYSTEM - AN EVOLUTIONARY
DESIGN
MALCOLM SA
P52 OF NAT ELECTRON CONF PROC 1975 (621.381/N27)

PERFORMANCE AND FIELD EXPERIENCE

SP-1 GROWTH AND PERFORMANCE
BUECHNER KM
NORTHERN ELECTRIC CO LTD TORONTO ONTARIO PRESENTED AT USITA
MIAMI FLA (OCT 1973)

SP-1 INTRODUCTION AND SERVICE EXPERIENCE
NAIK VB
P321-325 OF INT SWITCHING SYMP MIT 1972 (E173 1597)

SP-1 CENTREX - OPERATING COMPANY EXPERIENCE
BHATT AK
P22-1 OF IEEE INT CONF COMMUN 1975 11TH CONF REC VOL 2

SP-1 4-WIRE TOLL SWITCHER PERFORMANCE EVALUATION AND OPERATION
OF THE VERIFICATION TRIAL OFFICE
KNOX KC + MATTILA HK
P22-6 OF IEEE INT CONF COMMUN 1975 11TH CONF REC VOL 2
(621.38/I11C)

THUNDER BAY SP-1: CANADA'S GATEWAY TO ELECTRONIC TOLL SWITCHING
ABI-AAD A + HOMONICK H + MILBANK W + TOPPLE E
TELESIS 4 (1): 20-7 (1975)

SOFTWARE

CALL PROCESSING SOFTWARE SYSTEM FOR SP-1 ELECTRONIC SWITCHING
SYSTEM
HALL CD + GAGNIER R
NAT ELECTRON CONF 1968 24TH PROC P634-8 (E4/N27)

SP-1 ELECTRONIC SWITCHING SYSTEM - SOFTWARE
HALL CD
IEE CONF SWITCHING TECHNIQUES FOR TELECOMMUN NETWORKS
APR 1969 CONF PUB NO. 52 P246-9

SP-1 SOFTWARE FOR OPERATION AND MAINTENANCE
DENIS RF + GILLON NH + KENNEDI R
NORTH ELEC TELESIS 1 (4) 126-13 (JAN 1969)

Paper 14

EVOLUTION OF THE SP-1 TOLL SWITCHING SYSTEM

John S. Edwards

The SP-1 computer-controlled switching machine has been introduced into Canada's central offices for local calls. A second member of the family will prove to be a powerful influence in the toll network. The increasing use of four-wire transmission facilities dictates the use of a four-wire switcher in many locations.

The SP-1 project for a computerized central office was initiated in 1963 by Bell Canada, through its subsidiary manufacturing company, Northern Electric. This new office was to be a stored-program-controlled exchange, that is, one that utilizes a digital computer to perform the controlling functions for the office. The reasons for this decision have been fully explained previously[1]. Briefly, they are that such a machine is much faster and more adaptable than the relay control used in previous types of switching machines, is smaller, and less costly to maintain. New services can be introduced at any time by making modifications to the program that controls the office's operation, without hardware changes, and new subscribers can be added to the exchange with minimum disruption to the functioning of the rest of the office. The system, designated the SP-1 ESS, was the first

exchange of this type designed by Bell-Northern Research. During its early years the SP-1 project concentrated on a 2-wire machine for the central office function (see box on 2-wire and 4-wire switching on this page). It was in the 2-wire network that Bell Canada and other principal customers of Northern Electric required modernization of their switching equipment. Following a successful field trial in the Britannia exchange in western Ottawa[2,3], the SP-1 2-wire system was introduced into service in Aylmer, Quebec, in 1971[4].

A New System is Born

Just prior to the Britannia field trial in the fall of 1968, a study of the future of the SP-1 family of switching machines was begun under the auspices of the switching systems engineering department at the

---

WHY 4-WIRE SWITCHING?

The local telephone network, including subscriber telephone sets, uses simple two-wire transmission circuits. Conversations are carried in both directions over this single pair of wires. Switching machines in this local network therefore switch a single pair of wires for each connection setup. However, in a long-distance connection unidirectional amplifiers are required to maintain signal strength. In this case, the two directions of transmission have to be separated by a circuit known as a hybrid so that outgoing and incoming messages are carried on separate two-wire circuits. The result is four-wire transmission.

Technological advances have removed the necessity of actually employing wires and the transmission can now be effected over cable, microwave links, etc. Regardless of the method used, distances of more than a few miles are spanned by four-wire transmission systems.

When one four-wire transmission facility has to be connected through a switching machine to another four-wire transmission facility, it is desirable that the switching machine switch all four wires. The alternative is to connect the incoming four-wire circuit to a hybrid to yield a two-wire circuit, switch through a two-wire switching system and run the output through another hybrid to again yield four-wire transmission. Because of their inherent imperfection, hybrids are sources of echo and singing. By eliminating the hybrids on four-wire to four-wire circuits, a four-wire switcher permits lower end-to-end loss within set echo and singing requirements.

Thus four-wire switching provides considerable economy when switching four-wire circuits. The economy comes not only through the elimination of the hybrids which would otherwise be required in the switching office but also from the further elimination of repeater sites on some toll terminating facilities.

Incidentally, a four-wire switcher may actually switch more than four wires. The additional wires are used for supervisory and control signals.

Reprinted with permission from *Telesis*, vol. 2, pp. 8–15, Winter 1972.

laboratories. This study concluded that a 4-wire toll switching system using SP-1 concepts would be feasible and would fill a requirement in the DDD network. Accordingly, in January 1969, a task force under the direction of J. Jezioranski was established at Bell-Northern Research to consider the development implications of the 'toll SP-1'. The members of this task force included a number of senior SP-1 designers and representatives from the systems engineering division of the laboratories. The full force met in February 1969 for about three weeks, and drew up a preliminary proposal. This document, called the "blue book", was to serve as the planning guide for the project for two years.

In May 1969 an exploratory development project headed by Walter Ives was chartered. Initially his total staff numbered two managers—J. Jezioranski and the author. Their first task was to re-issue the blue book to correct some deficiencies and revise the design, as it was the prime document Northern Electric needed to evaluate funding for the project.

Early Design Effort

The proposal for the toll SP-1, as stated in the revised blue book, was to 'extend the SP-1 system to provide 4-wire toll facilities (which) will provide for a stand-alone system of from 200 to 4,000 incoming trunks' (see box on 4-wire switching on page 8). The report went on: 'Additionally, the proposed system will function in the lower range as a combined 2-wire local and 4-wire toll switch'. How were these figures derived? How confident were the members of the department in them? To answer these questions first consider the nature of the job. That is, what market did the designers see in 1969 for the new system? A study of the plans for almost all of the North American DDD network had revealed that in the period from 1974 to 1984 some 90 percent of the toll switching machines expected to be in service at that time would be under the 4,000 trunk limit. This indicated a great opportunity for a toll switching machine of the stored-program type, and prompted the proposal for the 4-wire SP-1. Having established that a potential market existed, the designers went on to consider the system requirements in detail.

There are two important parameters to consider for any switching system: network capacity and system capacity.

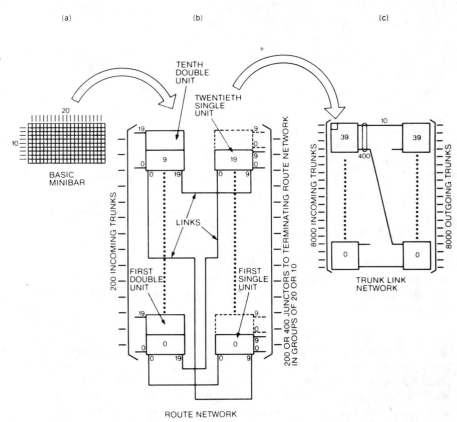

FIGURE 1. *The overall objectives of the design for the trunk link network were to provide a matrix of MINIBAR switches that can handle around 4000 trunks, with potential for expansion. The basic MINIBAR switch (a) has 200 individual sets of contacts (crosspoints) arranged in a 10 by 20 format. Each crosspoint set has six wires. Four of the wires make the required contacts to connect a call (two contacts per pair), one wire is used for internal office control, and one wire is spare. Thus 10 different 6-wire connections can be made between the 10 horizontal appearances and any 10 of the 20 vertical appearances. Each line shown within the switch represents one six-wire set. Numbers of basic MINIBAR switches are assembled in order to build up a network which is capable of connecting any one of 4000 incoming trunks to any one of 4000 outgoing trunks, with internal connections (links) apportioned among individual switches in the most efficient way. In the initial design (b), utilizing the basic MINIBAR, 20 by 20 double switches were assembled by connecting together two 10 by 20 basic switches. Then 10 double switches were joined together in a first stage, and linked to 20 single switches in the second stage. For simplicity, only the extreme inter-connecting links are shown. The resulting unit was then used as a building block for the trunk link network. Broken lines show where additional switches could be added to increase the network capacity. The first stage (c) of the network consisted of 40 of these units, and the second stage of 40 of their 'mirror images'. The resultant network has 8000 incoming and 8000 outgoing appearances. However, the number of links in the 20 by 20 arrangement of the double switches in the first stage is too large for the amount of traffic to be handled: they were not fully utilized.*

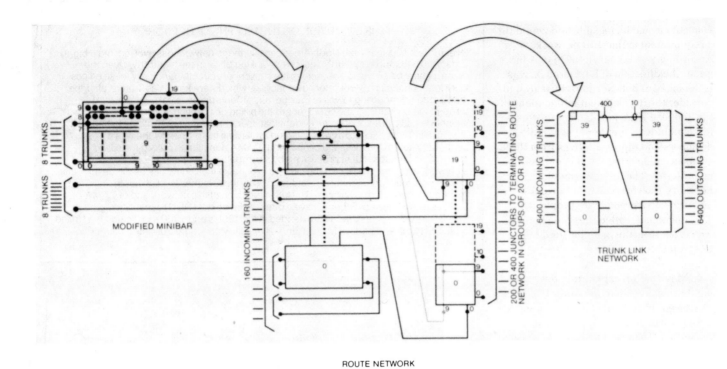

MODIFIED MINIBAR

ROUTE NETWORK

TRUNK LINK NETWORK

The network capacity is a measure of the number of calls that the system can handle simultaneously, while the system real-time capacity indicates how many calls can be handled in a given interval at a busy time.

Network Design Considerations

A 4-wire network is a simple concept, but its final configuration in a given switching system depends on many factors, some of which are discussed here.

The 4-wire machine would be required as soon as 1974. Thus there were only four years to design, manufacture and place the first unit into service. The MINIBAR* switch, already used in the SP-1 2 wire office was the obvious choice as the switching element. As any programmer is quick to tell you, most computers deal in binary numbers and powers of two. Thus, an eight-by-sixteen switch would perhaps be the most palatable for the computer-like SP-1 system. However, for reasons outlined in the next few paragraphs, the 'binary' switch is not an important system consideration. In early 1968, the network designers considered their options.

Their approach was as follows. In order to assess the optimum switching arrangement for a central office which is required to connect incoming trunks to outgoing trunks (the function of the

FIGURE 2. An alternative arrangement was devised in order to make more efficient use of the switches in the network. Each 10 by 20 MINIBAR was divided (a) into two functional switches. Levels 0-7 on each half were used for the incoming trunks, and levels 8 and 9 were employed to group the links. Thus each functional switch could handle 8 trunks, and the modified MINIBAR was able to take 16 trunks instead of 10 in the basic unit. This arrangement reduced the number of switches required for the first stage (b) to 10, for handling 160 incoming trunks. The coloured line indicates how a connection is made in this type of network. The final trunk link network (c) is made up from 40 of these modified units. The maximum number of appearances that this network could handle is thus 6400; but 10 modified MINIBARS (20 functional switches) could be added to expand the network to terminate 320 incoming trunks, with a maximum of 12,800 appearances. Broken lines show additional units.

4-wire machine) one must consider the total number of trunks, the length of time a typical telephone conversation lasts, how many conversations will be carried on a trunk, on average, and perhaps how long it takes to actually connect the incoming to the outgoing trunk. These data have been gathered over a long period of time by various telephone administrations and thus could be called upon during the design process. The length of time a call lasts depends upon the amount of information to be exchanged between the two parties and the cost of the call per minute. Cost has been the dominant factor up to now, but the North American trend toward lower long-distance price structures has modified this somewhat. (Certain members of the author's family quote rates as so much an hour!) In any event, a call lasting a little over three minutes (200 seconds), has been shown to be a good measure for the length of an average toll call (note the relationship to the three-minute minimum charge interval that has been in effect for several years).

Now statistically it is found that an average trunk may carry traffic for from one-third to two-thirds of the time that it is available for service. This allows for calls to be completed with a high probability. This fact, considered from a network point of view, leads to the conclusion that the simplest network would utilize the MINIBAR in its basic 10 by 20 format (a switch of this size has the capacity required to handle the calls arriving on the number of trunks specified for the 4-wire office). The designers first chose to create the base trunk link network (TLN) for the office by connecting together two such switches, making a 20 by 20 double unit, and then connecting 10 of these double units to a second group of 20 single switches via links, as shown in Figure 1. Sets of these networks and their mirror images were to be mounted on metal frames, called link frames, and interconnected to make up the TLN. Access between frames was to be provided by connectors known as junctors. However, the 20 by 20 arrangement of the first stage proved to have too many links for the amount of traffic it had to handle. They were not fully utilized.

In order to produce a more efficient working arrangement, an alternative network was fashioned. In this version, the physical 10 by 20 MINIBAR was divided into two halves. Levels 0-7 on each half were for trunks; levels 8 and 9 were for grouping the links, as shown in Figure 2. Again two such switches would be combined, resulting in a 32 by 20 switch. This network used fewer MINIBAR units, at the cost of increased design complexity. Computer simulations and computations of network capacity were performed in the summer of 1968 with the help of the systems engineering department of Bell-Northern Research to determine the relative capacities of these two networks. The second network was shown to carry a lower, but sufficiently high traffic load. Thus in this case economics decided against the simple solution, and the final design employed the 32 by 20 switch. This network could grow to 6,400 incoming trunk appearances. Where would the system capacity limits lie?

System Design

The method of determining the required capacity of any complex system is not easy. One usually proceeds from known systems and gradually develops a model or theory by which the limiting factors may be determined. In the case of the 4-wire machine, we already knew from the market survey results that there would be a strong demand for a machine with up to 4,000 trunks. That gave us our network capacity target figure. As regards the system capacity, we decided to start from the objective previously set for the 2-wire machine, since this unit had been created earlier, and was much nearer the market at that time. Its characteristic was therefore much more closely defined. The published objective, in terms of the number of *completed* calls per hour, was 36,000. Now the system real-time capacity is computed from the sum of two quantities: the amount of time

FIGURE 3. *This block diagram shows the main components of the 4-wire SP-1, grouped in three main functional areas: switching network, peripheral equipment, and central control. Calls are routed through the network under the direction of the central control, acting through the peripheral units. The maintenance centre is available for checking performance and identifying faults.*

Calls enter the switching machine from other offices over the incoming trunks. Signalling information for routing the call, also sent over the trunk, is passed through the receiver/sender link network into a receiver/sender. The call is routed to the appropriate outgoing trunk by closure of contacts in the MINIBAR switches of the trunk link network. (Both the trunk link network and the receiver/sender link network connections are established by their respective markers.) Instructions are passed to the markers from the central control complex over information interfaces known as buses: these buses also carry signals to the signal distributor to operate individual relays such as signalling relays in the trunk circuits. They also pass information about the state of the system from the matrix scanner to the control complex. The complex, a standard SP-1 subsystem, comprises duplicated processor units and associated program and call stores.

Here, the quality of two trunk circuits, one incoming and one outgoing, are being tested from the transmission test centre (coloured lines).

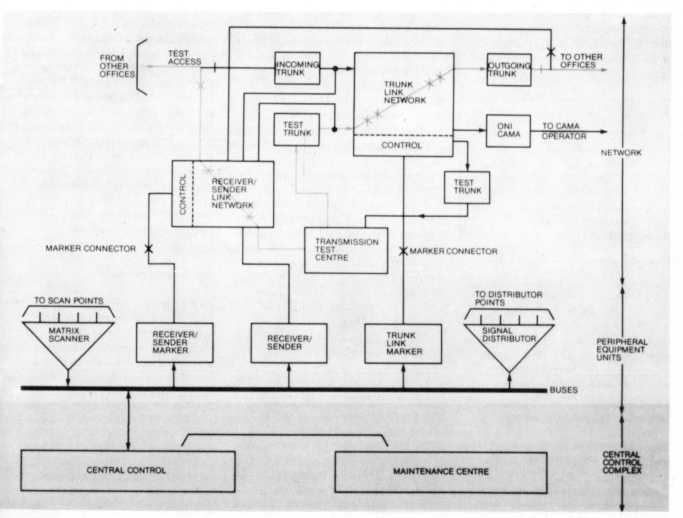

taken per call, multiplied by the number of calls, plus the amount of overhead time. The overhead time is that time which is continuously used by the stored-program control, even when no calls are being processed. The sum may be expressed as the number of seconds per hour, or as a percentage of total time available. In a conservative way, one may say that the real time used by each call in the 4-wire is no more than—and perhaps less than—in the 2-wire. Because there are no subscribers, only trunks, to maintain in the 4-wire, its overhead is less. Therefore the 4-wire version was expected to be able to handle more calls per hour than the 2-wire, and a call-processing target of 40,000 completed calls per hour was set. This calling rate was determined so that it would absorb only about 85 to 90 percent of the total time, so as to make the remaining time available for overload and unexpected maintenance functions.

Since each office has a different mix of trunks and traffic parameters, a precise fix on the capacity is not possible. What may be done, however, is to develop a consistent set of conservative figures to be used in general planning. The following simple relationship gives us a check on the consistency of our targets for the system capacity and the network capacity.

$$(n \times u) / t = c \quad (1)$$

where

n = number of trunks
u = usage for each trunk
t = time for each call
c = calls per hour

We know from the market survey that 4,000 trunks is the desired network capacity; from experience we assume a trunk is busy 2,000 seconds each hour when the average call lasts 200 seconds and finally we increase the 36,000 completed call limit of the 2-wire machine to 40,000 completed calls for the 4-wire. Substituting these figures on both sides of the identity, we get:

$$(4000 \text{ trunks} \times 2000 \text{ sec/trunk hour}) / (200 \text{ sec/call}) = 40000 \text{ calls/hour} \quad (2)$$

Since each side of the identity (2) may be supported, then for planning purposes

the limits we established earlier can be taken as valid. These are:

1. 40,000 completed calls/hour.

2. 4,000 incoming trunks.

3. 2,000 seconds busy per trunk per hour.

Future availability of a faster memory for the central processor will further increase the system's call processing capacity.

The ONI Story

It would obviously be impossible in the course of one short article to describe the development of all the different parts of the SP-1 4-wire system, but as an example of the many problems that had to be solved during the project, take the case of the feature known as Operator Number Identification (ONI). As the CAMA system was developed in the telephone network in the 1950's the idea was to have the central offices identify the calling party's telephone number by a technique known as Automatic Number Identification (ANI) and then send the number to the CAMA office. The CAMA office would then record and validate the number automatically. Older systems could not be economically so arranged and for some classes of subscriber, e.g.: multiparty, the central office cannot decide which customer to bill anyway. For these cases, an operator is required to identify the calling party's number. As the customer gives his number to the operator, she keys it into the system. After the number is validated by the system the operator is free to handle another call. The SP-1 required ONI because many of the subtending central offices were not equipped for ANI. During 1970 and 1971 considerable effort was expended to determine the best ONI arrangement—that is, at what point should the attendants' positions be interconnected to the rest of the SP-1 equipment. (Refer to the schematic view of the SP-1 4-wire[6], shown in Figure 3.)

The first suggestion for the ONI function attempted to simulate ANI. Since a digit receiver was required for ANI, the ONI position was to be connected directly to the existing receiver on the switching machine, see Figure 4. In order to allow for full access, a switch was required between the digit receivers and the ONI positions. A position link network was proposed. As this network

required one pair of wires for the ONI attendant to hear the subscriber, one pair to let the subscriber hear the attendant, one pair for the attendant to send digits to the digit receiver and one wire to control the network, a total of seven wires would be required. Since only six wires are available on the MINIBAR switch, it was suggested that the conversation between the attendant and the customer be converted to 2-wire at the receiver/sender and further switched through the receiver/sender link network, see Figure 5. This was expensive because converters would be required on all receiver/senders. The next suggestion was to use the TLN, since it already had a 4-wire talking connection. This approach was attractive because no modifications were required on the receiver/senders. It postulated a separate receiver attached directly to the ONI position trunks, see Figure 6. However, the ONI receiver here was found to be hard to maintain, and if it did fail, the entire position was put out of service. The next modification was to run cable around the TLN to the receiver/sender link network and set up a switch through it to one of the regular receivers for the ONI function, see Figure 7. As a separate cable would have to be engineered and maintained, it was decided to use instead one of the many switched paths through the TLN and employ programs to control setup of the connection to the ONI position digit receiver see Figure 8. Finally, in order to utilize regular call-processing programs for this job, the ONI position circuit was constructed of two trunk circuits, one incoming and one outgoing. This arrangement, which represents the current solution, allows for programs to deal with the ONI functions with a minimum amount of special treatment.

The Matrix Scanner

As the project evolved, pressures grew to increase the calling capacity of the system. This traditional development problem is customarily attacked in two ways. One is to attempt a complete redesign, to create a 'second generation' system. The second is to seek those subsystems, be they physical entities or programs, that use the major portion of system capacity and relieve them by some redesign. The first approach may yield order of magnitude improvements; the second may yield improvements of 20 to 30 percent. In SP-1 4-wire, the second approach was considered more practical

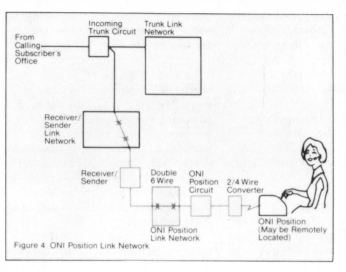

Figure 4. ONI Position Link Network

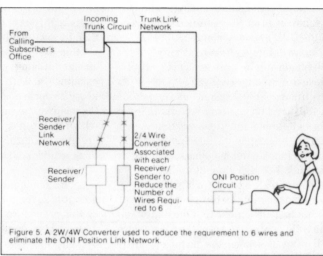

Figure 5. A 2W/4W Converter used to reduce the requirement to 6 wires and eliminate the ONI Position Link Network.

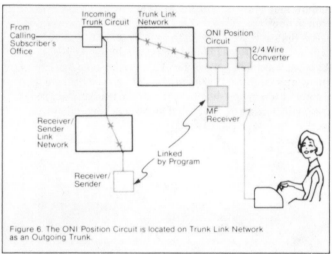

Figure 6. The ONI Position Circuit is located on Trunk Link Network as an Outgoing Trunk.

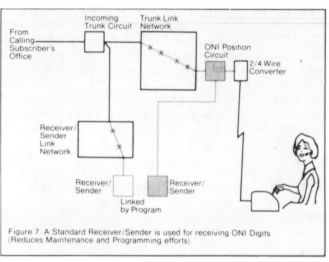

Figure 7. A Standard Receiver/Sender is used for receiving ONI Digits (Reduces Maintenance and Programming efforts).

FIGURE 4. This series of diagrams depicts the evolution of the feature known as Operator Number Identification (ONI). The attendant sits at a keyboard console at which she keys in the customer's number on long-distance calls. In the first case, the ONI position was to be connected directly to the receiver/sender on the switching machine. However, in a typical medium-sized office, there may be five receiver/sender link networks, 100 receiver/senders, and six ONI positions. Each incoming CAMA trunk must be able to access an ONI position, and so some form of switch must be fitted between the trunks and the positions. Initially, this switch was to be provided through the position link network, a separate switching circuit. However, this would have demanded a double six-wire network.

FIGURE 5. The next stage was to move the 2/4 wire converter to the receiver/sender, reducing the number of wires required for switching to six. It eliminated the need for the position link network since the receiver/sender link network could be used. However, a separate converter was required for each receiver/sender.

FIGURE 6. The next proposal located the ONI position on the trunk link network, and treated it as though it were an outgoing trunk. The TLN already has a 4-wire talking connection, and thus a reversion to one converter per ONI position was possible. An MF receiver was combined with the ONI position to accept the dialled digits. The two receivers were correlated by a program in the control complex. However, this ONI receiver would have required a separate maintenance program and if it failed the ONI position would be out of service.

FIGURE 7. The next modification employed a standard receiver/sender. A cable connected the ONI position circuit and the receiver/sender link network. The path from the ONI position to the receiver/sender was then completed by internal connections made in the RSLN under the direction of the central control complex. Because

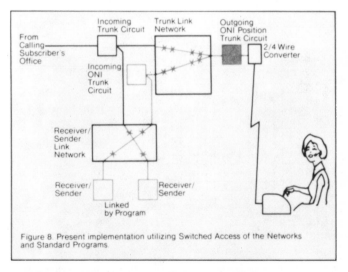

Figure 8. Present implementation utilizing Switched Access of the Networks and Standard Programs.

one of the standard receiver/sender units was used, maintenance was easier and programming effort needed to set up the connections was reduced. However, this separate cable would have to be installed and maintained, adding to cost.

FIGURE 8. The present solution utilizes one of the many switched paths through the trunk link network to connect the ONI position and the receiver/senders. Programs correlate the ONI position digit receiver and the other receiver/sender. In order to utilize already available call-processing programs to do this, the ONI position circuit is constructed to resemble two trunk circuits, one incoming and one outgoing. This allows programs to deal with the ONI functions with a minimum of special treatment.

A major consumer of capacity in the machine was easily identified. There are in the DDD network a large number of older switching systems. In many telephone administrations a majority of these are 'step-by-step' (SXS). This electromechanical system was invented in 1887, and its main characteristic from the switching point of view is that the dial on the customer's telephone directly controls the switching elements in the central office. For example, when the customer dials 5 the elements of the switching machine 'step' over five contacts. This implies that the digits from the SXS local office enter the SP-1 4-wire toll office as soon as the customer dials them. For example, if the customer dials 1-765-4321, as soon as the first 1 is dialled and before the 7 is dialled, the connection to the SP-1 must be ready to receive the digits. Since these come immediately, this is sometimes called 'immediate dial' operation. The time between the 1 and the 7 can be as little as 200-300 milliseconds. Some of this time is used by the

SXS system. The SP-1 family registers the digits in this case by a program rather than by establishing a physical connection to a physical digit receiver. The stringent timing requires the SP-1 to examine the state of the trunk circuit every 25 ms to ensure that all digits from the customer are collected. In an office with 6,400 trunks, with the trunks grouped in sets of 16, the 400 examinations would have to be made each 25 ms.

Each examination takes 30 microseconds; so the time spent by the system on this procedure would be 12 ms every 25 ms. This would imply that half of the system's time would be occupied in examining the state of the trunk circuits. The reader may wonder how many of these examinations result in new information for the system; that is, how many new pieces of dialling information are sent over the trunks in each examination period. Even in a busy interval, the probability is less than 1 per group of 16 trunks. If the system knew which rows to

examine in order to find the new information, the 400 examinations could be reduced to 44.

A new development effort was chartered, therefore, to devise some means of doing this, and the resultant apparatus, known as a matrix scanner, was arranged to identify the rows of trunks that had undergone a change since the last scan. Instead of scanning all the trunks individually, and devoting 30 microseconds to each, the matrix scanner looks at rows of 16 trunks at a time and only notes fresh data on each scan. It was grouped into four matrices of 15 rows with 16 scan points each. Any change in row 'n' sets the 'nth bit' of the change row to one, see Figure 9.

As the matrix scanner evolved we found that it would reduce the SP-1 overhead processing time by an order of magnitude. Therefore it became feasible to examine all the trunks every 25 ms. This led to the conclusion that trunks

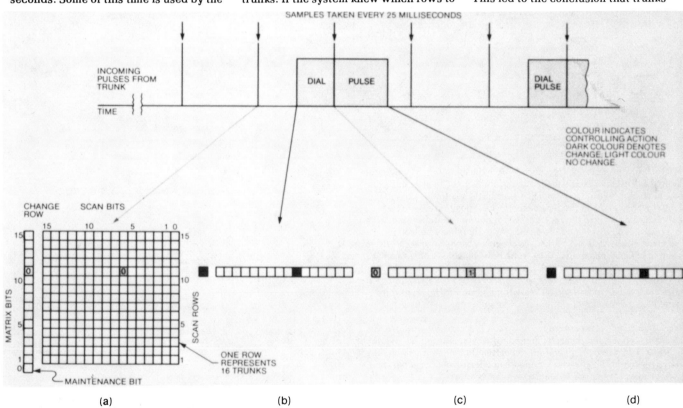

(a)   (b)   (c)   (d)

FIGURE 9. Many older central offices send dialled digits in a train of dc pulses immediately upon seizing a trunk circuit. One of the main innovations in the SP-1 4-wire system, the matrix scanner, allows these pulses to be gathered efficiently and passed to the central control complex without any hardware operations.

In order to register all the dialled digits, the machine must be able to scan each trunk at 25-millisecond intervals. However, it would waste the system's time to interrogate all trunks on every pass, as only fresh information is required. An extra row of scan points, called the change row, was added to indicate the change in state of each set of 16 trunks. If no change has occurred in that set since the last scan, the change row bit is 0; when one or more changes appear, the bit becomes 1. This acts as a flag to the scanning program to interrogate the indicated row.

This diagram shows what happens in one quadrant of the scanner as a dial pulse train arrives. Initially (a), the voltage on the trunk corresponds to a 0, which is shown on the scan point representing that trunk. Because no change has occurred since the last scan, the change row bit is also 0. The arrival of a dial pulse (b) causes a 1 to appear on the trunk scan point and alters the change row bit to 1. When the next scan is made (c), the program reads the change row, detects the change, and scans the indicated row, resetting the change row bit to 0. When the dial pulse has passed (d), the scan point reverts to 0, and the change row again becomes 1, indicating that a further change has occurred. This change would then be read and detected by the program in the same way.

would not have to be segregated according to scanning rates, as had been the custom in almost all previous stored-program machines.

A companion trunk circuit development was nearing completion in the laboratories at this time. The force of this project was to eliminate the need for custom engineering of the layout of the trunk frame, on which trunk cables are laid out in the central office. In the SP-1 4-wire, all incoming and outgoing trunk circuits have been packaged to fit into universal boxes with connectors to attach them to the cables. The trunk circuits are grouped into four identical units per box. Each box is only six inches high, four inches wide and eight inches deep. The universal trunk frame can mount 96 incoming trunks and the same number of outgoing trunks. With the development of the matrix scanner and the universal trunk frame, the 4-wire machine began to take shape.

Many other new features have been developed for the system besides those described above. For instance, a new cordless transmission test centre draws upon the power of the SP-1 central processor to set up connections between the centre and the trunk under test. This will reduce the work load of personnel who are performing routine transmission test functions. New network management tools have been evolved by the project team in close co-operation with the headquarters traffic personnel of Bell Canada. These tools allow the SP-1 to control its own operations, and report the results of its actions to the network manager, enabling him to query the system and to effect control directly when he wishes (see Table 1.)

The laboratory version of the system was completed at Bell-Northern Research in March 1970 and a second machine — a combined 2-wire and 4-wire machine made by Northern Electric — was installed in the laboratories in Ottawa in 1972. Both machines are undergoing continual evaluation. Final system checkout will be completed in time for

*Trademark of Northern Electric Company Limited.

delivery of the first commercial machine to Bell Canada for installation in Thunder Bay, Ontario, in March 1973.

Over the last four years the 4-wire project has ensured that the advantages of stored-program control envisaged in the early 1960's have been embodied in a machine suitable for switching duties in the toll network. This will enlist the general system benefits of speed, flexibility and low maintenance costs for a toll switching machine.

References

1. Telesis, Vol. 1, No. 4, January 1969, Special issue.

2. Electronic Switching Arrives, Telesis, Vol. 1, No. 9, Fall 1970, p. 301.

3. Bomba, J.S., SP-1 Electronic switching system field trial experience. Proceedings of the National Electronics Conference, 1970.

4. Downs, J., Gordon, B., Inshaw, P., and Shimokura, S., SP-1 Electronic Switching: A New Canadian System, Telesis, Vol. 2, No. 6, Fall 1972, pp. 2-10.

5. For an overview of network evolution, see Terreault, C., Planning the Telecommunications Network of the Future, Telesis, Vol. 2, No. 4, Spring 1972, pp. 2-8.

6. Edwards, J.S., SP-1 4-wire ESS, an evolutionary ESS system, International Switching Symposium Record, 1972.

TABLE 1 — TECHNICAL & ECONOMIC ADVANTAGES OF SP-1 4-WIRE ESS

New design features
- verified writing of CAMA data on magnetic tape
- electronic matrix scanner (advantages of autonomous scanner without complexity)
- fully connectorized frames
- all revenue-sensitive units connectorized
- continuous transmitted digit monitoring
- conversational mode for office data modifications

Automatic external trouble treatment
- carrier failure protection
- hit detection on incoming trunks
- external trouble data on magnetic tape
- sender retrial data on magnetic tape

New network management tools
- automatic distant office deloading
- answer peg count by trunk group (message traffic indicator)
- deflected peg count by trunk group (alternate route indicator)
- improved glare resolution
- emergency call denial and measurement by selected NPA or home NNX

Paper 15

Telephone Exchange Electronic No. 2 (TXE 2)

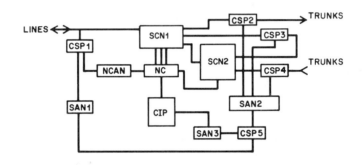

SCN1 = STAGES A , B , C
SCN2 = STAGE D
CIP   = CENTRAL CONTROL
CSP1 = LINE CIRCUIT
CSP2 = OUTGOING TRUNK CIRCUIT
CSP3 = INTRA-OFFICE TRUNK CIRCUIT
CSP4 = INCOMING TRUNK CIRCUIT
NC   = MARKER
SAN1 = LINE IDENTIFIER
SAN2 = REGISTER LINK
SAN3 =

FURTHER DEVELOPMENTS OF THE TXE2 (PENTEX) ELECTRONIC SWITCHING SYSTEM

G.A. Matthews & R.C. Long.

Introduction. Just over two years ago the first production TXE2 electronic exchange, which was designed by Messrs. Ericsson Telephones Limited under the auspices of the Joint Electronic Research Committee in collaboration with the British Post Office, was cut into service at Ambergate, Derbyshire, England; at present there are about 30 such exchanges in service and more are being installed at therate of one exchange per week, some overseas. The TXE2 system is designed for use as a local exchange in a variety of environments. It can serve as a local exchange with a self-contained numbering scheme, as a satellite exchange in a non-director linked numbering area or as a local exchange sharing a numbering scheme with many exchanges in the same numbering plan area. The early exchanges supplied to the Post Office are serving as local exchanges with self-contained numbering schemes; some of the exchanges now being supplied are required for incorporation in linked numbering schemes. The different exchange numbering scheme arrangements and means for increasing the range of the system to double the exchange capacity are described, together with some new subscriber facilities.

Brief Description. Although the system is adequately described elsewhere[1,2,3,4,5,6,7], it will assist to give a brief description here. The basis is a three/four stage bothway trunking network as shown in Fig. 1. Each of the stages of switching is made up of multiples of a basic 5 x 5 reed relay crosspoint switch, which allows smooth growth by small increments. In operation the line identifier produces the directory number of the calling subscriber and puts it into a free register. The register finder allows only one register at a time to have access to the common control equipment. The latter takes the subscriber's number to mark the calling subscriber and provide his class-of-service, chooses a free supervision circuit and a path to it from the marked subscriber through the A,B and C switches and completes the path also to the register. The common control equipment, which has taken an average of 50 ms for this operation,is released while the register accepts dialled digits from the subscriber. A change from one type of supervision circuit to another (say from own-exchange to an out-going route) is made during an inter-train pause by the register obtaining access to the common control equipment. Termination of a call is achieved by a further application of a register to the control.

Numbering Schemes. When the system was required to work as a local exchange with its own numbering scheme, four digits were used for the subscribers directory numbers. Access to the parent exchange and to adjacent exchanges was achieved by code dialling, which meant that the exchange had to discriminate on the first digit for calls to the parent exchange, own exchange and some adjacent exchanges, on the second digit for calls

G.A.Matthews is with Plessey Telecommunications Ltd., Beeston,Nottingham

R.C.Long is with the Post Office Telecommunications Headquarters
Development Department, London.

Reprinted with permission from *IEE Conf. Publ. 52, Switching Tech. Telecommun. Networks*, Apr. 21-25, 1969, pp. 38-42.

to other adjacent exchanges and on the third digit for some subscriber facilities.

Introduction of linked numbering schemes increased the digits in the subscriber's directory number from four to five or six, and required expansion in the routing facilities. The digit stores in the register were not increased above four, but after discrimination on the first one or two digits, the stores were cleared for re-use for own exchange calls. On adjacent exchange calls where three-digit discrimination was required, and on subscriber facility codes of four digits (such as subscriber's transfer of incoming calls) the digits were retained in the register stores until full discrimination was achieved.

On incoming calls four or five digits may be received depending on the number of digits absorbed in the routing train at the distant exchange. In those cases where more than four digits are received, the final four digits only are stored in the register.

Extension of the exchange. The common control time for setting up paths in the switching network is approx. 50 ms; from this it can be shown that the common equipment can handle at least 7,500 calls per hour. With an average call holding time of 2 minutes, this represents 250 erlangs, or with 3 minutes average call holding time, 375 erlangs of traffic. Thus the TXE2 system can cater for 2500 subscribers with an average calling rate of 0.05 erlang or over 4000 subscribers with an average calling rate of 0.03 erlang (assuming a call holding time of 2 minutes).

A method of combining two exchange units to double the capacity of the exchange has been developed, thus greatly extending the range of the system. The arrangement is indicated in Fig. 2. The main problem in adding a second unit is to direct incoming calls and own exchange calls to the correct unit. Incoming junctions are connected to either of the two units, and an incoming call over such a junction causes that incoming supervisory to be set up to a register in that unit.

Some restriction in numbering schemes will be imposed in that all numbers with the same thousands digit will be kept to one unit. Thus the register by inspection of the thousands digit will be able to decide whether the call that is to be terminated is to a subscriber in its own unit or to a subscriber in the other unit. As can be seen from Fig. 2 registers will have access to both common controls, and D switches will be doubled in size to provide links to the C switches in both units.

When the subscriber's number is received, the thousands digit determines which control the register must use; setting up is then completed in the normal manner.

This principle will allow the exchange to grow to about 7000 lines. Should it ever become necessary to provide three units, then these would be linked together with a form of reed group selector which would direct incoming calls to the correct unit.

Additional Subscriber Facilities. The versatility of the system is demonstrated by the following facilities which have been added to the system without difficulty.

The first, called 'Freefone', is to allow local or unit fee calls to be paid for by the <u>called</u> subscriber when a special code is dialled in addition to the subscriber's number. This is arranged by using the special code to connect the calling subscriber to a special line circuit; this in turn is connected to a new supervision circuit which picks up a new register in the same way as an incoming call. The remaining digits to be dialled i.e., the called subscriber's number, will result in this 'Freefone' supervision circuit being connected to the called subscriber through the switching network. When the called subscriber answers, the Freefone supervision circuit passes a meter pulse to the called subscriber's meter. This facility is especially useful for police, taxi services at stations and airports and for advertising purposes.

Another facility, known as 'Call Waiting', provides for a 'pip' of tone to be superimposed at regular intervals on an established call between subscribers 'A' and 'B' (say) to indicate that another call from subscriber 'C' is waiting for subscriber 'A'. On pressing a button switch on the telephone, the called subscriber 'A' will be transferred from the original call, which will be held, to subscriber 'C'; nothing will be heard by subscriber 'B'. Pressing the button switch again will re-establish the call between subscribers 'A' and 'B', subscriber 'C' connection being held, unless he hangs up.

A similar facility is a three-way conference call; here subscriber 'A' first establishes a call to subscriber 'B'; subscriber 'A' then presses a switch on his telephone which gives him dial tone and enables him to establish a call to subscriber 'C'. A further press of the button switch will connect all three subscribers together.

Both these facilities use an additional circuit, together with two standard line circuits, and they can be added to any exisiting TXE2 exchange.

Another useful facility that has been included in the design permits the subscriber to bar incoming calls and have them transferred to a recorded announcement. For this facility the subscriber dials a short code in a similar manner to that required for the standard transfer facility.

<u>Integrated Circuits</u>. As has been stated, the system is made up of a reed switching network controlled by circuits of transistors and reed relays. An investigation is now being made into the possibility of replacing the discrete component logic with integrated circuits, still retaining the reed switching network. The indications are that there will be three benefits; reduction in size, significant cost reduction and the ability to extend the range of a single unit to above 10,000 lines and 1,000 erlang of traffic. A parallel development will provide exchanges at the other end of the scale i.e., below 200 lines, and the P.A.X and the P.A.B.X.

<u>Conclusion</u>. At this time, about 30 exchanges varying from 600 to 2000 lines are in service. These are welcomed by subscribers for the additional facilities and improved service with noise-free speech path; by maintenance staff for the reduction and ease of maintenance and by the administration for the ease of introduction, ordering and extension. Further development with integrated circuits may enable

117

the system to be extended to wider fields of application.

Acknowledgements.   Acknowledgement is made to the Senior Director of Development of the General Post Office and to the Directors of Plessey Telecommunications Limited for permission to make use of the information contained in this paper.

References :

1.   'Pentex – a small electronic exchange'
       Ericsson Bulletin No. 50A, March 1965.

2.   G.A.Matthews: 'The Pentex electronic telephone exchange'
       IEEE Transaction on Communication Technology, June 1966,
       Vol COM-14, No.3, p.212.

3.   G.A.Matthews and C.F.G.Hillen: 'A small electronic exchange for
       the British Post Office'
       International Conference on Electronic Switching, Paris 1966.

4.   G.A.Matthews: 'The Pentex electronic telephone exchange system'
       Plessey Communication Journal, Vol.1, No.3, p.92.

5.   'Ambergate electronic telephone exchange'
       Plessey Communication Journal, Vol.1, No.3, p.90.

6.   G.A.Matthews: 'Field Trial of an electronic telephone exchange'
       Systems Technology, No.4, April 1968.

7.   R.C.Long and G.E.Gorringe: 'The TXE2 Electronic switching system'
       I.P.O.E.E Journal, Vol.61, Part 4, January 1969.

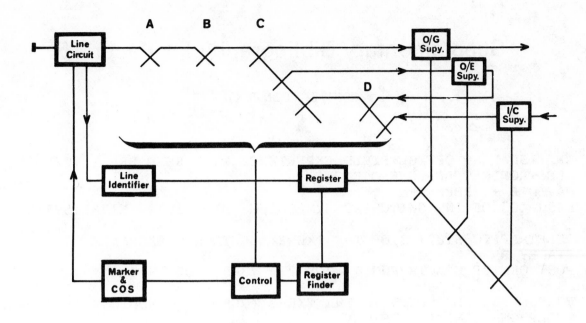

Fig.1   Simplified functional diagram

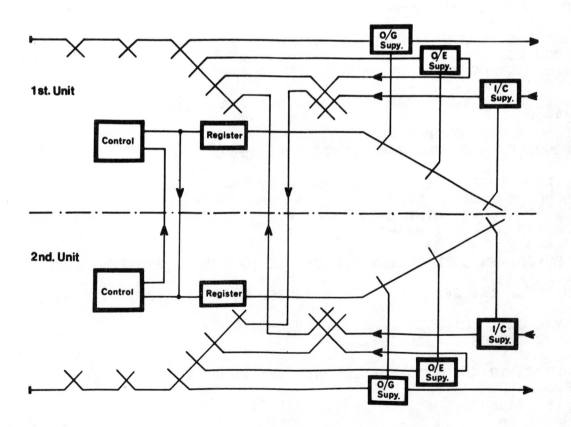

Fig.2   D-link extension

Supplementary Bibliography for Paper 15

TXE-2 (PENTEX)

BRITISH POST OFFICE FIELD EXPERIENCE WITH REED REALY (TXE-2)
ELECTRONIC TELEPHONE OFFICES
DAVID E + URBEN TFA
P400-405 OF INT SWITCHING SYMPOSIUM MIT, 1972 (E173 1597)

TELETRAFFIC STUDIES OF THE TXE-2 ELECTRONIC EXCHANGE
STACEY RR
POST OFFICE ELECTR ENG J 67 PT2: 73-9 (JUL 1974)

FURTHER DEVELOPMENTS IN THE TXE-2 (REED ELECTRONIC PROGRAMMABLE
TELEPHONE CENTRAL OFFICE)
TAYLOR GH + ORBELL AG
WESCON TECH PAP 14 (SESS 19/1): 1-9 (1970)

PROGRESS WITH TXE-2
CAPTER DAE + PALMER AJ
POST OFFICE TELECOMMUN J 26: 12-13 (AUTUMN 1974)

TEX-2 ELECTRONIC SWITCHING SYSTEM
LONG RC
IEEE INT COMMUN CONV RECORD JUN 1968 P91-7

ELECTRONIC TELEPHONE EXCHANGES TXE-2 A SMALL ELECTRONIC EXCHANGE
SYSTEM
LONG RC + GORRINGE GE
POST OFF ELEC ENG J 62 12-20 (APR 1969)

FIELD EXPERIENCE WITH THE TXE-2 SYSTEM
LONG RC + DAVIS E
IEE CONF SWITCHING TECHNIQUES FOR TELECOMMUN NETWORKS APR 1969
CONF PUB NO. 52 P32-7

DEVELOPMENTS IN PENTEX ELECTRONIC SWITCHING SYSTEMS
POLLARD JR
P517 OF INT SERV SYM RECORD MUNICH 1974 (621.381537/.59)

AMGERGATE CUT-OVER (PENTEX) (TXE-2)
SYST COMMUN 3 (JAN 1967)

PENTEX TRANSPORTABLE ELCTRONIC TELEPHONE EXCHANGE
BROOKS BMG
SYST TECHNOL NO. 18: 18-23 (FEB 1974)

AMBERGATE TXE-2 ELECTRONIC CENTRAL OFFICE
POST OFF TELECOMMUN J 19 NO. 1 2-5 (1967)

PENTEX ELECTRONIC TELEPHONE EXCHANGE SYSTEM
WEAVER AL + BROOKS BMG
SYST TECHNOL NO. 11: 17-25 (DEC 1970)

Paper 16

Telephone Exchange Electronic No. 4 (TXE 4)

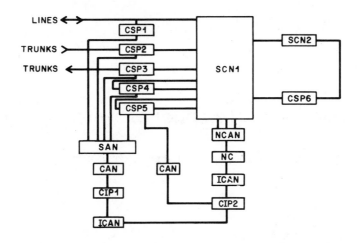

SCN1 = SWITCHES A, B-C NETWORKS
SCN2 = SWITCHES D
CIP1 = CYCLIC STORE UNITS
CIP2 = MAIN CONTROL UNITS
CSP1 = LINE CIRCUIT
CSP2 = INCOMING JUNCTION
CSP3 = OUTGOING JUNCTION
CSP4 = MISCELLANEOUS RELAY SET
CSP5 = REGISTER (SENDER)
CSP6 = LINK
NC   = MARKERS
NCAN = INTERROGATORS
SAN = SCANNER

A Processor Controlled Telephone Switching System—TXE4

PETER J. HINER, S. G. W. JOHNSTONE, KENNETH PIPER, AND J. P. RONAYNE

Abstract—Telephone subscribers require a service which is reliable and offers a wide range of facilities. System design is of vital importance in determining the ability of an administration to meet these requirements economically, and processor controlled exchanges can be designed to provide the necessary qualities of reliability and flexibility. This paper describes in outline the operation of the TXE4 system, and shows how it incorporates features which will enable an administration both to meet its present commitments and to look ahead to providing an enhanced service in the future.

INTRODUCTION

ANY new telephone exchange must demonstrate that it shows a substantial improvement over existing equipment. This paper describes TXE4, and discusses the reasons for improvements both to the administration and to the customer. Major improvements to the administration are the ability to dimension the exchange and to extend it to meet the wide variety of traffic patterns without undue overprovision of equipment, the reduction in maintenance costs caused by improved maintenance aids, the lower fault rate of the system, the removal of the need for regular routine maintenance, and the repeat attempt features which enable the system to automatically circumvent faulty items, and the opportunity to add some new facilities more easily due to the stored program control. For the subscriber, the transmission will be of better quality, the repeat attempt facility ensures a lower call failure rate, and new facilities will become available to those who want them.

REQUIREMENTS

There are two major aspects to the provision of a telephone service. From the user's viewpoint it is essential that the service should be responsive to his changing needs. It should readily provide a wide range of facilities and

Manuscript received December 11, 1973.
The authors are with Standard Telephones and Cables, Limited, London, England.

Reprinted from *IEEE Trans. Commun.*, vol. COM-22, pp. 1276–1282, Sept. 1974.

122

should be capable of altering the range provided as time goes on. Furthermore, the service should be a good one, calls demanded should be successful, the quality of connection should be high, and service should be available at all times.

Thus flexibility and quality of service are foremost in the user's mind. To satisfy the subscriber is the purpose of the administration, whose view of the telephone service is naturally rather different. First, telephone exchanges are machines to be kept in working order with minimum resources: hence they should be reliable. Since failures will occur it is also necessary that the system be easy to maintain; since attention cannot always be immediate, the system should not be critically affected by faults. Second, the day to day routine of adding and removing lines, altering numbers, and attending to subscribers' requests should be simple and rapid. Growth in the frequency of calls or in the number of subscribers served must be accomplished without disturbing the service given, and exchange growth should be possible in small steps, so that all the equipment installed is providing revenue.

Flexibility is also important to the administration. The ability to provide for new types of line and new facilities is part of their commitment to the user. However, they will also wish to benefit from improvements in technology without the upheaval involved in changing to a completely new system. From this consideration we can see that flexibility, service quality, maintainability, fault tolerance, easy growth, and piecemeal improvement are features of basic importance. These requirements must be properly balanced in the design of a modern system, especially if it is not to be quickly superseded by later developments.

FLEXIBLE SYSTEM

The essential elements of a TXE4 exchange can be seen in Fig. 1. The network block may be taken as representing one switching unit, a number of which are provided according to exchange size. Each switching unit is divided into "planes" (independent switching networks) with the A switches giving access to all planes, so that connection to an exchange termination may be made on any plane. Links are provided on odd numbered planes, and on the even planes there are D switches to provide connection between switching units. Subscribers, registers, trunk equipment, and miscellaneous relay sets are all accessed via A switches, and paths through the exchange always use the ABC switches and a link of an odd plane and the ABCD switches of an adjacent even plane: either end of the connection may be on the odd plane. A typical connection (from subscriber to register) is shown in Fig. 2.

All the A switch terminations (subscribers, registers, etc.) are scanned in sequence and the state of each termination (calling, busy, etc.) is combined with data from the cyclic stores. This information is presented in a con-

tinuously operating cycle to the main control units, enabling them to determine the state of each line, its class of service (type of line and any special facilities or limits to service), its directory number (number dialed to access a subscriber), and its equipment number (point of connection of the line to the exchange, which needs no fixed relationship to the directory number). The cyclic stores also provide translation and number length information (for determination of junction route, routing digits, and end of dialing).

When a main control unit recognizes a calling line, it stores the information relating to that line and then searches the cyclic stores for a free register. When one is found, the main control unit reads from the cyclic store the register identity and equipment number. The equipment numbers, which define the two ends of the connection, are then sent to interrogators and markers, which find the available paths, select the best path according to predetermined rules (designed to use the switching network as efficiently as possible), and mark that path (i.e., operate the reed relay crosspoints necessary to make the required connection). The connection from subscriber to register is thus set up as shown in Fig. 2, and dial tone is returned.

Digits received from the subscriber are passed by the register to the main control unit for storage, and these digits are used to search the cyclic stores for translation information (to discriminate between local and outgoing calls, determine required subscriber's equipment number or outgoing route number, etc.). When the required termination is known, the main control unit causes a connection to be set to it, similar to that from originating subscriber to register. A local to local connection is shown in Fig. 3; the path from subscriber to register is released after completion of the path from subscriber to subscriber; note that for the latter a bridge link is used, to provide a transmission bridge and call supervision.

Certain features of the system are worthy of note. The paths consist of repeated connections, which are simple to control, thus allowing efficient use of program. The connection to register does not require use of any auxiliary switch network, does not predetermine any point of connection of the final transmission path, and is released when no longer required. State of line and class of service information from the cyclic stores enable the control to avoid busy terminations without abortive marking: for example a busy outgoing junction route can be determined from cyclic store information, enabling the control to continue immediately with alternative routing.

However, the overall capability is much more important than individual merits, in that the system has inherent flexibility. The path setting functions are simple subroutines of the control program which are selected as a result of decisions made at two major points. First, when the initial demand for service is received, the class of service information, which accompanies the calling signal,

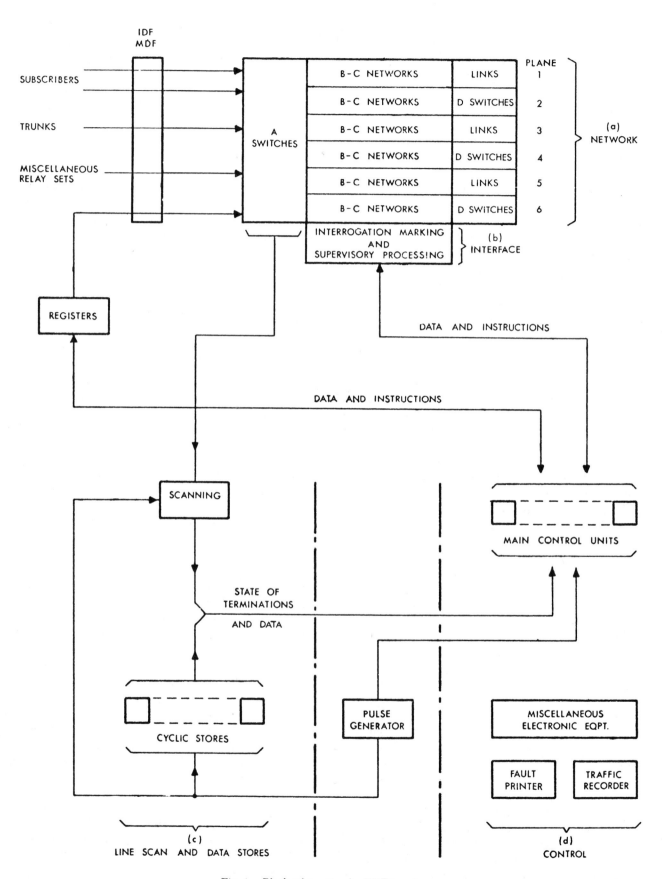

Fig. 1.   Block schematic of a TXE4 exchange.

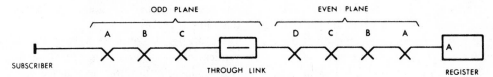

Fig. 2. Subscriber to register connection.

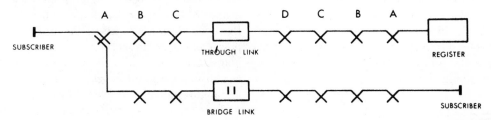

Fig. 3. Local to local connection.

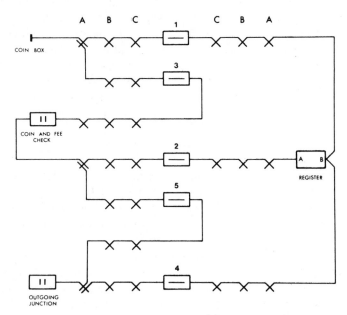

Fig. 4. Coin box to outgoing junction connection.

enables the control to select the appropriate connection: it can determine the type of register (loop-disconnect, MF4, etc.) to be connected, or route the call to a tone circuit if the line is barred to outgoing calls; it can also cause a coin and fee checking relay set to be associated with a coin box line and so on. There is therefore no need for path of entry discrimination, auxiliary relay sets (such as C & FC) are fully available, and association of a particular facility with a line can be achieved by entering the appropriate class of service information in the cyclic store.

The second major decision point comes when the call is to be connected to the required destination. Information from the cyclic store enables the control to select a suitable subroutine, to cause connection to an outgoing junction, to a local subscriber, to a tone circuit, or elsewhere. Association of auxiliary equipment (e.g., outgoing sender,

Freefone relay set) is determined by the terminating class of service: such equipment is connected via the normal switching network and is released when no longer required (e.g., a C & FC relay set would be released if the terminating connection were to a line with a Freefone facility).

The flexibility of the system may be seen clearly in the following example of a connection from coin box line to outgoing junction relay set shown in Fig. 4. (The diagram is simplified by omission of D switching stages, and the links are numbered to show the order of connection of paths.)

Path 1 is set up to the B terminal of a register (normally used as an outgoing sender terminal). This path is set up to make the calling line busy while a C & FC relay set is being found and connected, and to enable continuity checks to be performed on paths 2 and 3. When paths 2 and 3 are complete, path 1 is released and the register sends a dial tone. Path 4 is set up when sufficient digits have been received to identify an outgoing junction, and this path is used for outgoing sending from the register. Meanwhile path 5 is set up but the link in this path is not switched through until register sending is complete. Then paths 2 and 4 are released, leaving only paths 3 and 5 to be held for the duration of the call.

The continuity of each path is checked and successful path completion is signaled by the register to the main control unit. It will be shown that this facility is important both in improving the service to the subscriber and in assisting exchange administration.

QUALITY OF SERVICE

The provision of a wide range of facilities to the subscriber is of secondary importance to providing a good reliable service. TXE4 incorporates a number of features designed to reduce the number of call failures caused by congestion or faulty equipment, to minimize the chance of complete loss of service to a subscriber, and to provide good transmission.

Since overall path selection is employed, TXE4 avoids the problem of stage by stage selection, where a call may become committed to a path which leads to a dead end. It was seen from Fig. 3 that the final path is set from subscriber to subscriber (or from subscriber to outgoing junction, etc.); the choice of final path is therefore not constrained by starting from a point of concentration, such as the point of register connection after a preselection switching stage. This also reduces the probability of blocking.

Interrogation may be repeated up to four times if a free path cannot be found immediately. For a point to point connection (e.g., subscriber to subscriber) an intentional delay of about a hundred milliseconds is introduced between each interrogation attempt, to allow the possibility of a path becoming free. When connection is to be made to one of a group of circuits (e.g., to an outgoing junction relay set), failure to find a free path causes the control to perform a new search in the cyclic store, probably resulting in selection of a different circuit from the group.

The path checking facility allows the control to detect faults in the switching network or associated equipment. Failure to mark a path successfully causes the control to initiate a repeat interrogation and marking sequence, normally using different equipment. Not only are call failures thus greatly reduced, but, because of the high speed of the system, repeat attempts do not cause an appreciable delay to call connection.

Two additional repeat attempts are used to secure emergency (999) calls. If all four attempts fail, the control will use an alternative routing procedure to reroute the call to normal operator (100) circuits, allowing yet another two attempts. Thus it would be theoretically possible for an emergency call to generate 24 interrogation and 6 marking attempts.

Naturally, all common control functions are secured by replication or other means. Additionally, in many areas, continual self-checking is carried out, so that faulty equipment can be automatically removed from service, to prevent it causing call failures.

The system is secured in a number of ways to reduce the chance of loss of service to any subscribers. Areas such as the cyclic stores are internally secured against faults or power failure. The sectionalization of switching units into planes gives each subscriber access to several independent switch networks, interrogators, and markers. All registers and main control units are fully available to all subscribers, with a low probability that successive calls from a subscriber would be handled by the same equipment. All outgoing junctions and other peripheral relay sets are chosen on a random basis to avoid the problems that could arise from faults in early choice equipment.

Metallic contacts are used for path switching in TXE4, to avoid any difficulty of interworking with existing telephone networks. The reed relay is chosen because it has the speed of operation necessary to match electronic control and its sealed contacts are protected against the environment, so providing a reliable low-noise transmission path.

ADMINISTRATION

Provision of a reliable service to subscribers inevitably involves exchange maintenance. Inherent reliability reduces fault incidence and a system that is fault tolerant allows the emphasis to be on corrective rather than preventive maintenance. Still it is desirable that the system should incorporate features to reduce the cost of maintenance by making it as easy and rapid as possible.

In addition to built-in check circuits and alarms, a facility for local or remote printout of faults in major items of equipment is provided by TXE4. A particularly valuable use of the fault printer is for identifying faults in the switching network, since every failure to set up an exchange connection causes printout of the identities of control and switching equipment involved. The use of standard switching paths leads to standard printout, regardless of the trunking sequence, thus simplifying analysis of the data and identification of the faulty equipment.

Automatic routiners, controlled by program in the main control units, can be used to test interrogator markers, registers, supervisory circuits, and subscribers' lines. The routiners are linked to fault print equipment, and the facility for remote printout makes remote control or routining viable.

Use of standard functional blocks in the system simplifies maintenance procedure, and sectionalization of the exchange allows maintenance work to be carried out without disturbing exchange service. Plug-in units are used throughout, so that faulty units can be replaced and taken to a repair center.

Exchange administration includes handling changes in subscriber facility requirements and sudden variations in traffic load. The cyclic stores ease both the changing of subscriber facilities, by class of service alteration, and the redistribution of traffic, by virtue of the variable relationship between directory and equipment numbers. Overloading in one switching unit as a result of a sudden increase in traffic (e.g., from a computer bureau) could be alleviated by moving lines to another unit, and this can be done without any change to directory numbers.

One directory number suffices for all lines in a PBX group: not only is there a saving in directory numbers, but also the lines in a group can be distributed as required to spread the traffic load over a number of switching units, and new lines can be added to the group at will.

GROWTH

Growth in telephone exchanges is a multidimensional problem, and the ability to change each dimension independently is vital to the economic provision of service.

Telephone networks have three important growth parameters. The number of lines connected, the pattern of traffic generated, and the amount of traffic carried. The last item has an inbuilt subdivision which becomes significant in considering common control systems. This is the division between call setting time, when the exchange control is involved, and conversation time, during which a low level of supervision is satisfactory.

In TXE4 each of these aspects of growth is effected in a different part of the system, thus permitting each to be dimensioned according to requirements.

Additional capacity for lines is provided by equipping further cyclic store racks, which also carry the A switches and line circuits for the new subscribers. Basic additional traffic capacity is provided by adding further switching units (network blocks) and control equipment (main control units and registers). The relative quantities of control and network are determined at any time by the ratio of call setting to conversation time.

The D switch stage in TXE4 provides the necessary interconnection between switching units without the need for frames or jumpers. Thus on extension, the new units via the additional D stage switches have access to all existing lines without any effect on existing cabling.

In each case of addition, the new racks are connected to the working exchange by plug-in cabling, which enables full testing of the new equipment, including the interconnecting cables, before association with working apparatus. The modularity of the system further assists the growth function by allowing the power to be removed from individual racks while interconnection is made, thus eliminating hazards to equipment or traffic.

Variations in traffic pattern may require changes to equipment already in service. Should the balance between traffic to other exchanges and terminating traffic alter, adjustment of the bridge to through link ratio would be required. In TXE4 a wide latitude is built in, and alteration of ratio is a simple process of unplugging one type of unit and plugging in another.

Provision is also made in the design for a fine adjustment of traffic should this be desired. Each of the switching units is made up of an array of fully interconnected switches and the array can be reduced in size to effect economies merely by leaving rack positions unequipped. At the A switch stage, traffic to the switching units is concentrated by commoning of plug-in A switches. The optimum concentration can be readily achieved by modifying the commoning and this is carried out by alteration of plug-in cables, with the attendant advantage of speed and security.

FUTURE

In considering the future network in which a system will operate, the designer is faced with a host of uncertainties. Although a widening range of facilities will be demanded by subscribers, the nature of the facilities and their popularity are not clear. New types of line and new signaling schemes will undoubtedly arise but the detail of their operation is undefined. New devices, possessing valuable properties, can move from laboratory to production in a few years.

In the face of these uncertainties the safest approach is to generalize and this is the foundation of the TXE4 solution to the problem.

Facilities provided at very low penetration would be applied direct to the required line. At higher penetrations, the facility requirement can be flagged by class of service and the main control unit program can then arrange for connection to appropriate equipment via the network by using an existing or new serial trunking sequence. At this stage the equipment providing the required facility is concentrated in a fully available group and can be provided purely on a traffic basis. In this way facilities such as early morning calls, call waiting, and camp on busy could be provided to any subscriber.

Similarly, new types of line can be identified to the control by class of service in the cyclic store. Such lines can then be specially connected as desired. As an example, a line from a computer installation could be connected to subscriber lines without the normal supervisory bridge to permit remote interrogation of gas or electricity meters.

The revision of the main control program to allow for new facilities or new trunking sequences is readily carried out by changing the plug-in units containing the program information. Some facilities may be of such a type or be required at such high penetration that software implementation is appropriate. Again, the necessary changes to programs are carried out by change of plug-in units.

The acceptance of new signaling schemes or changes to existing schemes is assisted by the supervisory processing function in TXE4. This concentrates the timing and decision features of the supervisory relay sets. Thus alterations to these features or the addition of new sequences can be quickly introduced. The processing function is provided on a modular basis with the switching units, and modification can be carried out without complete loss of service.

The modular arrangement of TXE4 also allows the system to be altered in a piecemeal fashion to take advantage of revised designs bringing cost or performance advantages, or to allow for introduction of completely fresh techniques. One example of this improvement is the current development of a replacement for the existing cyclic store module, to provide for remote alteration of the stored data.

CONCLUSION

By considering the basic needs of a telephone service, the features required in a modern system have been identified. These have been incorporated in the TXE4 system to provide an economic solution to present day requirements.

A fundamental aim of the development was to ensure that TXE4 would assist future enhancement of the telephone network. Processor control of a general purpose switching network provides an open ended design, which can readily adapt to future conditions.

ACKNOWLEDGMENT

The authors wish to thank Standard Telephones and Cables Ltd., for permission to publish the information in this paper. The consideration, decisions, and designs discussed in the paper are the result of many years of cooperative effort between the British Post Office and telephone manufacturers.

Supplementary Bibliography for Paper 16

TXE-4

REED RELAY PROGRAM CONTROLLED TELEPHONE EXCHANGE (TXE 4)
PIPER K + HARLAND G
IEEE CONF SWITCHING TECHNIQUES FOR TELECOMMUN NETWORKS
APR 1969 CONF PUB NO. 52 P62-5

TELEPHONES IN THE UK: CAUTIOUS PROGRESS (TEX-4)
PAYNE M
IEEE SPECTRUM 12: 42-5 (JUN 1975)

TRAFFIC CHARACTERISTICS OF THE TXE-4 ELECTRONIC EXCHANGE
A. F. PAIS
POST OFFICE ELECTRICAL ENGINEERS
JOURNAL VOL. 68 - PART III OCT. 1975

TXE 4 ELECTRONIC EXCHANGE SYSTEM
PART 1 - OVERALL DESCRIPTION AND GENERAL OPERATION
J. V. GOODMAN AND J. L. PHILLIPS
POST OFFICE ELECTRICAL ENGINEER JOURNAL
JAN. 1976 - VOL. 68. PT.4 - PP196-203

Paper 17

Local Metaconta System (10C)

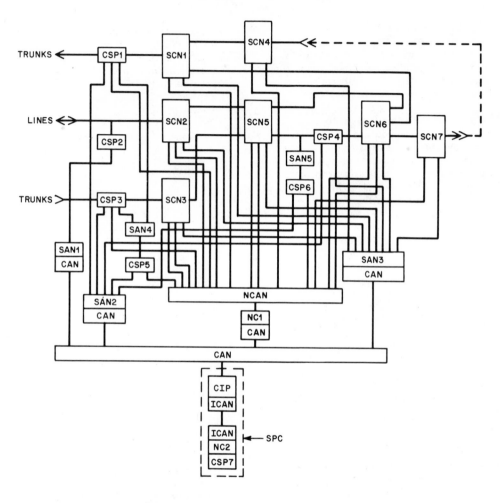

SCN1 = (TCP) – TRUNK CONCENTRATOR NETWORK
SCN2 = (LCP) – LINE CONCENTRATOR NETWORK
SCN3 = (TEP) – TRUNK EXPANSION NETWORK
SCN4 = (JTP) – JUNCTOR TERMINATING NETWORK
SCN5 = (MXR) – MIXING NETWORK
SCN6 = (JXP) – JUNCTOR MIXING NETWORK
SCN7 = (JDP) – JUNCTOR DISTRIBUTION NETWORK
CAN = PERIPHERAL REGISTER AND BUS
CIP = CENTRAL PROCESSOR
CSP1 = OUTGOING TRUNK CIRCUIT
CSP2 = LINE CIRCUIT
CSP3 = INCOMING TRUNK CIRCUIT
CSP4 = FEED JUNCTOR
CSP5 = MULTI–FREQUENCY–RECEIVER AND SENDER
CSP6 = PUSH–KEY RECEIVER
CSP7 = CALL STORE

NC1 = MARKER–DRIVER
NC2 = NETWORK MAP
SAN1 = LINE TESTER
SAN2 = COMBINED CIRCUIT TESTER
SAN3 = LINK TESTER
SAN4 = JUNCTION SIGNAL NETWORK
SAN5 = PUSH–KEY RECEIVER NETWORK
SPC = PROCESSOR

THE 10-C SYSTEM,
A STORED-PROGRAM CONTROLLED REED SWITCHING SYSTEM

H.H. Adelaar
Bell Telephone Manufacturing Company
Antwerp, Belgium

Introduction

The 10-C system comprises modular multi-stage link switching networks composed of reed crosspoint matrices, controlled by a stored-program central processor system.

The main features and advantages attached to the use of miniature sealed dry reed contact assemblies as crosspoints of the switching matrix, as well as those resulting from the use of centralized stored program control have been discussed elsewhere (1)(2). Most prominent among the advantages are : high switching speed, noise-free high quality transmission, long life without maintenance, and space reduction, for the reeds; and high control capacity, flexibility and adaptability, improved traffic control and management, resulting in efficient use of cable routes and office equipment, and a variety of new subscribers' facilities, for the stored program control.

This paper is in the first place concerned with the system aspects peculiar to reed crosspoints and to the central control arrangement; it particularly intends to illustrate the way in which these aspects have been taken advantage of in designing the 10-C system.

Basically, in designing this system, the aim has been to achieve an optimum match, in spite of their apparent dissimilarity, between the switching networks and the central control. This implies that not only was the control arrangement to be matched to the requirements of the network, but also the network was to be shaped with a view to achieving maximum simplicity and efficiency in formulating the control programs in terms of computer language; moreover, where feasible, the aim has been to reduce the amount of per call data to be processed in or through the peripheral control circuitry, so that the latter could be simplified and reduced in size with a resulting increase in intrinsic reliability and easy maintainability.

A second guiding principle in 10-C design has been the objective of ensuring the required standards of reliability and dependability with the simplest possible means.

These basic principles will be illustrated with reference to the following description of the 10-C terminal exchange system, a first installation of which has been put into service in Wilrijk near Antwerp on September 25th of last year, now almost 9 months ago.

High Switching Speed

For new generation switching systems, high speed switching is a prime requirement, especially in view of : 1° the development of high speed signalling methods using a network of independent signalling data links (CCITT N° 6 system), and 2° the trend towards short messages, which is expected to occur in the composition of telephone traffic. Moreover, as the use of subscriber trunk dialling extends at a rapid pace, more calls will have to be switched through many switches in tandem, and this will again put increasing stress on the importance of high speed switching.

A reed crosspoint switches in 1 to 2 ms. In the 10-C system, owing to the fast serial marking procedure, it takes only 17 ms in all, to extend a connection through four consecutive switching stages. As general-purpose junctors are used, and the release of all paths is controlled by contacts in the junctor, the average number of marker operations is about 3, so that each marker can handle up to 20 000 calls per hour. A single marker would be sufficient for a 2048-line package, when the rate of calls in both directions taken together does not exceed 10 calls/hour/line. Actually, in the cases hitherto considered the call rate was less than half this number. Therefore the functions of relay driving and path setting have been combined in a single marker-driver, a duplex set of which is provided for each 2048-line package.

High speed service is also required for extending paths to signal receivers, as this enables registers in distant exchanges to

Reprinted from *1968 IEEE Int. Conf. Commun. Rec.*, June 1968, pp. 38-45.

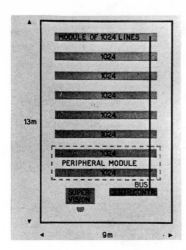

Fig. 1 - 10-C Exchange for 8,192 lines.

discharge their contents in the shortest possible time, and this should be independent of the load or overload condition which may prevail in the speech network. Therefore separate signal switching networks have been provided in the 10-C system.

Modular Construction

The rapid increase of the dial telephone user population calls for frequent additions of switching equipment. The modular construction of the 10-C networks provides easy expansion with a minimum of initial investment. Figure 1 shows, as an example, the lay-out of a 10-C terminal exchange for 8,192 lines. As illustrated in this figure, the network is composed of a plurality of self-contained network units, each serving a group of 1024 lines. Two such units, as shown in figure 2, together with peripheral network control circuits (markers, drivers, testers) and common pools of signal receivers and senders, form a peripheral package serving 2048 lines.

As shown more particularly in figure 3, each network unit comprises a full-availability group of general purpose junctors and two groups of terminals for incoming and outgoing trunks respectively, as well as link switching networks providing paths from subscribers' lines to junctors (LCP, MXP), and vice versa, from incoming trunks to junctors (TEP, MXP), and from junctors to outgoing trunks (JXP, TCP). In a dependent terminal office, almost all originating traffic may be leaving the office on outgoing trunks, while incoming trunks supply almost 100 % of the terminating traffic. The 10-C networks have been dimensioned for this case; if necessary, some tandem traffic can also be handled.

Thus each network unit is a self-contained module which, complemented with a set of peripheral control circuits and a central processor system, can serve as a complete 1024-line office. In order to cope with growth, modules can be added as required. Interconnection between modules will then be provided via small additional networks (JDPe,o and JTP1...n) of which JDPe and JDPo give access to even and odd-numbered modules respectively, whereas a JTP-network is added for each added module. With the aid of a tie frame, new modules can be connected, without disturbing the existing wire connections.

Figure 4 shows a traffic flow diagram for this module, in which it has been assumed that average subscriber traffic is 0.05 Erlang per line in either direction, and 20 % of the traffic is locally terminated. As will be seen in this graph, the by-path mixing network JXP is used preferentially for outgoing calls, which are routed through TCP as long as free trunks in the wanted direction are available, whereas terminating calls are directed preferentially through JDP and JTP. Thus, if the different outgoing directions are about equally represented in each module, a substantial part of the traffic can be handled within the module, whereas intermodule traffic is kept to a minimum.

In offices containing only one module, the JDP-JTP array reduces to a two-stage network identical to JXP, and the total outgoing plus terminating traffic can be handled between the two networks operating in parallel.

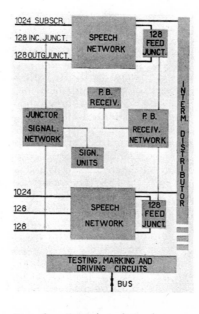

Fig. 2 - Peripheral Package.

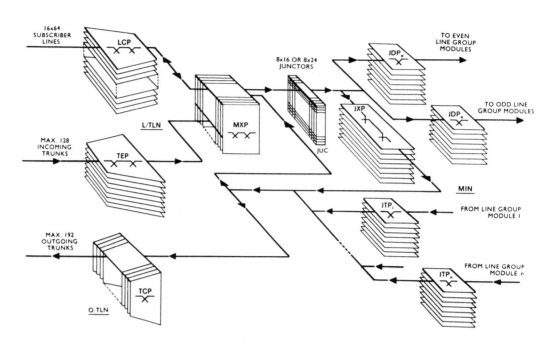

16x64 SUBSCRIBER LINES

LCP

L/TLN

MAX. 128 INCOMING TRUNKS

TEP

MXP

MAX. 192 OUTGOING TRUNKS

TCP

O.TLN

8x16 OR 8x24 JUNCTORS

JUC

JXP

JDPe

JDPo

MIN

JTPi

JTPn

TO EVEN LINE GROUP MODULES

TO ODD LINE GROUP MODULES

FROM LINE GROUP MODULE 1

FROM LINE GROUP MODULE n

Fig. 3 - Network Module.

High Crosspoint Efficiency

Economic use of crosspoints, in terms of a minimum number of crosspoints per line or per Erlang, is achieved in the 10-C system owing to the use of small size matrices in conjunction with "conjugate selection", whereby for each call extension all available network paths can be tested and any path, when free, may be used. As an example, for assumed traffic values as indicated in figure 5, the distribution of crosspoints (per line) over the different switching stages is given in Table 1. It will be seen that the variable part, which increases with the number of modules used in the exchange, is small. For example, for normal traffic (2 x 0.05 E per line), the number of crosspoints per line increases from 12.25 to 17 as the exchange capacity grows from 1 000 to 20 000 lines. Obviously the largest number of crosspoints occurs in the first concentration stage (LC0). For this stage, in the normal traffic case, a grading pattern has been chosen as shown in figure 6. As in N° 1 ESS, each line has access to a selection of 4 out of 8 A-links, but in 10-C the selection is a different one for each of the 16 lines, the pattern being directly related to the binary line coordinates. Computer simulation experiments have shown that, when exponential traffic distribution is assumed, the blocking probabilities are somewhat lower than for a pattern where the lines are grouped in four groups of four (3).

Table 1 :

| Network | Number of Crosspoints per Line | | |
	Low	Traffic Normal	High
LC_0	4	4	6
LC_1	1	2	3
MX_0	3/4	1 1/2	2 1/4
MX_1	3/4	1 1/2	2 1/4
TE_0	5/16	1/4	9/16
TE_1	-	1/2	3/4
TCP	5/16	1/2	3/4
JX_0	1/4	1/2	9/8
JX_1	1/8	1/4	3/8
JDPe	1/4	1/2	9/8
JDPo	1/4	1/2	9/8
JTP	1/8 n	1/4 n	3/8 n
	8 + 1/8 n	12 + 1/4 n	19 5/16 + 3/8 n

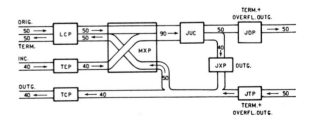

ORIG.
50
50
TERM.
LCP
50
50

INC.
40
TEP
40

OUTG.
40
TCP
40

MXP

90
JUC
50

50

40
JXP
OUTG.

50

JTP
50

TERM.+ OVERFL.OUTG.

JDP
50

TERM.+ OVERFL.OUTG.

Fig. 4 - Traffic Flow in Network Module.

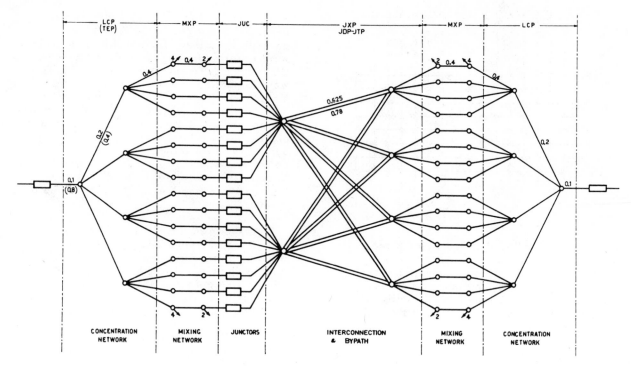

Fig. 7 - Path Diversity Graph.

A path diversity graph for subscriber-to-subscriber connections in this module is given in figure 7. The worst case from a traffic handling quality point of view, is where there is only one module, and accordingly all traffic is to be routed through one JDP-JTP combination in parallel with JXP. The graph in figure 7 applies to this case, and the numbers next to the branches indicate the probabilities of the corresponding links being busy, if both-way traffic per line is 0.1 E. The same graph is also valid for incoming calls, provided the value between brackets is taken for the busy probability of the A-links.

As appears from this graph, each junctor has access, via JDP and JTP, to 16 paths through the mixing network MXP for completion of the call. A junctor, when seized in preselection, can thus be used again for call completion in about 75 percent of the cases; in the remaining cases a new route is selected via another free junctor. In this way valuable time is saved for the processor as well as the marker.

The congestion probability values found with the aid of this graph have since been improved upon by full-scale simulation using a Kosten model (4).

On 930,000 simulated calls the following values are found :
Preselection   0.0035
Subs to subs calls   0.014
Subs to trunk calls   0.0053 (3 trunk routes)
Trunk to subs calls   0.0050 (3 trunk routes).

Binary Network Structure

The structure adopted for the speech and signal switching networks is of a binary nature, i.e. the various elements such as input and output terminals, crosspoints, matrices, links and junctors are grouped in powers of 2, and binary coordinates are used to designate these elements, so that each element or group of similar elements can be addressed by means of a binary address adapted to fit in a binary computer instruction format.

For instance, in an office comprising up to 16 modules, coordinates may be used as follows :

$U_0 \ldots U_3$ Modules
$X_0 \ldots X_9$ LCP line terminals
$Y_0 \ldots Y_6$ MXP junctor terminals
$Y'_0 \ldots Y'_6$ MXP re-entrant terminals
$Z_0 \ldots Z_5$ TEP incoming trunk terminals
$R_0 \ldots R_5$ TCP outgoing trunk terminals.

Fig. 5 - Flow Chart.

133

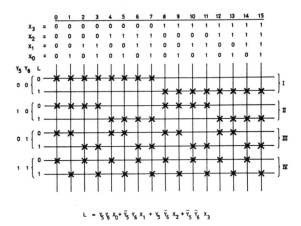

	0	1	2	3	4	5	6	7	8	9	10	11	12	13	14	15
X_3 =	0	0	0	0	0	0	0	0	1	1	1	1	1	1	1	1
X_2 =	0	0	0	0	1	1	1	1	0	0	0	0	1	1	1	1
X_1 =	0	0	1	1	0	0	1	1	0	0	1	1	0	0	1	1
X_0 =	0	1	0	1	0	1	0	1	0	1	0	1	0	1	0	1

$$L = \bar{Y}_5 \bar{Y}_6 X_0 + \bar{Y}_5 Y_6 X_1 + Y_5 \bar{Y}_6 X_2 + \bar{Y}_5 \bar{Y}_6 X_3$$

Fig. 6 - Grading Pattern in Line Stage.

As any path through the network is uniquely identified by the terminals between which it extends, marking as well as driving orders can be formulated in terms of these coordinates.

In order to illustrate the use of these coordinates, the procedure used for setting up a path between a calling line and a free junctor will now be described with reference to figures 8 and 9.

As soon as a call is detected, the coordinates X0...X9 of the calling line are established. Then a link testing procedure is initiated, in which A- B- and C-links are tested in groups of 16.

For the A-link test, coordinates U0 and X9...X5 are used as a test address. In order to single out the 4 links accessible to the caller, the 16-bit busy/idle word is first masked with the access pattern :

$$\bar{X}_3 X_3 \bar{X}_2 X_2 \bar{X}_1 X_1 \bar{X}_0 X_0 \bar{X}_3 X_3 \bar{X}_2 X_2 \bar{X}_1 X_1 \bar{X}_0 X_0$$

and then with another mask which eliminates the second or first half-word according to whether

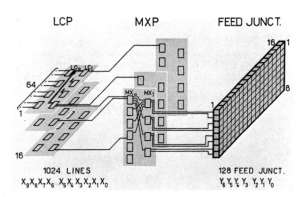

Fig. 8 - Connections in Line Link Network.

LCP   MXP   FEED JUNCT.

1024 LINES
$X_9 X_8 X_7 X_6 \ X_5 X_4 X_3 X_2 X_1 X_0$

128 FEED JUNCT.
$Y_6 Y_5 Y_4 \ Y_3 \ Y_2 Y_1 Y_0$

X4 is 0 or 1. The resulting 4-bit word is expanded according to the B-link accessibility, then aligned with the busy/idle word resulting from the B-link test which uses U0 and X9...X6 as a test address. The test word so obtained reveals the coordinates Y6...Y3 of the vertical MX-planes that can be used for the call. The C-links in these planes are now tested in groups of 16 divided over 4 planes, using U0 and X9X8X6X5 as a test address, and the busy/idle states of corresponding junctors are fetched from memory, in order to determine the coordinates U0 Y6...Y0 of a free junctor to which a free path extends.

As shown in figure 9 the latter coordinates are decoded and used in an access matrix, to apply positive marking to the selected junctor. Then the pulling potential sources are connected as shown in the drawing, to selected pulling multiples in the successive switching stages, under the control of

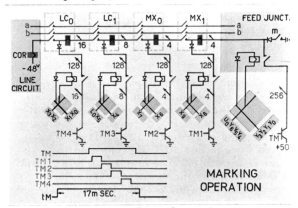

Fig. 9 - Marking Operation.

coordinates X9X8, X7X6, L0X5X4 and X3X2X1X0 respectively. L0 is an auxiliary coordinate, necessary to distinguish between the two A-links extending between the selected LC0 and LC1 matrices, and can be calculated as shown in figure 6.

Owing to the geometrical network structure thus being adapted to the binary instruction format, the entire path search operation can be neatly integrated in the output handling program which controls marker operation. As each single link group test takes only 20 µsecs. and 3 such tests are sufficient in all but a few cases, the path searching operation adds only a negligible amount to marker operation time.

In order to ensure maximum marker efficiency, especially under high traffic conditions, the marker-driver output program is initiated by means of a program interrupt, as soon as the marker-driver has terminated its previous job.

Bus System and Interface

As mentioned before (2) a duplicate processor system is used, with the processors working in load-sharing mode. For communication with the central processors, each peripheral package has two 26-bit peripheral registers, each comprising 16 flip-flops for data input and output plus 10 flip-flops for checking and control purposes. Via a set of gates each register is connected to a 41-lead peripheral bus.

The processor, besides instructions for memory fetch and store, arithmetic, logical, shift, control, jump and skip instructions, also has input/output instructions for data transfer from its accumulator to its peripheral bus and vice versa, and for setting a flip-flop or sensing a line.

In order to transfer data to or from a selected peripheral register, the package address is decoded in an address and function analyser to select and open the gates towards the wanted register.

By these arrangements, each processor can transfer, via its own bus, 16 bit test orders and double-, triple- or quadruple-word marking and driving orders, fetch test results and sense, set or reset control flip-flops to, from or in any selected 2048-line package, respectively.

For communication between the two processors, two interprocessor buffers, one for each direction, are used. Whenever one processor sends a message to the other, a high level interrupt is actuated in the latter.

Program Organization

Call handling programs are used to fetch information from the periphery, process this information and emit the switching orders found to be required. They deal with peripheral devices in different ways :

Passive Devices.

Passive input devices (line testers and combined circuit testers) are supervised according to a stored time schedule which is initiated periodically at 14 ms intervals by a clock. Initially, numerical information is collected by scanning the calling side scan points in all junctors and the outputs of all signal and push-button tone frequency receivers. Then the program turns to "slow" supervision by sensing scan points in one or two groups of 16 junctors (terminating side), incoming trunks and outgoing trunks respectively, to end up with the scanning of e.g. 8 groups of 16 lines each.

Each 16-bit scan result is compared with a "last-look" word fetched from memory.

For each call in the fast supervision phase a register buffer is seized in memory, in which the numerical codes as well as other relevant information is stored. The programs used during this phase comprise mismatch detection and identification as well as pulse timing and counting, so that the assembly of numerical information can mainly be treated by those programs working with the register buffers.

In the slow supervision phase, if a scan point is found to exhibit a change, its coordinates are stored in a hopper for further treatment by the appropriate base level program.

There are 10 programs in the clock interrupt schedule. Normally the execution of these programs takes substantially less than 7 ms and the remaining time can be used by the 14 base level programs and some of the 14 on-line test programs, until the next clock interrupt causes the cycle to be repeated.

As the clock interrupts alternate at 7 ms intervals, the processors will not interfere with each other : while one communicates with the periphery, the other processes the information previously received. Moreover the line scan schedules of both processors are 180° out of phase so that on the average, each processor picks up the same number of calls.

Active Devices.

Active input devices, such as the interprocessor buffers can cause an interrupt at any time, in order to cause the processor to accept a message.

Active output devices, such as the marker-drivers, can activate an interrupt line in order to sollicit new instructions which may be waiting in an output hopper.

Base Level Programs

The base level programs scan buffers and hoppers for work, which will finally result in network testing orders, marking orders and relay driving orders being placed in appropriate output hoppers, and messages being sent to the interprocessor buffer.

Size of Programs

Careful attention has been paid to minimizing the number of instructions in call handling programs.

The 10 clock interrupt programs, 4

tester-marker-driver programs and 14 base level programs comprise 2,600 + 2,700 + 1,600 = 6,900 instruction words, to which must be added 6,300 words contained in subroutines, i.e. 13,200 words in all.

Base level programs further comprise 2,100 words of on-line test programs and about 3,900 words of man/machine communication programs.

Another 1,100 words are devoted to start up and automatic recovery, and miscellaneous items bring the score up to 21,600 words. Finally a field of abt. 750 words is kept open for the introduction of "on-demand" programs which may be used for routine tests and/or statistics.

Reliability

As will be seen, the on-line tests are kept to a minimum, sufficient to indicate the incidence of vital faults in one or the other processor, the bus system or the peripheral control circuits. Routine tests and diagnostic tests are available on tape, the former to be introduced as desired into the on-demand program field, and the latter to be used off-line after a fault has been detected.

This concept is found to be feasible owing to the simplicity of the circuits and functions, the low number of components involved and their intrinsic high reliability which minimize the requirements of various check circuits and programs, and which justify a high mean time between simplex system failure prediction.

Automatic Recovery

Each processor can work in any of 5 modes : on-line, copy, reading mode, halt and test.

A processor goes to halt in any of the following cases :
1. Parity fault on memory read-out.
2. Repeated time-out on marker-driver response.
3. Wrong results from all peripheral registers.
4. Repeated failure in passing an on-line test.
5. Maintenance key thrown.

Without human intervention the system always tries to restore itself to normal. The processor modes are supervised by the automatic supervisor in the system console. Whenever a processor is found in the halt condition, the maintenance key being at rest, the automatic supervisor interrupts the other processor to initiate the take-over program. This program ensures that control of all calls in the conversation phase is taken over by the on-line processor, whereas calls in the dialling phase are put in parking condition.

The automatic supervisor also causes the stand-by program tape to be re-wound, whereafter the off-line processor is forced to reading mode. By means of a hard-ware loader, function tests are loaded successively. Each time a test has been loaded, the processor goes to test mode, in order to execute the test. If the test is successful, the processor goes to reading mode to load the next test. If not, the process is repeated. When all tests are successful, the operational program is loaded and the processor goes to copy mode for copying network and call data via the inter-processor channel from the on-line processor. Then after a final check the processor goes on-line again.

If both processors go off-line, the automatic supervisor selects one for automatic reload, then tries the other one. In that case all calls in progress are lost. As soon as the first processor is restored to normal, it proceeds to release all connections in order to liberate all circuits.

Line Classes

As installed at Wilrijk, the system provides for 30 different line classes which may be combined as required. Many more can be added, if desired. A line class indicator table stored in memory has one bit for each line to indicate whether the line has special features or not. In this way the memory space required for the translation table can be minimized and much time can be saved if many lines do not have such features.

Man-Machine Communication

At present the man-machine communication programs provide for 17 different teletype input/output operations, such as
- read or write a specific word in memory,
- change a line class,
- print out all equipment numbers pertaining to a specific subscriber number,
- print out list of abbreviated dialling codes,
- add a new line to a PABX group, etc.

Each request or order is repeated by the machine, which automatically adds date and time. If a line is to be displaced, the machine replies with the new and the old equipment number.

Conclusion

10-C development started in January 1965 By September 1967, a terminal exchange comprising one 1024 line unit, extensible to 10,000 line capacity, was connected to the Belgian telephone network. This operation has taken 120 engineering men-years, 36 of which were devoted to programming.

The work now in progress comprises design of a faster processor which will permit expansion of the terminal exchange to 20,000 lines or more; development of combined local and toll exchanges, and remote controlled switching centres; 10-C telex exchanges; as well as various application studies.

Acknowledgement

The success of the 10-C system is largely due to the enthusiastic cooperation of all engineers and programmers who formed the 10-C development team under the inspiring conduction of J. Van Goethem, M. Verbeeck and S. Kobus.

This paper has been improved owing to comments and suggestions of J.D. Beierle, A. Termote and J. Broux.

References

1. N° 1 Electronic Switching System : System Organization and Objectives by W. Keister, R.W. Ketchledge and H.E. Vaughan. Bell Syst. Techn. Journ., Vol. XLIII, Sept. 1964, N° 5, Part 1, pages 1831-1844.

2. "Semi-electronic Reed Crosspoint Telephone Switching System 10-CX" by H.H. Adelaar and J. Masure, Electr. Communication, Vol. 42, Number 1, 1967, pages 33-46.

3. "N° 1 ESS Switching Network Plan" by A. Feiner and W.S. Hayward. Bell Syst. Techn. Journ., Vol. XLIII, Sept. 1964, N° 5, Part 2, pages 2193-2220.

4. Internal Communication from the Traffic Studies Division, ITT Laboratorios de España.

Supplementary Bibliography for Paper 17

10C LOCAL

INITIAL EXPERIENCE WITH THE 10C SWITCHING SYSTEM
BROUX JA
ELEC COMMUN 43 (4) 323-8 (1968)

METACONTA SWITCHING SYSTEM REVIEWED AFTER 7 YEARS
BROUX JA
ELEC. COMMUN 50 NO. 3: 170-8, 1975

TECHNICAL POSSIBILITIES OF THE LOCAL EXCHANGE
METACONTA 10C
SILA V
ELEKTROTEH. VESTN. 41 (5-8): 183-9 (MAY-SEPT. 1974) (IN SOLVENE)

OPERATIONAL AVAILABILITY AND MAINTENANCE FACILITIES FOR THE ITT 3200 PROCESSOR IN THE METACONTA SWITCHING SYSTEM
CAGNAC T + PENET X
ELECT COMMUN ITT 49 (4): 400 (1974)

INPUT-OUTPUT PART OF TELEPHONE EXCHANGE METACONTA 10C
KLANCAR S + SKRJANEC M
ELEKTROTEH. VESTN. 41 (5-8): 190-3 (MAY-SEPT. 1974) (IN SLOVENE)

Paper 18

Toll Metaconta System (10C)

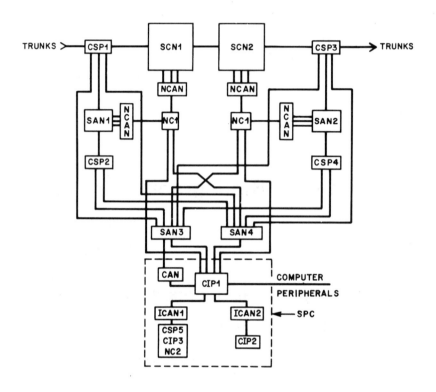

SCN1 = INCOMING NETWORK		ICAN1 = MEMORY BUS
SCN2 = OUTGOING NETWORK		ICAN2 = DIRECT INPUT/OUTPUT BUS
CIP1 = CENTRAL COMPUTER		NC1 = MARKERS- LOW
CIP2 = PROGRAM MEMORY		SPEED DRIVERS
CIP3 = TRANSLATION MEMORY	MEMORY BLOCKS	NC2 = NETWORK MAP
CSP5 = DATA MEMORY		SAN1 = RECEIVER LINK
CSP1 = INCOMING JUNCTORS		SAN2 = SENDER LINK
CSP2 = RECEIVERS		SAN3 = HIGH SPEED TESTER
CSP3 = OUTGOING JUNCTORS		SAN4 = HIGH SPEED DRIVER
CSP4 = SENDERS		SPC = PROCESSOR SYSTEM

An Introduction to the 10C Trunk Exchange System.

B. J. McKINLEY, B.A., M.I.E. (Aust.)

In April 1968 the APO sought from manufacturers through the world, a trunk exchange capable of handling the large quality of trunk traffic expected in the Sydney network commencing in the early 1970's. Following an evaluation of the offers received an exchange consisting of 10C equipment to be supplied by Standard Telephones and Cables Pty. Ltd. was selected.

The 10C system is an electronic trunk system which has a maximum capacity of 64,000 lines. This article surveys the functions of the major parts of the system and outlines the means by which these parts interact to process traffic.

INTRODUCTION

The ARM system was adopted as the standard APO trunk equipment in 1959, but the first exchange was not installed at Haymarket in Sydney until 1967. The maximum size of a single ARM exchange is 4000 inlets and 4000 outlets, and it is possible to increase the size by "twinning" to 8000 inlets and 8000 outlets.

It became obvious toward the middle 1960s that if the trunk growth continued to increase at the rate then current, and if, for economic reasons, all the trunk traffic in the larger cities was to continue to be handled through a minimum number of switching points, then trunk exchanges of greater capacity than ARM could provide, would be needed at the major trunk centres in the 1970s.

Following the preparation of a specification, quotations were sought from telephone manufacturing companies, on a world wide basis, for the supply of a trunk exchange for Pitt, Sydney, which could accommodate up to 50,000 lines (inlets/outlets). Tenders for this equipment closed in January 1969.

After a detailed evaluation of tenders which considered not only the equipment itself, but took into account associated economic factors such as operating staff, building requirements, air conditioning, power, loading of trunk lines, etc., based on the best information and assessments then available, the decision was taken in September 1969 to purchase a 12,000 line, 10C trunk exchange from Standard Telephones and Cables Pty. Ltd. (STC) to be installed in the Pitt St. building in Sydney. The equipment for this exchange was to be manufactured by Bell Telephone Manufacturing Company (BTMC) of Antwerp an associated company with STC in the International Telephone & Telegraphs group (ITT).

About this time, the APO decided to use the 10C system as an alternative to the ARM system as dictated by economic considerations of the particular switching centres.

Subsequently, two further contracts for trunk exchanges were let to STC namely, 8000 lines for Lonsdale (Melbourne) and 8000 lines for Waymouth (Adelaide). The Pitt exchange will be commissioned in two stages with the STD section scheduled for November 1973 and the Manual assistance section about 18 months later. Following the decision to purchase 10C equipment, the ability of a processor controlled exchange to provide a more sophisticated manual assistance position was realised. At the time when the detailed specification of all the facilities to be included in these positions was finalised, it was not possible for the contractor to complete design, manufacture and installation of the manual assistance equipment at the date by which the STD facility was required at Pitt. It was therefore decided to press ahead with the STD exchange at Pitt, and to introduce the manual assistance facility after the completion of the Waymouth exchange which would be the prototype installation for the combined STD and manual assistance centre. Currently, Waymouth and Lonsdale are scheduled for commissioning in 1974/75.

FUNCTIONS PERFORMED BY THE IOC EQUIPMENT

The 10C equipment will be used in the network in a similar manner to ARM exchanges. The 10C system switches on a 4 wire basis and can grow to a maximum of 32,000 inlets and 32,000 outlets. It will be used for transit switching of trunk traffic, as well as an interconnecting point between the two and four wire networks. It will have a rate determining function, and will return metering informa-

Reprinted with permission from *Telecommun. J. Austr.*, vol. 23, pp. 85–93, June 1973.

tion to dependent exchanges, when required, in a similar manner to the ARM exchanges.

Integrated manual assistance positions will be provided, similar in some respects to the AFG positions associated with ARM exchanges. From the design and operational viewpoints the 10C positions are significantly more advanced than the AFG equipment.

One important feature of the 10C equipment which is not currently included in the ARM equipment used in Australia is the Centralised Interception Service. The L. M. Ericsson ARF local switching system used for terminal exchanges has the capability of marking subscribers so that calls terminating on ARF exchange equipment will be re-routed to a centralised point which will be the 10C trunk exchange, where specialised handling of the call can be arranged.

10C EQUIPMENT — GENERAL

Hardware

From a hardware viewpoint, a 10C trunk exchange consists essentially of:

Telephone Switching Section

This Section basically consists of:
  (i) junctors which are the interface between the exchange and the external trunks and junctions;
  (ii) the switching matrix which is a five wire, six stage reed relay selector.

Telephone Periphery

The telephone periphery equipment is the interface between the processors and the conventional exchange items (junctors and switching matrix).

The Central Processor System

The processor system consists of:
  (i) the central processor unit (CPU) which gathers information from the periphery, performs logical operations on this information, and, based on the conclusions, issues orders to the periphery for driving the junctors or the switching matrix;
  (ii) the memory (a ferrite core system) in which the exchange program, translation tables and variable data are stored.

Computer Periphery

The computer peripherals consist of magnetic tape and disc drives, paper tape readers, and teleprinters, which are items of equipment normally associated with computer installations. Paper tape punches and line printers may also be associated with this computer.

Bus System

The bus system interlinks the computer and all peripheral equipment and is the means by which information necessary for the operation of the exchange is conveyed between the various items of equipment.

Software

Software is the instructions and data stored in memory which controls the operation of the exchange. The operational program can be sub-divided into a number of interconnected software packages:

Signalling Package

This package controls the reception of, and responses to, both line and information signalling, including time supervision for the various functions. It communicates (links) with other packages as required for this purpose.

Marker/Driver Package

This package controls the operation of the switching matrix, and collects information from other packages to generate final driving orders to the telephone periphery. Thus, other packages which require some operation in the telephone switching section are linked to this package.

Man-machine Package

All inputs (and outputs) from the computer periphery to the CPU are controlled by this package. All decisions by other packages to give teletype outputs, for example, are referred to this package. It also checks incoming messages for correct format before further processing.

Manual Assistance Package

The operation of all manual assistance positions and associated monitors and supervisors positions are controlled in this package. It will, for example, treat key operations, light lamps and display relevant information and refer action necessary for decisions taken to other packages such as Man-machine or Marker/Driver.

Intercept Package

This package controls the interception facilities provided by the exchange, and, in conjunction with the Manual Assistance package, controls the manual positions associated with this service. As before, it is linked to other packages as necessary.

On-line Test Package

The tests which are continuously run on the exchange are contained in and controlled by this package, e.g. CPU Console test. The tests done are of varying priority, some being done very early in each processor cycle of 10 ms and others towards the end. Thus, in those cycles where the work load is high, the execution of some of these test programs will be delayed until the processor has time available.

Test Equipment Package

This package contains the programs for controlling exchange test equipment such as the Traffic Route Tester and Automatic Call Sender. Again, this package is linked to others as necessary.

Take-over and Recovery Package

In the event of a fault developing in the system, particularly in the processor (CPU, memory, controllers, etc.), decisions must be in-built which enable the equipment to prevent calls being lost (take-over) and to recover from the fault situation. This package contains the programs necessary to control these functions. Such actions can involve reconfiguration of memory block allocations, program re-loading, etc.

On Demand Package

This package contains those programs which are not normally required for the correct operation of the exchange and therefore are not being continuously executed.

The programs are stored on paper tape and read into a reserved area of memory 'on-demand' via a medium speed paper tape reader. This reserved area will be much less than the sum of the on-demand programs, thus giving more economical usage of memory. The package contains such programs as detailed diagnostic tests, traffic dispersion and occupancy, etc.

PHILOSOPHY OF STORED PROGRAM CONTROL (SPC)

Before considering each of the above areas in greater detail it is of value to consider the basic philosophy of processor controlled exchanges. Processors are machines which are capable of performing both arithmetical and logical type calculations. A telephone exchange consists of items of equipment which perform logical operations based on informa-

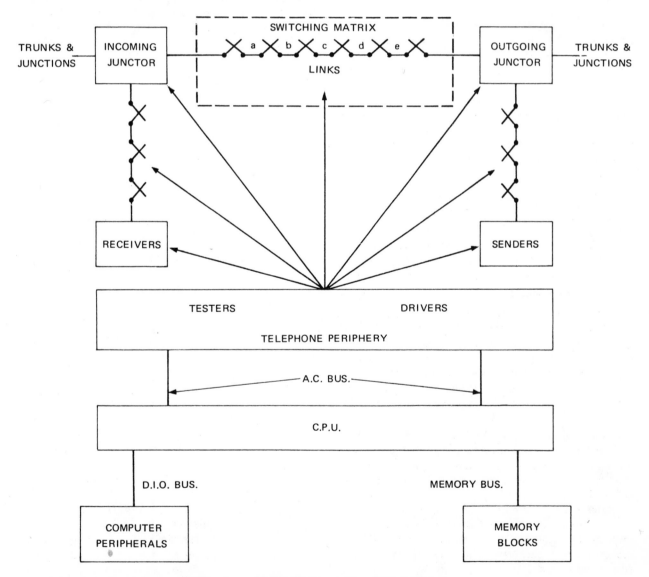

Fig. 1 — Major Divisions of a 10C Exchange

tion received from external sources. In conventional electromechanical exchanges, these logical operations are generally performed by relays. The intelligence in electromechanical systems can be widely dispersed as in step-by-step systems, or concentrated in blocks as in common control systems such as the ARF system. Greater concentration of control generally leads to economic advantages and the possibility of more sophisticated facilities. The extent to which common equipment can control individual items is a function, amongst other factors, of the speed of operation of the control equipment. As processors can perform logical operations in microseconds, they are able to directly control more equipment than common control systems using relays, where the logical operations occupy tens of milli-seconds. Advantage has been taken of this speed of operation of processors in electronic exchanges, to extend centralised control not only to the selector stages, as in electromechanical systems, but also to individual trunk and junction terminations.

The core of this centralised control is the CPU operating under SPC conditions, i.e. the sum of the software packages listed above. This software is arranged so that it is continuously running in the CPU in a cyclic fashion. The individual programs which make up the different packages are arranged in order of priority, and the processor executes these programs, covering all functions required in the exchange, at a fixed multiple of the basic cyclic rate.

IOC EQUIPMENT — DESCRIPTION AND OPERATION

Following this brief description of the basic philosophy, we shall now explore, in a little more detail the functions and the interrelationships of the various components of a Metaconta 10C electronic exchange. Fig. 1 outlines the major divisions of a 10C exchange.

Telephone Switching Section

Junctors (Trunk or Junction Line Terminations)

Junctors in the Metaconta 10C system consist of some 7 to 10 relays plus solid state detectors, transmission bridge, etc. These components produce variations to conditions on test points, provide metering reversals, holding for switching matrix crosspoints and coupling to signalling senders and receivers.

Collection of Information on Scanning

The junctors are controlled by the processor through test points and drive points. A test point will change potential, when conditions change on the external circuit to which it is connected. Fig. 2 indicates the basic elements of a test point.

At intervals of 100 milli-seconds, the processor inspects the state of this test point via the bus sysem and the peripheral equipment to determine any change. This is known as scanning.

It is important to note that the processor controls

all actions in the exchange. The junctors, for example, do not send advice to the processor about a change of state. Instead, during its routine operations, the processor interrogates the test points in groups of 32 via the telephone periphery and later, requests the results to be returned to it. In this manner the processor knows the source of all information it receives.

Depending on the state of the component controlling the test point, a different condition (logic 0 or 1) is returned to the processor. The software signalling package compares this information with information from the previous scan stored within the processor's memory, and enables the processor to deduce what is happening on the particular circuit and take appropriate action.

Orders for Action or Driving

After the processor determines what action is necessary in the telephone exchange equipment (i.e. in the junctors or the switching matric), it calls on

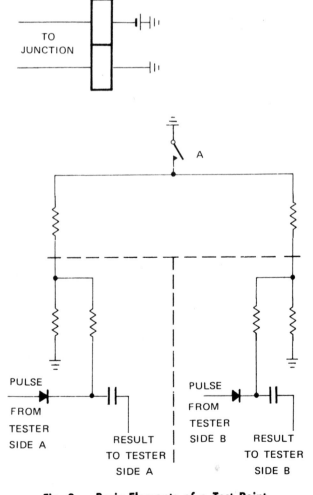

Fig. 2 — Basic Elements of a Test Point

TJA, Vol. 23, No. 2, 1973

the marker-driver package to transmit an instruction to the particular equipment items, which causes the required action. In most instances, this results in a relay operation in the device concerned, which locks and is released only when so instructed by a subsequent order from the processor.

Fig. 3 shows, for comparison, a 10C junctor card and an ARM relay set both of which are used to connect an incoming four wire physical circuit to the respective exchanges where the exchange initiates multimetering signals. The difference in the absolute size and the logic in each of the equipment items is readily apparent. What must be appreciated, is that the logic contained in the ARM termination has been removed from the 10C termination and resides in the program of the processor.

The Switching Stage

The switching stage in the 10C trunk exchange consists of a six stage reed relay matrix. The crosspoints themselves consist of five reed elements (four for the transmission path and one for the holding wire) surrounded by a single coil which operates the five reed inserts.

A basic building module consists of 16 reed crosspoints assembled into a 4 inlet, 4 outlet configuration. These can then be used either directly as a 4 x 4 unit or extended to 4 x 8, 8 x 8 or 8 x 16 to form the particular switching stage.

Fig. 4 shows an 8 x 8 reed crosspoint matrix. It is plugged into the rack via the connections on the left hand side of the card and consequently can be readily replaced.

The exchange itself at the maximum size of 32,000 inlets and 32,000 outlets, has a minimum number of 16 paths between any inlet and any outlet. The connections between the various stages comprising the exchange, are arranged in an orderly manner, to ensure that, from a knowledge of the exchange numbers of the calling inlet and a selected outlet, the 16 possible paths can be determined out of the 64,000 paths (C links) through the maximum size exchange.

The switching process is initiated by the processor selecting an outlet in the required route via the translation tables, following which it calculates the location of the C links (the link at the centre of the exchange between the two middle switching stages) from which the inlet and outlet are accessible. After tentative selection of one free C link, it calculates the address of the crosspoints forming the one possible path between each end of the C link, and the inlet and outlet. The processor then examines the condition of the crosspoints which is stored in the common data memory blocks. If all crosspoints on this path are not free it selects a second C link and tries again. When a free path is found, the processor sends appropriate instructions, via the

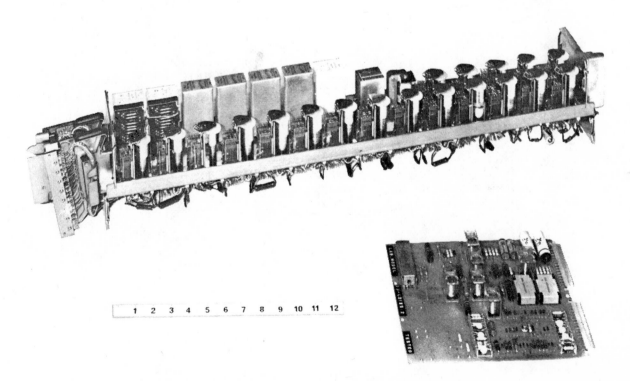

| 1 | 2 | 3 | 4 | 5 | 6 | 7 | 8 | 9 | 10 | 11 | 12 |

Fig. 3 — 10C Junction Card and ARM Relay Set

periphery, to operate the selected crosspoints and establish the required path between inlet and outlet.

Telephone Periphery

The time intervals in which the processor operates is in the order of microseconds, while the components in the telephone switching section operate in tens of milli-second intervals. The equipment known as the telephone periphery is the interface between these two different time environments. The bus system carrying data to and from the processor is connected to registers in the peripheral devices. These registers store the data in bistable elements which operate in microsecond intervals. The output of the register is steered through a series of diodes which produce a single active output for each different combination stored in the register. This output is used to initiate the particular function required. That section of the register in a particular unit which receives information from the address section of the bus is continually changing as orders are transmitted to the different peripheral units connected to the bus. The data section of the register however will only change when the address digits received correspond to the address of the peripheral unit which, after decoding, opens the gates for the data section of that register to accept data. Thus, after receipt of an order for a particular device connected to a peripheral unit, the order will remain in the register, and consequently on the device, until the processor next addresses the peripheral unit and changes the information in the register.

Thus the output of the peripheral unit towards

Fig. 4 — 8 x 8 Reed Crosspoint Matrix

TJA, Vol. 23, No. 2, 1973

the telephone switching part of the exchange will persist for a period after the input has been set at microsecond speeds. The period this condition remains on the output, being dependent on the intervals between which the processor addresses the particular peripheral unit, can thus be controlled and made to match or exceed the operating time of the components in the devices.

The telephone peripheral equipment can be divided into two major categories, testers and the drivers:

Testers

Testers are the units through which the processor determines what is happening in the telephone switching part of the exchange. The tester, which is addressed by the processor over the address bus system, admits into its peripheral register the data transmitted on the data bus.

This data is decoded and one active output results. This active output is connected to 32 test points of some particular group of peripheral devices. Depending on the state of these test points, pulses are returned on 32 leads to the peripheral register. Thus, the information stored in the 32 bits of the peripheral register, indicate whether each of the 32 devices interrogated are operated or released.

The processor will address the peripheral register again after an interval greater than eight microseconds (the functioning time of the tester) and read out the 32 bit word stored in it, which indicates the condition of the test points.

There are two separate bus systems from the processors to the testers and, in fact, to all peripheral equipment. The peripheral equipment itself is duplicated up to the actual test point of the individual device. This arrangement increases the security of the equipment, with complete duplication of the tester and the bus system back to the processors. Thus, in the event of a fault occurring in one of these areas, the second processor can take over control. The system is secure against one fault in the bus or peripheral equipment. However, one fault in the actual peripheral device (individual junctor) can result in that junctor being unusable.

During periods when there is no effective traffic to a peripheral unit such as a tester, the processor conducts 'on-line' tests to assure itself that the unit can function correctly. These tests consist of sending words in which all bits are "O" and, alternatively, all bits are "1". Each of these words, when received correctly in a peripheral unit which is functioning satisfactorily, will cause a particular test point to be activated.

By interrogating this test point the processor can deduce whether the peripheral unit is functioning correctly. If a satisfactory result is not obtained, the processor can initiate a procedure which will ensure

that it no longer handles traffic to that particular unit. It also advises the maintenance staff via a teleprinter of the situation so that corrective action may be taken.

Drivers

The driver is the peripheral unit through which the processor causes action to be taken in the telephone exchange.

The driver is addressed by the processor in a similar manner to the tester, and the selected driver accepts data into its register. When this order is decoded one of the circuit elements in one of the peripheral devices served by the driver is caused to operate or release.

Like the testers, the drivers have an all "0", all "1" test for continued satisfactory operation.

Test of Effectiveness of Order

There is no test to confirm operation of the circuit element in the individual device following each drive instruction. However, after an instruction to set a particular connection through the exchange, a continuity test is applied on the speech wires between the incoming and outgoing junctors which confirms that the connection is established. There is no test, for example, to confirm that, following an order, the answer supervisory signal has been transmitted by a junctor.

THE PROCESSOR SYSTEM

Central Processor Unit (CPU)

The processor used in the 10C trunk exchange is known as the ITT 3200. The processor is a machine which makes logical decisions and carries out arithmetical calculations under the control of a program stored in its memory. The data on which the processor operates, is obtained from the telephone switching part of the exchange, from the computer peripherals, or extracted from memory. Following the operations made on this data, the processor issues appropriate orders to the equipment it controls.

Memory

The core memory is a series of ferrite cores arranged in words of 32 bits and in blocks of 16K words (K = 1024 = 2^{10}). In the 10C trunk exchange, the memory is divided into three categories:

(a) the private memory, of which there is one copy per processor with access restricted to that processor. The private memory contains the program packages which control the operations of the CPU.

(b) the translation memory, which is duplicated, is accessible to all processors and contains all the information about the particular trunk groups, the individual circuits of the trunk groups on the switchblock, the charging information peculiar to the particular exchange, number length analysis, and other trunk network information.

(c) data memory is a non-duplicated memory, accessible to all processors and containing a temporary record of the particular connections established in the exchange at any stage in a call. This information is continually changing as the CPU proceeds to set up and break down the required connections through the exchange.

Information is loaded into and extracted from memory by the CPU in 0.85 microseconds. This interval is the factor which, in the main, limits the number of operations the CPU can perform in a given period, and is the most significant factor in limiting the number of calls which can be handled by the CPU. The ITT 3200 processor can handle up to 215,000 calls per hour. The limit is also affected by the complexity of the calls. For example, control of a call being switched by a manual assistance operator will occupy the CPU for a much longer period, than a relatively simple STD call. It is expected at this stage that six processors will be required to serve a 64,000 line exchange. For security, one more processor, than is necessary for traffic reasons, is provided as safeguard against processor failure.

Program

The program is a list of instructions stored in memory which controls the operation of the CPU. The CPU operates on a cycle of:

(i) extract an instruction from store;
(ii) obtain the data from the location specified in the instruction;
(iii) operate on the data as specified in the instruction;
(iv) direct the processed data to the location specified in the instruction. (This could be returned to store or sent to the peripheral equipment as an order for action.)

The instructions which can be executed by a CPU are determined by the logical processes which have been built into the equipment. (These logical processes are determined by the detailed circuitry which constitute the CPU.) Not all CPU's can carry out the same logical processes, hence some are more suitable for particular applications than others. The ITT 3200, for example has been designed to efficiently undertake the logical operations required to perform communications switching while other CPU's have been designed for functions such as scientific calculations.

COMPUTER PERIPHERALS

The following items of hardware which are normally associated with computers are used in 10C exchanges to permit communications between the machine and operators.

Magnetic Tape Drives

Tape drives are used for two purposes:

Reload of Program

There are various indications that an error has occurred in the private program. In an operating exchange it is not likely that the error is due to a logic fault in the program itself. Rather it is more likely to be transient, or a failure in hardware. The error is indicated for example by the CPU receiving a non-existent instruction, or by detection of incorrect parity in an instruction word.

If the processor suspects an error in its private program it requests a re-load of the program from its dedicated magnetic tape drive. During the reload process, tests are performed at various stages to ensure the processor is operating correctly. These tests constitute a series of tasks which the CPU must be able to successfully complete as a check on its "sanity", before it is permitted to again handle traffic.

Recording of Data

There are four tape drives which record information from which traffic statistics for the exchange can be derived, and details of manual assistance traffic used to debit the appropriate charge to the calling subscribers.

This information is recorded on two tapes simultaneously, while the remaining two are in the standby condition and will be immediately taken into service at failure of one of the active drives, or at a scheduled changeover time.

Teletypes

These are used for various purposes by exchange staff to communicate with the processor to modify operation, obtain statistical information, request the execution of an "on demand" program, receive fault reports, etc.

Disc Drives

Disc drives are a much less expensive form of mass storage than ferrite core, and have a much faster access time than magnetic tape. These units are used to store infrequently used information such as number-to-name translation tables, details associated with subscribers interception service and details of manually assisted calls during the 15 minutes after the call is completed and before the call record is written onto magnetic tape.

Paper Tape Readers

These are used to read "on-demand" (O/D) programs into the processor store. These programs are special purpose, seldom used programs which for economy of ferrite core store are held off line on paper tape, and must be loaded by exchange staff when the particular function is required to be performed. O/D programs are used for detailed diagnosis of fault conditions, to provide service observation facilities, etc.

BUS SYSTEM

There are several bus systems used in a 10C exchange. A bus is a number of wires on which data pulses are transmitted between the various items of equipment constituting the processing system, or between this system and the telephone periphery.

As time delays on buses slow down the speed of the computer, it is desirable to keep the buses as physically short as possible — a bus introduces a propagation delay of about five nano-seconds per metre to the data pulses used. A further constraint on bus lengths is imposed by the distortion and 'skew' of pulses relative to each other as they pass along the buses.

DC Memory Bus

The bus system interconnecting the CPU to its memory blocks is designed to be as short as possible, because the propagation time in this area has a significant influence on the speed of the CPU and hence on the number of calls which can be handled by the CPU. The maximum length of the memory bus is 30 metres, but restrictions placed on the bus configuration by the number of loads (16) and the maximum distance from the CPU to any load (15 metres) can prevent this figure being realised.

Direct Input/Output (DIO) Bus

This bus connects the CPU's with the computer periphery controllers, and experiences similar limitations to the memory bus. As the traffic on this bus is not as intense as that on the memory bus, it is not so critical to minimise its length.

AC Bus

The bus sysem which connects the CPU with the telephone switching section of the exchange is known as the AC bus, and can be up to 300 metres long. This consists of 150 metres from the CPU to a bus repeater, and 150 metres from the repeater to the actual peripheral unit. The increased length is realised at the expense of increased holding time on the bus for any one signal, and by the inclusion of senders and receivers in each bus to amplify the signals which also contribute to an increased holding time for each signal.

The AC bus consists of a bundle of twisted pairs, one pair for each bit transmitted. There are 16 pairs to transmit, address and control information from the CPU to peripheral equipment, three to transmit control information from the peripheral equipment, and 32 to convey data in each direction under the control of the processor.

Signalling on AC Bus

Pulses on the pairs of the bus system experience propagation delays which are a function of the characteristics of the pair itself, and the associated senders and receivers included in the bus.

To overcome this differential propagation time, a pulse is transmitted on one of the control pairs after the signals have been sent on the data pairs. This pulse opens an electronic gate to the register in the peripheral equipment and allows the input to the register to be read simultaneously, and at a time which takes full account of the delays and distortion introduced by the bus.

Signal transmissions on the AC bus uses a compelled sequence technique. The signals are applied by the processor which waits for a signal, the condition code, to be returned to indicate that the transmitted signals have been received. Such a technique enables the occupation time of the bus to be limited to the minimum required for transmission of the necessary information. Thus the occupation time needed to signal to the most distant equipment does not necessarily determine the time which must be allowed to signal to equipment close to the CPU.

Thus the CPU on receipt of the condition code signal from the periphery knows whether the data has been received satisfactorily, and if not, it is given an indication by the condition code of the condition in the peripheral unit which affects its operation and the CPU can take appropriate action.

CONCLUSION

The telephone switching hardware of the 10C system, as is common with all processor controlled systems, is relatively simple compared to the electromechanical system. The logic, in the case of the processor controlled systems resides in the program or software and the operation of the exchange requires effective interaction between the software and hardware of the systems. Within limits this program may be readily altered to enable different facilities to be provided from the same configuration of hardware.

As this article is being written, the operational programs are being tested in a model of the Pitt exchange which has been built at BTM factory in Antwerp. This operational program has already been tested by a simulation process in which a processor which is programmed to resemble an exchange is connected to the bus system of normal exchange processors, to ensure as far as possible that all necessary logical operations can be performed.

The test performed on the model, known as system test, will test the interaction between hardware and software as far as is possible in a model. Both of these test procedures are being undertaken to ensure that, under traffic conditions at commissioning, the exchange will function with a minimum of interruption.

Supplementary Bibliography for Paper 18

10C TOLL

10C SEMI-ELECTRONIC TOLL AND TRANSIT SWITCHING SYSTEM
ADELAAR HH + BEIERLE JD + VANGOCTHEM J
IEE CONF SWITCHING TECHNIQUES FOR TELECOMMUN NETWORKS
APR 1969 CONF PUB NO. 52 P88-91

SWITCHING NETWORKS FOR 10C TOLL AND TRANSIT EXCHANGES
ADELAAR HH
P35-39 - 35-46 OF IEEE-ICC 1970 CONF REC VOL 2 70-CP-369
COM-IEEE TRANS COMMUN TECHNOL 19: 2-8 (FEB 1971)

10C TOLL TELEPHONE SWITCHING SYSTEM
ADELAAR HH + BEIERLE JD
ELEC COMMUN 44 (2): 92-5 (1969)

10C TOLL TELEPHONE SWITCHING SYSTEM CENTRAL PROCESSOR
BEIERLE JD
P27-19 - 27-23 OF IEEE-ICC, 1970 CONF RCD VOL 2 70-CP-323 COM

SPECIAL FACILITIES IN METACONTA 10C LARGE TOLL APPLICATION
BEIERLE JD
P121-128 OF INT SW SYMP MIT 1972 (E173-1597)

METACONTA 10C TOLL EXCHANGES GENERAL DESCRIPTION AND SOFTWARE
DESIGN
JANSSENS J
ELEC COMMUN 48 (3): 239-47 (1973)

TRANSIT TELEPHONE EXCHANGE METACONTA 10C
UNK M
ELEKTROTEH VESN 41 (3-4): 117-21 (MAR/APR 1974) (IN SLOVENE)

   SYSTEM CONSOLE IN TOLL EXCHANGE METACONTA 10C FROM THE VIEW
OF TEST EQUIPMENT
PISKAR R
ELEKTROTEH VESTN 41 (3-4): 126-9 (MAR/APR 1974) (IN SOLVENE)

PERIPHERAL CIRCUITS FOR METACONTA 10C TRANSIT EXCHANGE
MOHAR T
ELEKTROTEH VESTN 41 (3-4): 121-5 (MAR/APR 1974) (IN SLOVENE)

THE 10C STORED PROGRAM TRUNK EXCHANGE
HOLT RJ + PAGE-HANIFY G + DEDRICK H
TELECOMMUN J AUSTRALIA 25 (1): 4-12 (1975)

Paper 19

Local Latching Metaconta (L) System (10R, 11A)

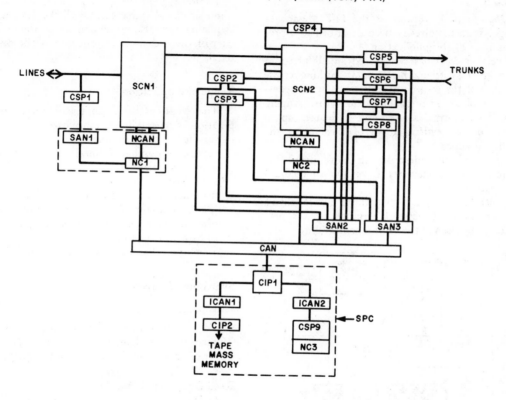

```
CAN   = PERIPHERAL BUS          ICAN1 = INPUT OUTPUT CHANNEL
CIP1  = CENTRAL PROCESSOR UNIT  ICAN2 = MEMORY UNIT CONTROL
CIP2  = DEVICE CONTROLLER       NC1   = LINE MARKER
CSP1  = LINE CIRCUIT            NC2   = GROUP MARKER
CSP2  = SENDER                  NC3   = NETWORK MAP
CSP3  = RECEIVER                SAN1  = LINE SCANNER
CSP4  = TAX SENDING DEVICE              (COMBINED WITH NC1)
CSP5  = OUTGOING JUNCTOR        SAN2  = SLOW DRIVER
CSP6  = INCOMING JUNCTOR        SAN3  = FAST DRIVER SCANNER
CSP7  = LOCAL FEED JUNCTOR      SPC   = CENTRAL CONTROL UNIT
CSP8  = DIAL PULSE AND PUSH
          BUTTON RECEIVERS
CSP9  = MEMORY BLOCK
```

Metaconta L Medium Size Local Exchanges

The METACONTA* family of exchanges is an established ITT switching system that has proved to be an important development in stored program control exchanges. The Metaconta L version is part of that family and is now applied for the first time to medium size local exchanges. It uses the ITT 1600 processor for control of reed relay or Miniswitch crosspoints and offers a large number of new features to both the subscriber and Administration.

J. P. DARTOIS
Compagnie Générale Constructions Téléphoniques, Paris

Introduction

The Metaconta L version of the ITT Metaconta switching system has already been described in a preceding number of this publication [1].

This version combines centralized stored program control with a switching network of latching crosspoints either of the reed or Miniswitch types. It comprises a complete series of exchange types, ranging from small concentrators and slave exchanges up to large local or toll exchanges, all of them using the same technical approach.

The present article describes in more detail the application of the Metaconta L version to medium size local exchanges.

The general Metaconta L diagram (Figure 1) shows the switching network, network terminal circuits, network access devices, and the central control unit.

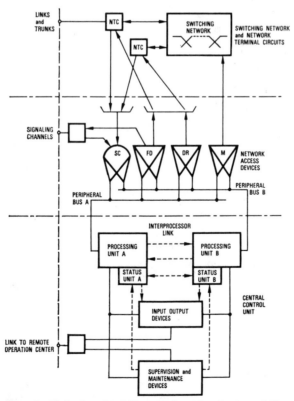

Figure 1 - Block schematic of Metaconta L version showing switching network and network terminal circuits, network access devices, and the central control unit.

SC	- scanner	M - marker
FD	- fast driver	NTC - network terminal circuit.
DR	- slow driver	

Figure 2 gives the corresponding diagram for medium size local exchanges. Of all the devices, only the switching network, which constitutes the most specific part of the exchanges considered, will be described in detail.

Range of Application

The overall exchange limit is obtained from a combination of partial limits, as follows:
— for the switching network
maximum number of lines: 32 000
maximum total traffic: 3 200 erlangs
— for the control
maximum number of busy hour call attempts
(BHCA): about 60 000, depending on the facilities offered, the type and number of signaling systems to be handled, et cetera.
Some typical exchange sizes are given in Table 1.

Switching Network

Crosspoints

To comply with specific customer preferences, two Metaconta L exchange options are offered which differ basically only in the type of crosspoint used.

Reed Option (10 R Version)

In the reed option, the switching network is built up with magnetic latching reed matrices, composed of reed crosspoints (Figure 3). This crosspoint and its operating characteristics have been the subject of two publications [2, 3].

Various types of plug-in unit are used:
— At the subscriber switching stage, the plug-in units consist of 96 two-wire crosspoints grouped into 4 matrices of 4 inlets and (4 + 2) outlets each. The two extra outlets feed the subscriber line circuits in the free or in the lock-out conditions. The unit can accommodate 16 subscribers and includes electronic devices for sensing the subscriber line states. In the case of low traffic per line, a special grading has been designed and appears under the form of a $16 \times (8 + 2)$ switch with availability 4.
— In all other switching stages, the plug-in units consist of 128 two-wire crosspoints, which can be grouped in 3 different ways:
— four 8×4 two-wire crosspoint matrices.

* A trademark of ITT System

Reprinted with permission from *Elec. Commun.*, vol. 48, no. 3, pp. 216–226, 1973.

Table 1 – Typical exchange sizes

Number of lines	Average traffic per line (erlang)	Additional transit traffic (erlangs)	Average call duration (seconds)	Number of BHCA	Subscriber facilities and environment complexity
30 000	0·08	0	150	57 600	Normal
20 000	0·12	100	150	60 000	Low
10 000	0·14	100	100	54 000	Significant

— two 8×8 two-wire crosspoint matrices
— one 16×8 two-wire crosspoint matrix.

Miniswitch Option (11 A Version)

In the Miniswitch option, the speech network is built up with the Miniswitch (Figure 4), composed of mechanical latching crosspoints [4, 5]. The Miniswitch constitutes a plug-in unit by itself.

At the subscriber stage, and depending on the line traffic, the Miniswitch permits:
— one 16 × (8+2) two-wire crosspoint matrix, for a traffic per line lower than 0·16 erlang, or
— two 8 × (8+2) two-wire crosspoint matrices, for higher line traffic.

In all other switching stages, 16 × 16 two-wire crosspoint matrices are used.

Structure

The switching network is a modular multistage link system of the nonfolded type in which calls are established according to an end-to-end conditional selection principle. There is no separate signaling network and 2-wire crosspoints are used for balanced transmission of voice and signals. The speech network is represented by a map in the central control unit memory thus avoiding the use of a third wire for electrical holding of the connections or for testing the states of the switches.

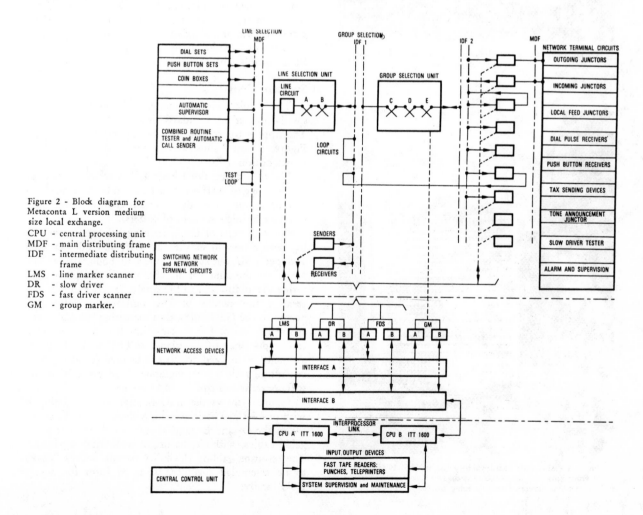

Figure 2 - Block diagram for Metaconta L version medium size local exchange.
CPU - central processing unit
MDF - main distributing frame
IDF - intermediate distributing frame
LMS - line marker scanner
DR - slow driver
FDS - fast driver scanner
GM - group marker.

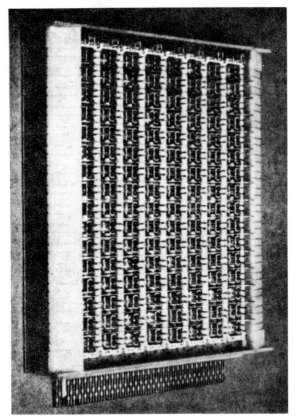

Figure 3 - A 16 × 8 two-wire crosspoint matrix using Herkon reed relays.

Figure 4 - Miniswitch board which consists of 16 × 16 two-wire crosspoints. This board is used in all switching stages of the switching network except the subscriber connection stage.

The units composing the switching network are divided into two types according to their function:
— Line selection units (LSU) which ensure the concentration/expansion of traffic coming from/going towards the subscribers of the exchange. There are two LSU switching stages in the Miniswitch network, and 3 in the reed network.
— Group selection units (GSU) which perform the mixing of the various traffic flows. There are 3 GSU switching stages in the Miniswitch network and 4 in the reed network.

Various terminal circuits are connected to these units, for example, subscriber lines, private branch exchanges (PBX's), coin boxes, incoming and outgoing junctors, senders, receivers, local feed junctors, and miscellaneous junctors.

The switching network itself (not considering any limitations due to the control unit) covers the range from about 200 to 3 200 erlangs. This range is divided into a limited number of basic steps, each step characterizing one standard network configuration, with one given GSU equipment and one given link distribution between LSU's and GSU's. Table 2 illustrates the 8 standard configurations considered for the Miniswitch network.

Figure 5 shows, in both the reed and Miniswitch options, a network diagram for a 10 000-line exchange with a traffic per line of 0·14 erlang and an additional transit traffic of 100 erlangs. Note that any other distribution of local, outgoing, incoming, and transit traffic is possible with the same structure.

Standard Units

The whole switching network is built up from a small number of standard units, LSU's and GSU's. This applies to both the Miniswitch and reed networks. Figures 6 und 7 illustrate the units used in the Miniswitch option.

Figure 6 shows the 4 basic LSU's which permit the whole range of traffic rate per line to be covered. Each LSU is characterized by a certain concentration ratio (number of inlets/number of outlets).

For each type of LSU, the range of traffic per line has been chosen in such a way that the loads per LSU and per LSU outlet are limited to boundary values, which are the same for all LSU's. It is also possible to refine the adaptation to the traffic rate per line by decreasing the number of LSU outlets physically connected to the GSU inlets, thus increasing the LSU concentration ratio. For instance, to handle an average traffic per line of 0·12 erlang, an LSU with 512 inlets and only 96 utilized outlets can be used (resulting concentration ratio = 5·33; maximum load per LSU outlet still constant and equal to 0·64 erlang).

Figure 7 shows the GSU family, which is built up with one 3-stage basic switching block. The linkage between the D- and E-stages is realized by 16-pair pluggable cables, without the use of a distributing frame. The resulting cabling flexibility permits several blocks to be assembled together, so as to form the actual GSU family.

Table 2 – Miniswitch network: standard configurations

Configuration number	Range of application (erlangs)	Corresponding quantity of GSU equipment	Number of lines at	
			0·10 erlang per line	0·16 erlang per line
1	0 — 250	$\frac{1}{4}$	2 000	1 500
2	250 — 450	$\frac{1}{2}$	4 000	2 800
3	450 — 650	$\frac{3}{4}$	6 000	4 000
4	650 — 850	1	8 000	5 300
5	850 — 1 200	$1\frac{1}{2}$	12 000	7 500
6	1 200 — 1 600	2	16 000	10 000
7	1 600 — 2 400	3	24 000	15 000
8	2 400 — 3 200	4	32 000	20 000

(a)

(b)

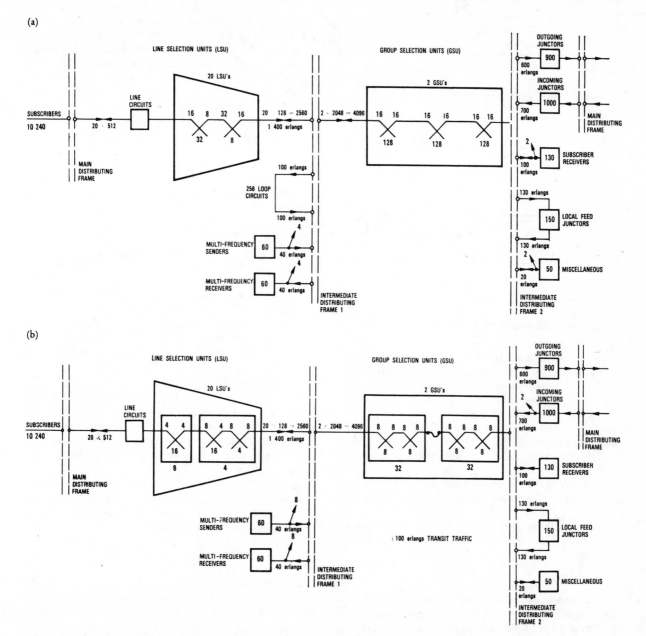

Figure 5 - Network diagram for medium size local exchange with 10 000 lines at 0·14 erlang per line and an additional transit traffic of 100 erlangs.
a) Miniswitch option   b) reed option.

LINE SELECTION UNIT GEOMETRY (SYMBOLIC REPRESENTATION)	MAXIMUM TRAFFIC PER LINE (erlang)	CONCENTRATION RATIO
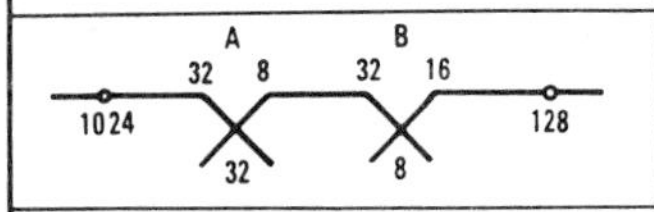 A: 1024 — 32/8, B: 32/16 — 128, 32/8	≤ 0.08	8
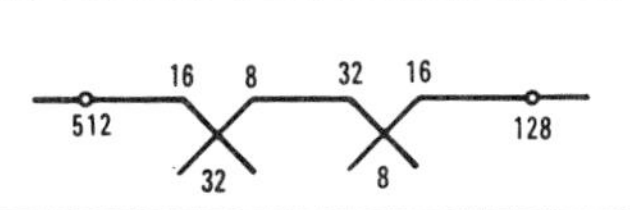 512 — 16/8, 32/16 — 128, 32/8	≤ 0.16	4
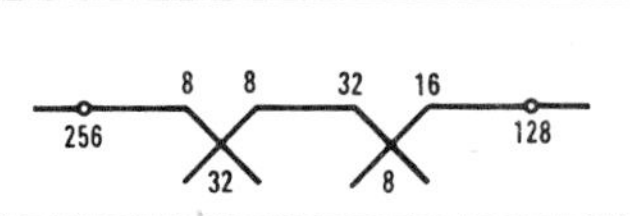 256 — 8/8, 32/16 — 128, 32/8	≤ 0.32	2
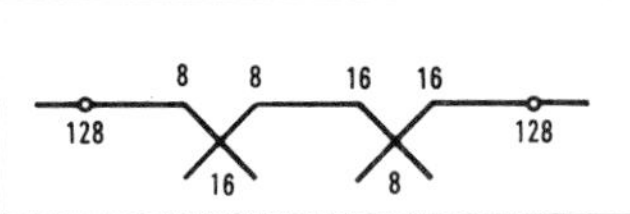 128 — 8/8, 16/16 — 128, 16/8	≤ 0.64	1

Figure 6 - Standard line selection units (Miniswitch option).

(a) GROUP SELECTION UNIT BASIC SWITCHING BLOCK

(b) GROUP SELECTION UNIT FAMILY

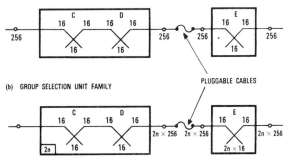

PLUGGABLE CABLES

Figure 7 - Standard group selection units (Miniswitch option).

Interconnection and Related Features

The most important aspect to consider in the switching network design is the definition of adequate interconnection rules, either inside the standard units (LSU's and GSU's), or between these units (at the level of the intermediate distributing frame IDF1 — see Figure 5), or for the connection of the network terminal circuits (at the level of IDF1 and IDF2). This definition has a direct impact on:

— IDF structure and the possibility of carrying out extensions easily
— network traffic handling properties
— efficiency of network control by the central control unit.

Solutions have been found [6, 7] which have greatly helped in achieving the features and properties described later.

IDF Structure

As already indicated, each standard network configuration is characterized by a single interconnection pattern between LSU's and GSU's. The corresponding link distribution is performed via the IDF in two separate steps:

— Macro-distribution, realized at the level of the cables connecting the units to the IDF. The use of standard plug-in cables permits, by cable re-allocation, simple changing from one connection pattern to another, thus considerably simplifying exchange extensions.
— Micro-distribution, realized by jumpers inside the IDF. This distribution is fixed and modular, that is, there is only one module type which is used for both IDF1 and IDF2, and which covers all exchange applications. The modules are wired in the factory and installed once and for all on-site.

This particular IDF structure makes it possible to implement exchange extensions by possible cable re-allocations only. In fact, many extensions can be performed without any modification to the existing cabling, merely by progressively installing and connecting new LSU's and new junctors according to requirements. For the extensions which necessitate changing from one standard configuration to another during the exchange lifetime, the corresponding cable re-allocation is reduced to a minimum, because:

— one family of cables only is concerned (those connecting the GSU inlets/outlets to the IDF's)
— inside this family, there is always a minimum percentage of cables that do not have to be moved.

Extensions are consequently performed with a minimum disturbance in traffic handling and service quality.

Grade of Service

All types of connection inside the network are established with full access to all groups of junctors and negligible internal blocking (less than 0·5 percent for a point-to-point connection and less than 0·1 percent for a point-to-two-points connection).

Moreover, the switching network offers an excellent resistance to traffic overloads. In the case of a 20-percent overload, the above mentioned internal blocking values are less than 1 percent and less than 0·2 percent, respectively.

Control

With respect to processing and supervision of the network by the central control unit, several elements contribute to give a greater simplicity, among which are:

— Use of switching matrices having a number of inlets and outlets in powers of 2, and grouping of these matrices also in powers of 2 into the switching stages.
— Simplicity and regularity of the various link distributions which permit very simple and fast path search in memory.
— Homogeneity in the processing of the various traffic flows. The network is such that each of its crosspoints can be used for carrying several types of communications (local, incoming, outgoing, et cetera). In addition, the signaling network is not different from the speech network and consequently

no special processing is necessary for establishing the signaling connections within the switching network.

Network Terminal Circuits

The NTC's can be divided into two categories:
— Circuits interfacing the switching network inlets/outlets with the external network of cables connecting the exchange to the subscriber sets and to other exchanges. In this category are the subscriber line circuits, and the incoming, outgoing, and both-way trunk circuits.
— Auxiliary or service circuits that are connected to the switching network only. There is a wide variety of such circuits, among which are the senders, receivers, tone junctors, speaking machine circuits, operator circuits, loop circuits, and local feed junctors.

NTC's have been simplified as far as possible by vesting all the complex logic and control functions in the central control unit. The circuits have been specialized; that is, the various functions required in a call are performed by several circuits acting in turn during the setting-up of the call. These two options were retained to minimize hardware and consequently to increase reliability and decrease power consumption.

Here again, standardization has received considerable attention, particularly in the following two areas:
— Standard manufacturing of the printed boards, combined with a standard wiring of the subrack back panels. This permits, in most of the cases, the change from one type of NTC to another simply by interchanging the corresponding plug-in units and by up-dating the central control unit memory.
— Straightforward procedures for grouping the NTC's inside the NTC racks, and addressing and connecting them to the speech network. These procedures,

while providing good flexibility, allow reductions in memory requirements, job engineering, and installation effort.

Network Access Devices

In medium size local exchanges, the network access devices (NAD's) are as follows (Figure 2):
— Line marker scanner (LMS), controlling up to 8 LSU's of the type shown in Figure 5, including the line circuits. A detailed description of this device has already been given [8].
— Group unit marker (GUM), controlling one complete GSU (2 048 inlets and 2 048 outlets).
— Slow driver (DR) controlling a maximum of 512 NTC's other than line circuits.
— Fast driver scanner (FDS) for the exchange NTC's (except line circuits). A detailed description of this device has already been given [9].

A high degree of security has been achieved, both in reliability and traffic handling aspects, by making use of active duplication and modularization principles.

All NAD's are fully duplicated, thus ensuring that single failures have no effect on traffic handling. To minimize the effects of possible simultaneous failures in each part of a duplicated NAD, a hierarchical organization has been introduced where needed. As an example, the FDS is organized as follows:
— one reduced centralized part directly controls up to 16 modular parts
— each modular part controls a maximum of 512 NTC's via up to 6 terminal parts
— each terminal part directly controls a maximum of 10 groups of 16 NTC's.

Consequently, two simultaneous failures in the same FDS part is an event of very low probability which, in most cases, disturbs only a limited number of junctors.

Central Control Unit

The central control unit (CCU) (Figure 8) organization and operation principles are the same for all Metaconta L exchanges and have already been described [1, 10]. For a medium size local exchange the main variation consists in the choice of the different modules. This choice has been made with a view to covering the desired range of application with maximum efficiency and an optimized cost; it mainly concerns the processors, memories, and input/output equipments.

Processor Modules
ITT 1600 Processor

The ITT 1600 processor is a third generation high speed digital processor, built up with integrated circuits and intended for centrally controlled telephone exchanges. In addition to a complete set of general purpose instructions to handle immediate logical and arithmetic problems, special instructions have been introduced to increase the power for telephone functions.

Figure 8 - Central control unit showing, from left to right, the duplicated processor peripheral devices, ITT 1600 processor main frames and memory blocks, and the maintenance and supervision devices.

These special instructions facilitate bit and slice manipulations of data.

The ITT 1600 processor is a 16-bit binary parallel type of machine. It has a modular structure and the modules can be interconnected in different numbers and ways, depending on the application, traffic range, reliability requirements, and peripheral equipments connected.

Memory Modules

The memory is of a random access type with a word length of 17 bits (16 bits + 1 parity bit) and a maximum capacity of $2^{16} = 65\,536$ words consisting of 8 blocks of 8 192 words. The machine can also accommodate blocks of 16 384 or 32 768 words. Beyond 65 536 words, an optional bank switch allows expansion up to 131 072 words.

The memory is a ferrite core type, with an access time of 0·35 microsecond and a cycle time of 0·85 microsecond.

Input/Output Devices and Interfaces

A standard set of input/output devices is available, from which devices may be provided according to each specific application. They are:
— teleprinter: keyboard, paper tape reader, and paper tape punch (all at 10 characters per second)
— bidirectional paper tape reader (1 000 characters per second) and spooler
— paper tape punch (110 characters per second)
— line printer (400 lines per minute)
— magnetic tape unit (9 tracks, 800 characters per inch, 75 or 112 inches per second)
— magnetic drum, disks, et cetera.

In addition to this, the ITT 1600 processor is provided with special facilities such as:
— interprocessor communication link, enabling two processor main frames to interwork
— automatic program reload circuits, used for automatic recovery procedures
— real-time clock, status unit, et cetera.

Principle of Operation

Full active duplication is applied to the central control unit according to the load sharing principle, a basic feature of the Metaconta system [1, 10, 11]. This principle includes two units that treat telephone traffic simultaneously and share the traffic load. The most important advantages resulting from this technique can be summarized as follows:
— Excellent overload capacity. Bursts of traffic up to 60 percent higher than the nominal value are processed without significant penalty in setting-up time.
— Reliability. Unavoidable software errors could theoretically cause the two units to fail simultaneously. With the use of the call load sharing principle (in which the two machines treat different calls), the probability of such an event is reduced.
— Ability to grow and change. The possibility of distributing traffic unevenly over the two processing

Table 3 – Main dimensional standards for two types of rack

Dimension	Low racks (7 subracks)	High racks (11 subracks)
Height	1 975 millimeters	2 950 millimeters
Pitch	970 millimeters	970 millimeters
Depth	400 millimeters	400 millimeters
Weight (average)	330 kilograms force	530 kilograms force
Floor load (average)	300 kilograms force per square meter	490 kilograms force per square meter

units in any desired proportion permits simple testing of program modifications and/or additions under reduced load in one processing unit, thus not endangering the total traffic. This is also true when making extensions.

Software

The software package is the nucleus of the system. It includes two main types of programs:
— Operational programs which are the programs controlling the real-time system operation.
— Test and maintenance programs used either as maintenance aids to localize hardware failures or to test new or modified equipments (installations, extensions).

Operational Programs

Resident Package

All these programs permanently reside in memory. They may be divided into:

Figure 9 - General view of the UNISWEP racks housing the equipment.

— Call processing programs that control all the call treatment, including charging, statistics recording, and so on.

— Man/machine communication programs, the purpose of which is to handle communications between the system and the operating personnel and also to permit the loading of on-demand programs.

— On-line test and defensive programs that observe abnormal behavior of the system and either restore normal conditions or make appropriate decisions to disconnect faulty devices.

— Start-up and recovery programs that handle the system status evolution. In this group are included programs taking over the calls when one machine fails.

On-Demand Package

These programs have to be called for by the operating personnel through a teleprinter message. The requested program is automatically loaded in a common memory area and initiated by the monitor as a normal resident program. The on-demand programs carry out such functions as:

— traffic observation
— charging information dump
— call tracing
— routine tests.

Start-Up Programs

These programs are used for automatic start or restart of the system. They do not require to be permanently resident in memory but are automatically loaded and initiated. An important category consists of the automatic test programs which are used to check the equipment before an automatic start or restart is decided.

Test and Maintenance Programs
On-Demand Programs

Here use is similar to the on-demand programs of the operational package. These programs are intended for the maintenance of the telephone periphery. They are also appropriate for installation and extension tests of the same equipments.

Off-Line Programs

These programs are loaded and executed in a processing unit which is in maintenance mode. They provide for fault location within the processor, memories, and input/output devices. They are also used for extension of a processor and wherever the on-demand maintenance programs are not sufficient.

Equipment Practice
UNISWEP* Technique

The Metaconta L version of the Metaconta system uses the new UNISWEP switching equipment practice [12].

---

* A trademark of ITT System

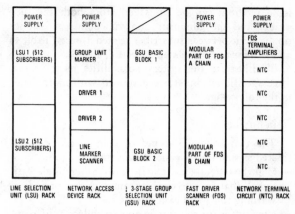

Figure 10 - Typical terminal exchange rack equipments (7 shelves per rack). Each rack is 1 975 millimeters high.

Two standard rack heights have been selected, one housing 7 subracks, the other 11 subracks. Table 3 summarizes the main dimensional standards for these two types of rack and the corresponding weights and floor loads (average fully equipped racks).

Distributing Frames

Medium size local exchanges are generally equipped with the ITT miniaturized main distributing frame (MDF), especially adapted for economy in floor space and ease of maintenance. The floor space required for this MDF is only one third of that for a conventional MDF, and jumpers can be run single handed by a man standing at floor level. These MDF's can be supplied with protection or with fuses and/or lightning protectors. However, an MDF with any type of protection can be supplied as required by the administration.

As already indicated, intermediate distributing frames (IDF's) have a particular structure using prewired modules. As a consequence, IDF's are very concentrated; one standard rack provides the interconnections between two families of 6 000 two-wire crosspoints (typically corresponding to a 15 000 line exchange at 0·16 erlang per line).

Equipment Layout

The mounting of all apparatus on standard plug-in units enables equipment layouts to be standardized, so that rack equipments are very similar over a wide range of exchange sizes (Figure 9).

Examples of standard rack layouts are shown in Figure 10. A typical floor plan for a 10 000 line exchange at 0·14 erlang per line is given in Figure 11. Due to miniaturization of the apparatus, the design of the system, and the special features of the UNISWEP equipment practice, floor space required is only about 100 subscriber lines per square meter.

Service Features and Facilities

Tables 4 and 5 list the main standard features and facilities provided in Metaconta L exchanges. Although some facilities can be envisaged from both the subscriber and the administration viewpoints, a distinction is made between subscriber related aspects (Table 4) and administration related aspects (Table 5).

To illustrate the system possibilities in this area, some specific examples are described with more detail in the following.

Coin Box Lines

The two following types of coin boxes are considered as standard for the Metaconta L version:
— Coin boxes for local traffic with either single cash signal (battery reversal at answer), or periodical warning tones and cash signals.
— Coin boxes for toll traffic able to collect 3 different kinds of coin.
Different methods of handling coin boxes can be provided as an option.

The following facilities may also be implemented for coin boxes:
— Prepay or semi-post pay as specified.
— Calls to specified destinations, obtainable without initial coin deposit (emergency, operator, et cetera).

PABX's

Facilities or options offered for private automatic branch exchanges (PABX's) are as follows:
— unlimited number of trunks per PABX
— sequential trunk scanning from a random starting point

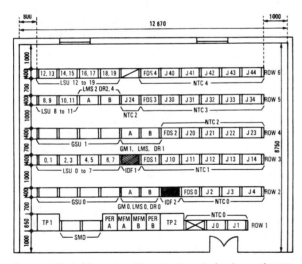

Figure 11 - Typical layout in a Metaconta L terminal exchange of 10 000 lines housed in UNISWEP equipment practice (7 subracks high).

LSU - line selection unit
GSU - group selection unit
DR - slow driver
FDS - fast driver scanner
GM - group marker
NTC - network terminal circuit
LMS - line marker scanner
PER - peripheral or input/output devices

SMD - supervision/maintenance devices
MFM - ITT 1600 processor main frame and memories
IDF - intermediate distributing frame
TP - teleprinter
J - junctor.

Dimensions shown are in millimeters. Other dimensions are:
Rack height 1 975 millimeters
Ceiling height 2 750 millimeters
Floor area 105 square meters
Floor load 300 kilograms force per square meter.

Table 4 – Service features and facilities — Subscriber related

Line classes	Subscriber facilities
One-party lines — with dial or push button type subscriber sets — with or without special charging categories	Abbreviated numbering — 1 or 2 digits — for individual lines, or groups of lines, or for all lines
Two-party lines — with or without secrecy, separate ringing, separate charging, revertive call facility	Transfer of terminating calls
	Conversation hold and transfer
	Calling party's ring back
Multi-party lines (up to 10 main stations) — without secrecy — with selective or semi-selective ringing	Toll call offering
	Hot line Automatic wake-up
PABX's — unlimited number of trunks — uni- or bidirectional trunks — with or without in-dialing	Doctor on duty service
	Do not disturb service
	Absentee service
	Immediate time and charge information
Coin box lines — local traffic — toll traffic — special applications	Conference calls
	Centrex facilities (optional)
Restricted lines — to own exchange — to urban, regional, national, or toll areas — to some specified routes	
Priority lines — toll essential — essential — priority during emergency, overload situations, et cetera	

— lines unidirectional or bidirectional
— night service; connection to a pre-assigned line of the PABX group
— calling line identification; a PABX line can be identified under the directory number of the group
— choice of PABX extension number post dialing (in-dialing)
— any line of a PABX group individually accessible for service or maintenance.

Transfer

This is a facility whereby the calls to a first subscriber line, the transferred party, are re-routed to another line, the receiving party. Transfer is always possible when both transferred and receiving parties are connected to the same exchange. When the receiving and/or the originating parties belong to exchanges different from the Metaconta L exchange of

Table 5 — Service features and facilities — Administration related

Administration facilities
Inter-office signaling — DC signaling codes (step by step, Rotary 7A and 7D, R6 with register or direct control, North America DC codes) — AC pulse signaling codes — MF signaling codes for register controlled exchanges (MFCR 2 code, MF Socotel, North America MF codes) — direct data transmission over common signaling link between processor controlled exchanges of the time or space division types.
Charging — control of charge indicators at subscriber premises — metering on a single fee or a multi-fee basis — free number service.
Numbering — full flexibility for equipment number — directory number translation — for local calls, national toll calls, international toll calls — PABX's with direct inward dialing.
Routing — prefix translation for outgoing or transit calls — alternate or overflow routing on route busy or congestion condition — re-signaling on route busy or congestion condition — called side release control.
Maintenance — plug-in boards — automatic fault detection and identification means by diagnostic programs.
Operation — generalized use of teleprinters — possibility of a remote centralized maintenance and operation center.

the transferred party, calls may also be transferred if metering or transmission considerations do not prevent the setting up of such a transit connection.

Predetermined Transfers

The terminating calls may be re-routed to one out of 3 receiving stations. The subscriber dials from his station a prefix XY 8 followed by a digit identifying the receiving station to which he wants the calls to be transferred.

By dialing the unlatch code XY 1 from his station, he can restore the normal condition, that is, receive terminating calls again.

Variable Transfer

A subscriber with this facility can request that his terminating calls be re-routed to any other directory number. He then dials XY 9 followed by the number to which he wishes to address his incoming calls. The unlatch code is the same as for the predetermined transfer.

On-Demand Transfer

This facility is open to any line. The subscriber calls an information operator and requests that his terminating calls be provisionally re-routed to a given directory number or to an absentee operator. After checking the agreement of the wouldbe receiving party, the

operator asks the exchange to carry out the transfer. The transferred subscriber may still originate calls but he will be reminded of his condition by the special dial tone received. He must apply to the information operator to recover normal conditions. This on-demand facility is charged according to the administration's specifications.

Does Not Answer and Busy Line Transfer

A call to a subscriber with this facility is automatically re-routed if the subscriber called is busy or does not answer within a given time limit.

Calling Party's Ring Back

On receiving the busy tone the calling party flashes his switch hook or dials the appropriate suffix. He is informed by a special receiving tone that his call is registered and he may hang up. He can be rung back when the called party becomes free (this is possible if the called party belongs to the same exchange or another processor controlled exchange) or when a trunk of the wanted direction becomes free. This facility may be cancelled when the calling party off-hooks for a new call (originating or terminating) or after a predetermined time limit.

Maintenance

The central control unit and the vital parts of the

network access devices are permanently checked by the system hardware and are automatically isolated in the case of a fault. The maintenance personnel are immediately informed of this event by an alarm and a teleprinter message. The use of the plug-in technique and of appropriate diagnostic and test programs easily permits personnel to identify and locate the faulty board, replace it, and test the circuit concerned before it is put back into service. Faulty boards are normally sent to a maintenance center for repair.

Operation

Exchange operation is facilitated by convenient man/machine communication means. Most of the activities involved, such as re-routing and/or re-allocation of trunks, traffic statistics, gathering of charging records, changes in subscriber classes and/or facilities, and so on, are performed by teleprinter messages using the man/machine equipment. This current exchange operation can be carried out from a distant operations center, common to several exchanges.

References

[1] S. Kobus, J. A. de Miguel, and A. Régnier: Metaconta L: Stored Program Control of Latching Crosspoint Matrices: *Electrical Communication*, 1971, volume 46, no 4, pp 235—245.

[2] A. Régnier: Point de Croisement à Contacts Scellés et à Maintien Magnétique: *Commutation & Electronique*, October 1965, no 10.

[3] A. Régnier and J. Payer: Matrices de Points de Croisement à Contacts Scellés et à Maintien Magnétique: *Commutation & Electronique*, January 1972, no 36.

[4] C. Vazquez and G. Dufresnoy: Miniswitch: A Miniature Crosspoint Switch: *Electrical Communication*, 1969, volume 44, no 4, pp 288—292.

[5] C. Chiroux: Testing the Miniswitch: *Electrical Communication*, 1969, volume 44, no 4, pp 293—298.

[6] J. P. Dartois: Improvements to Switching Networks: *French Patent* registered no 70 11616, 1 April 1970, publication no 2 086 535.

[7] J. J. Perrot: Considérations Théoriques sur les Règles Pratiques de Distribution dans un Système Maillé: *Commutation & Electronique*, July 1972, no 38, pp 42—50.

[8] C. Bouchet: Conception d'un Explorateur-Marqueur de Lignes Pour Centraux Semi-Electroniques: *Commutation & Electronique*, July 1971, no 34.

[9] C. Bouchet: Conception d'un Explorateur-Distributeur Rapide Pour Centraux Semi-Electroniques du Type Spatial: *Commutation & Electronique*, October 1972, no 39.

[10] H. H. Adelaar: The 10-C System, a Stored-Program Controlled Reed Switching System: *Proceedings of the Institute of Electrical and Electronics Engineers International Conference on Communications*, Philadelphia, 14 June 1968, New York, Lewis Winner, IEEE Cat. no 68 C 20-COM, pp 38—45.

[11] S. Kobus, A. Kruithof, and L. Viellevoye: Central Control Philosophy for the Metaconta L Switching System: *Electrical Communication*, 1972, volume 47, no 3, pp 159—163.

[12] S. W. Evans, V. R. Henson, and P. J. Risley: UNISWEP: a New Equipment Practice for Switching Systems: *Electrical Communication*, 1972, volume 47, no 3, pp 140—150.

Supplementary Bibliography for Paper 19

METACONTA L

SECURITY AND RELIABIITY ASPECTS IN METACONTA L
DARTOIS JP + GOUARS BE + VIELLEVOYE L
ELEC. COMMUN 50 NO. 3: 197-185, 1975

ELECTRICAL DESIGN OF METACONTA L EXCHANGES
TYSZKA JM
ELEC. COMMUN 49(4): 392-9 (1974)

METACONTA-L TERMINAL EXCHANGES: CALL PROCESSING
SOFTWARE STRUCTURE
KRUITHOF A + VERHEYDEN JP
ELEC COMMUN 50 (2): 113-22 (1975)

METACONTA SWITCHING SYSTEM
NORDSIECK H
ELECT COMMUN 46(3): 233-4

THE METACONTA L ELECTRONIC SWITCHING SYSTEM-SYSTEM
STRUCTURE AND CALL PROCESSING DESCRIPTION
NEVERGOLD RU + THOMPSON AW
P39-28T039-33 OF INT CONF COMMUN 1973, V2 (T/I11C)
100761

APPLICATION OF THE METACONTA* (10R) SYSTEM IN
ROISSY AIRPORT (FRANCE)
TRELUT J
P 585-591 OF INT SWITCHING SYMP, MIT, 1972 (E173 I597)

FIELD EXPERIENCE WITH FIRST METACONTA L (11A) MEDIUM
SIZE LOCAL EXCHANGE AT RABAT
DANIS R + DARTOIS JP
ELEC COMMUN 48(4): 329-43 (1973)

METACONTA L. 10-R EXCHANGE SWITCHING NETWORK
PERROT JJ + REGNIER A
ELEC COMMUN 48(3): 227-38 (1973)

LAS VEGAS ELECTRONIC TELEPHONE EXCHANGE. ORGANIZATION
OF THE PROGRAMS (10R, METACONTA-L)
NEVERGOLD RU + THOMPSON AW
COMMUT ELECTRON NO 42:65-81 (JUL 1973) (IN FRENCH)

CENTRAL CONTROL PHILOSOPHY FOR THE METACONTA* TELEPHONE
SWITCHING SYSTEM
KOBUS S + KRUTHOF A + VIELLEVOYE L
P509-513 OF INT SWITCHING SYMP, MIT, 1972 (E173 I597):
ELEC COMMUN 47(3): 159-63 (1972)

EXPERIENCE WITH METACONTA SOFTWARE
KOBUS S + KRUITHOF A + DE BRUYNE G + JANSSENS J
P514 OF INT SWITCHING SYMP RECORD, MUNICH, 1974
(621.381537/I59)

Paper 20

Electronic System No. 10 (E10)

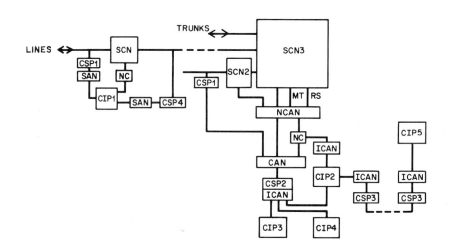

SCN1 = CONCENTRATION NETWORK
SCN2 = SPACE CONCENTRATOR
SCN3 = SWITCHING GROUPS (MT=BUFFER MEMORY: RS=OUTPUT REGISTER STAGES)
CIP1 = CENTRAL CONTROL LOGIC
CIP2 = CONTROL UNIT (OC)
CIP3 = TRANSLATOR
CIP4 = CHARGING UNIT (CU)
CIP5 = CENTRAL UNITS
CSP1 = LINE CIRCUIT
CSP2 = MULTIREGISTER.(MR)
CSP3 = STANDARD INTERPOSES
CSP4 = SIGNALING UNIT
NC = MARKER (MQ)
NCAC = ACCESS LOGIC (MC)

CITEDIS Production PCM Public Telephone Switching System

PIERRE FRITZ

Abstract—After a short review of the interest in digital switching and network integration, a description of the CITEDIS system organization is given (CITEDIS is a digital exchange now in production), outlining its specific features and possibilities. The industrial aspect of CITEDIS manufacturing and the present manufacturing rate are then given.

INTRODUCTION

MOST MAJOR telephone administrations or companies think of their future networks as integrated networks. However, there are divergences as to when this integration will be started or achieved, or as to the best way to start integration of an existing network. Nonetheless, integration is widely considered as the desirable trend for telecommunication networks.

Two important developments are included in the "integration" concept. The first is the merging of previously independent telephone transmission and switching systems into one digital network; this means that switching machines will directly interface with transmission systems at the primary multiplex level (1.544 Mbit/s or 2.048 Mbit/s, since these two types of primary multiplexes are recommended by CCITT). The second development is the use of the digital network, not only for telephone, but also for transmission or switching of other signals (such as data, facsimile, etc.). The digital network handles (transmits and switches) isochronous bit streams at 64 kbit/s (time slots). Various signals can be accomodated by this bit rate. Signals which require a higher bit rate may use a whole number of time slots of primary (or higher) digital multiplexes. Slower signals may be multiplexed together to share a common 64 kbit/s bit stream.

The advantages inherent to an integrated network are well known.[1] One may recall briefly the technical advantages (little transmission impairment (if any) in the network, no attenuation), the operational advantages (flexibility of the network which accepts all types of signals, ease of fault supervision), and economical advantages (no need for primary multiplexers–demultiplexers at the interface with transmission systems, switching network technology).

The outstanding growth of digital transmission at the primary level (1.544 or 2.048 Mbit/s) already provides the basic transmission support for the integration of the network.

We are presently moving toward the industrial emergence of digital switching systems, the second basic element of integrated networks. The CITEDIS system,[2] which is manufactured by *Société Lannionnaise d'Electronique*, Citerel, France, is the first digital switch to have reached the stage of industrial production. This system has been developed under the sponsorship of the Centre National d'Etudes des Telecommunications of the French Post, Telegraph, and Telephone Administration. The following short description of this system outlines its characteristic features and shows its ability to tackle the problems of telephony in the coming decades.

SYSTEM DESCRIPTION

From control point of view, this digital switch is somewhat unconventional, since it has a two-level control system (Fig. 1). The first level of control performs real-time tasks; that is mainly the tasks directly associated with the setting up and releasing of calls. This first-level control is carried out by means of specialized microprogrammed computers (multiregisters), helped by such auxiliary equipment as translators and metering units. The second level performs all tasks with less stringent time requirements, but which require a much higher degree of flexibility and sophistication: the man–machine interface (loading or reloading if translator stores, putting part of the equipment out of operation to perform tests, etc.); supervision (registering fault messages, interpreting and printing them); test of equipment for fault location, etc.

This second-level control (or information processing center (IPC)) system is an universal computer, which is commercially available (e.g., C.I.I. MITRA 15), and may be shared by a number of switches. A data link at 64 kbit/s (one time slot of a primary multiplex) is used between the IPC and each switch. It enables the latter to be remotely controlled from the IPC.

The basic block in the system is the time division digital switching network with its associated first-level control and auxiliary equipment. The basic switching network may connect a maximum of 120 2.048 Mbit/s pulse-code-modulation (PCM) primary inlets, and an equivalent number of outlets, that is 3600 both-way PCM telephone channels. Being a purely time division switching network, hence, nonblocking, it is, therefore, possible to connect up to 1800 calls simultaneously, whichever pair of PCM junctions are connected together. This nonblocking switching system has been achieved while keeping switch-

Manuscript received November 20, 1973.

The author is with the Société Lannionnaise d'Electronique, Citerel, France.

[1] See A. E. Pinet, "Telecommunications integrated network," *IEEE Trans. Commun.* (Concise Papers), vol. COM-21, pp. 916–919, Aug. 1973.

[2] CITEDIS is marketed by CIT-ALCATEL.

Reprinted from *IEEE Trans. Commun.*, vol. COM-22, pp. 1264–1268, Sept. 1974.

163

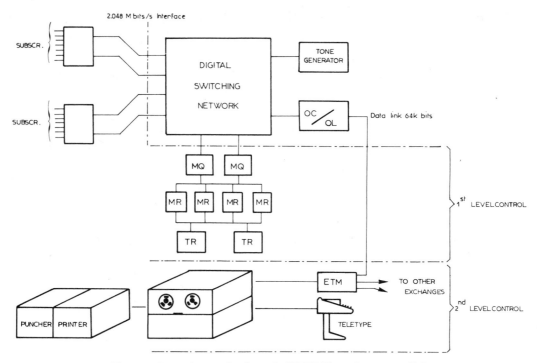

Fig. 1. General organization of CITEDIS exchange, outlining two-level control system.

ing speed at a reasonable level (8 Mbit/s) by the use of parallel highways (8 wires carrying the 8 codes bits), and by the use of up to 4 such parallel highways. Each "super multiplex" carried by a highway is assembled by taking PCM 8-bits samples from a memory which can accommodate one frame for every input PCM primary multiplex, this ensures nonblocking. The total buffer memory capacity in the switching network therefore, amounts to 32 bits per channel. A control memory provides cyclically the addresses of the buffer memories to be read; this control memory is also used as a "map" of the switching network (therefore, no other map is needed in the control system). Safety is achieved by splitting the network into 4 independent units. Each unit, corresponding to one highway, is also divided into two independent parts. Naturally, the switching network can be subequipped to provide economically a smaller number of channels.

The switching network is able to work asynchronously; that is, a "spilling memory" is provided for every PCM system connected, so that the only care to be taken is to make sure that clock accuracies are sufficient to provide a "spilling rate" compatible with speech quality (10^{-6} is considered very satisfactory).

The first level of control is performed, as explained earlier, by specialized computers called "multiregisters." These computers have a very simple structure, reflecting the fact that the operations to be performed, to set up or release a call, are of a simple and repetitive nature. The time sharing of the computing circuits is accomplished in the most straightforward way: the multiregister works cyclically and every call being processed is allocated a fixed fraction of a cycle. With a cycle period of 8 ms and the possibility of having 66 calls processed simultaneously

(corresponding to 66 registers) every call is allocated 120 μs of computing time, repeated every 8 ms.

Sampling of signaling information is performed by the multiregisters themselves. The multiregister sampling period is, therefore, also the signaling information sampling rate. The multiregister is a microprogrammed computer. A set of 63 microinstructions (each 40-bits long), particularly adapted to the problems encountered in telephony, is stored in a READ-ONLY memory. The program itself may contain up to 2000 instructions (also 40 bits long, and also stored in a read-only memory). The work memory (with 320 bits per register), operated in a cyclic mode, is of the looped shift-register type.

The auxiliary equipments incorporate markers (which, in fact, are microcomputers which dispatch information between switching network, multiregisters, and auxiliary equipment), translator (which stores all information concerning subscribers, circuits, and routing), metering units (which computes data necessary for call charging), and tone generators (tones are digitally generated and connected to the subscribers or circuits through the switching network; this applies not only to tones but also to frequencies of MFC codes).

Frequencies received from circuits using MFC codes are analyzed by a set of digital filters. All digital frequency sending and receiving equipment are located in the tone generators which are connected to the switching network by a number of 2.048 Mbit/s bit streams.

Safety is achieved in the first-level control by duplication. Markers and translators are duplicated and translating tables are also stored in the second-level control systems. Multiregisters are at least duplicated, and up to eight multiregisters (working on a load-sharing basis)

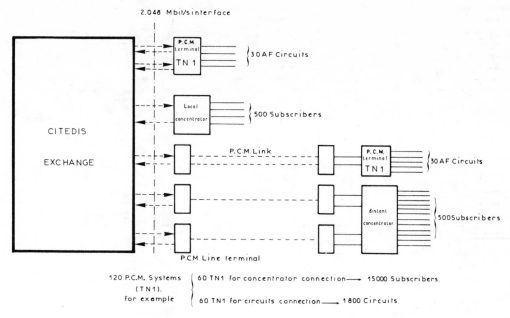

Fig. 2. Subscribers and circuit connection to CITEDIS digital network.

may be provided. Naturally, links carrying information are duplicated, and supervised by an error-detection system, so that a faulty bus is isolated.

The basic block (with individual or shared second-level control) may be used as a small capacity transit exchange (3600 channels). If digital transmission is provided all around, it can directly interface with digital line terminal equipment. If FDM transmission is used, standard PCM transmission terminals are used to provide voice frequency and E and M wire interfacing.

Concentrators may be used to connect subscribers (Fig. 2); a concentrator is connected to the digital switching network by two PCM multiplexes—that is 60 channels. Traffic capacity of concentrators is, therefore, limited to approximately 43 Erlangs (no facility is provided to bypass the capital switching network, for traffic between subscribers is connected to the same concentrator). A concentrator, therefore, incorporates D/A and A/D facilities for 60 channels, subscribers relay sets (power bridge, loop supervision etc.), and a three-stage space division switching network to concentrate 500 subscribers on the 60 junctions. For subscribers with a traffic higher than 0.085 Erlang/line the concentrators may be subequipped in terms of subscribers. A different type of space-division concentrator, the one with a lower concentration ratio has to be used if traffic per subscriber is much higher than 0.15 Erlang/line, or if a mixture of very high traffic and medium traffic subscribers has to be connected.

Since the concentrator is linked to the switch by two PCM systems, concentrators can be cheaply and easily located remotely from the switch; this provides considerable flexibility in the system. Assuming that 60 PCM systems (that is one half of the full capacity of the switch) are used to connect concentrators with 500 subscribers per concentrator, and assuming that the other 60 PCM systems are used to provide circuits, the capacity in terms of subscribers for a basic block is 15 000.

For large transit centers, the capacity of one basic block (3600 circuits) is obviously too small; by coupling several basic blocks in the same way as if they were independent exchanges (i.e., each block having its own first-level control system, the second level being shared by all the basic blocks), one may constitute a much larger exchange (Fig. 3). This approach to the large exchange problem may appear somewhat uneconomical, but when the facts that the first-level control is fairly cheap and that circuits between blocks use a simple separate common channel signaling system are taken into consideration, one may conclude that this approach is perfectly valid.

The blocks may be specialized for ingoing or outgoing circuits, or may not be specialized and accept both type of circuits. In the first case, the number of links to be provided between blocks is smaller than in the second case, since the ingoing blocks need links only to outgoing blocks. This results in a larger number of junctions in each link, and consequently a better efficiency of the whole exchange, but with a slight reduction of flexibility. The maximum size of such multiblock exchanges depends upon the type chosen (with specialized or more specialized blocks), and of overload or traffic unbalance considerations. (The effect of traffic unbalance may be cancelled by scattering circuits of the same origin or destination on several blocks, so that any specific overload will be shared by several links between blocks). A figure of 36 000 circuits (18 000 outgoing + 18 000 ingoing) is a reasonable limit (using 20 specialized blocks, and assuming that for every block half of the circuits are used for interconnection between blocks or, in other words, that 180 junctions are available between any ingoing and any outgoing block).

The CITEDIS system, therefore, is able to handle all

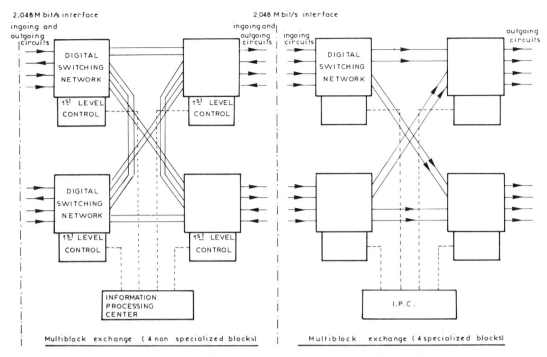

Fig. 3. Two different ways to interconnect CITEDIS basic blocks, in order to implement large capacity transit centers.

telephone problems from the case of medium telephone density zones (where the flexibility inherent to PCM connected concentrators is very efficient), to the case of large transit exchanges (where the use of PCM transmission, at primary or secondary level, is a precious feature of such transit exchanges, especially in large urban areas where VF transmission has been used so intensely that cable ducts are scarce and must be used as efficiently as possible).

The fact that second-level control may be centralized at one location serving an entire multiexchange area, and handling all management and maintenance functions, leads to an immediate and greatly appreciated cost saving, staff levels being considerably reduced.

From the industrial point of view, the CITEDIS system is an electronic system, with very few electromechanical components, since the use of relays is restricted to the concentrators.

The concentrators space division switching network uses 7 to 12 reed relays per subscriber (depending upon the type of concentrators); a little more than 2 relays per subscriber are used for supervision of subscribers' loops. Since the relays play a minor role in the switching system, evolution of technology in this field could be easily accomodated. Apart from these relays, the system employs only logic circuits, mainly standard TTL or MSI IC of widely available types, such as scratch-pad memories (64 or 256 bits per package). In fact, the system was designed with the idea of making the best use of these MSI IC's. Since by the time the project was launched, the dramatic cost reduction of TTL IC's and MSI IC's was by no mean obvious; hence this reduction appeared at the right time to make the system economically competitive, so that industrial production could start.

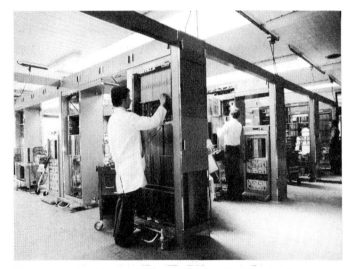

Fig. 4. Testing of exchanges in Lannion Factory. Exchanges are assembled in their operating configuration, and tested before being sent to site.

After the test zone in Brittany, France (15 000 subscribers in the vicinity of Lannion), the transit application is going to be experimented (switching centers of St. Brieuc, in 1974, and Tuileries, Paris, in 1975).

Presently, production has started at a rate of approximately 30 000 lines per year (Fig. 4), and another 15 000 subscriber lines will have been put into service by the end of 1973, in a number of towns. Production rate is going to be increased in the next years to a 100 000 lines per year.

CONCLUSION

As a conclusion, one may consider that the rise of PCM transmission at primary level, and the fall of IC's cost have made time division switching an industrial reality.

This is only a first step towards the integration of the network, and one may expect the next step to be the industrial emergence of medium speed PCM transmission, which is already apparent from the development of both cable and radio-link systems. When these systems appear, time division switching will be mature and widespread enough to allow a bigger and faster step towards integration.

Supplementary Bibliography for Paper 20

E10 AND CITEDIS

SYSTEM GENERAL

THE INTRODUCTION OF ELECTRONIC SWITCHING IN POLAND (E10)
DEGAULLE B + KOLCDZIEJCZAK J + DUVAUA PH
COMMUT ELECTRON NC 50 NO. 50: 25: 38 (JUL 1975)

THE E10 SYSTEM EQUIPPING OF THE AREA OF LEMANS
CABANNE A
ECHO RECH NO. 78: 28-33 (OCT 1974) (IN FRENCH)

SUB SYSTEM

E10 SYSTEM: SYNCHRONIZING GROUP FOR MULTIPLEXED CIRCUITS (GSC)
FEURSTEIN M + MARTIN M
COMMUT ELECTRON NO. 48: 7-19 (JAN 1975)

MULTI-REGISTER IN E10 (CITEDIS) TELEPHONE EXCHANGES
MAYER Z
PREZEGL TELEKOMUN 47 (5): 164-7 (1974) (IN POLISH)

COMMUNICATION BANKS IN TELEPHONE EXCHANGE SYSTEM E10
MAYER Z
PRZEGL TELEKOMUN 47 (2): 75-80 (1974) (IN POLISH)

FIELD EXPERIENCE, MAINTENANCE

E10 SYSTEM: LOAD AND TRAFFIC OBSERVATION
COUDREUSE JP
COMMUT ELECTRON NO. 43: 86-93 (OCT 1973) (IN FRENCH)

E10 SYSTEM THE MAINTENANCE CENTRE AND ITS ENVIRONMENT
PITTE JM + LOGETTE JC
COMMUTAL ELECTRON (45): 28-36 (APR 1974)

MAINTENANCE AND ADMINISTRATIVE FUNCTIONS IN THE E10 SYSTEM
REVEL M + MEREU JN
P442 OF INT SWITCHING SYMP RECORD MUNICH 1974 (621.381537/.59)

TEMPORARY COMMUNICATION SYSTEM E10: RESULTS OF EXPERIMENTS AND DEVELOPMENT
HARDY D
P47-32-47-35 OF IEEE INT CONF COMMUN 1971 CONF REC (TI11C)

E10 SYSTEM FAILURE LOCALIZATION BY THE DATA PROCESSING CENTRE
VAUTRIN G + SIMON Y
COMMUT ELECTRON NO. 50:   19-24 (JUL 1975)

E10 SYSTEM: EQUIPMENTS RELIABILITY
BASSINET J
COMMUT ELECTRON NO. 48:   27-33 (JAN 1975)

E10 TIME DIVISION ELECTRONIC SWITCHING SYSTEM OPERATING
AND MAINTENANCE FUNCTIONS
REVEL M + MEREUR JN
COMMUT ELECTRON NO. 47:   16-25 (OCT 1974) (IN FRENCH)

SERVICE EXPLOITATION CENTRE IN CITEDIS SYSTEM - DESCRIPTION
OF PROGRAM
SMIGAJ B
PREZEGL TELEKOMUN 47 NO. 9:   314-17 (1974) (IN POLISH)

MANAGEMENT CENTER OF THE CITEDIS SYSTEM
BAJURSKI W + BOGOBOWICZ M + HILDEBRANDT A
PREZEGL TELEKOMUN 47 (1):   5-11 (1974) (IN POLISH)

THE E10 SYSTEM.   VERSION B OF THE MPC,
C. VAUTRIN + P. CAIZERGUES
COMMUTATION & ELECTRONIQUE, JANUARY 1976 (PP5-15)   NO. 52

———————————————

Paper 21

Electronic System No. 11 (E11)

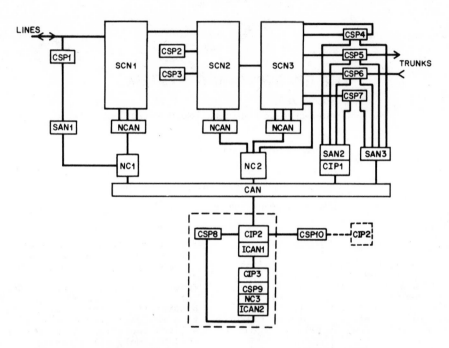

SCN1 = LINE SWITCHING UNIT
SCN2 = INTERMEDIATE SWITCHING UNIT
SCN3 = TRUNK SWITCHING UNIT
CAN   = TRANSMISSION INTERFACE
CIP1 = AUTONOMOUS SCANNER
CIP2 = MAIN FRAME
CIP3 = MEMORY CONTROLLER
CSP1 = LINE CIRCUIT
CSP2 = TRUNK RECEIVER
CSP3 = TRUNK SENDER
CSP4 = LOCAL FEED JUNCTOR
CSP5 = OUTGOING TRUNK CIRCUIT

CSP6 = INCOMING TRUNK CIRCUIT
CSP7 = SUBSCRIBER RECEIVER
CSP8 = DIRECT MEMORY ACCESS
CSP9 = CENTRAL MEMORY
CSP10 = INTPROCESS LINK
NC1   = LINE MARKER
NC2   = GROUP MARKER
NC3   = NETWORK MAP
SAN1 = LINE SCANNER
SAN2 = FAST DRIVER
SAN3 = SLOW DRIVER
SPC   = PROCESSOR

THE E11 SWITCHING SYSTEM

C. Rozmaryn
Centre National d'Etudes des Télécommunications

J. Trelut
Le Matériel Téléphonique

L. Viellevoye
Compagnie Générale de Constructions Téléphoniques

Issy les Moulineaux, France

ABSTRACT

After a description of the general organization of the E11 system, a stored program controlled telephone switching system, this paper puts the emphasis on some specific points : partition of the non-duplicated parts of the equipment into "defense units", software structure and partition, software security, program debugging.

1. INTRODUCTION

The E11 System is a stored program controlled system with space division switching network. It is developped for large local exchanges (up to 64000 lines, 100.000 busy hour calls) and it is based both on specifications set up by the French Administration and on the structures and the principles of the Metaconta L System :

.Control by two LCT 3200 processors working together according to the "call load sharing" mode - [1] [2]

.Two-wire switching network with reed latching crosspoint and Map in memory technique [3]

.Relations of the processors, with the switching network and the junctors, through two separate sets of telephone peripherals, called the "network access devices", each set being devoted to one processor, the number of links between the homologous devices of the two sets being as small as possible.
The main objectives of the French Administration are :

- to define guides in order to obtain a good maintainability of the product.

- to normalize interfaces with the operating personnel (signalling systems, man-machine communications, programming language)

Several E11 offices can be connected to an operation and maintenance center from which it is possible to perform traffic observation, statistics analysis, fault messages analysis etc...
A given operation and maintenance center may control not only E11 offices, but also other E1 type offices. (up to 15 E1 offices or the equivalent of 200.000 lines).

2. GENERAL ORGANIZATION OF THE SYSTEM.

It includes 3 main parts
- the switching section
- the signalling section
- the central control

2.1 The switching section (fig. 1)

It includes the switching network itself and its associated peripherals : markers and line scanners.

The switching network is built up with 3 types of blocks, called switching units : the line switching units (LSU's), the intermediate switching units (ISU's) and the trunk switching units (TSU's). The sizes of the ISU's and TSU's are always the same (512 inlets, 512 outlets ; 2 and 3 stages). All LSU's have the same number of outlets (128) but the number of inlets which, in fact, is the number of connected subscriber lines, depends on the traffic per subscriber line - (6 LSU configurations are defined, for traffic range from 0,05 Erlang/line to 0,6 Erlang/line).

Reprinted with permission from *1974 Int. Switching Symp. Rec.*, Sept. 9–13, 1974.

These network blocks are interconnected through intermediate distribution frames IDF1 and IDF2. The total number of stages from one inlet of the network to one outlet is 8. The size of the basic switch is 8x8. In the LSU's, 4x4 switches and 8x4 switches are also used.

Paths are set or released, in the switching network, via the markers ; a group marker controls a number of ISU's and/or TSU's according to the traffic handled by these switching units (maximum 8) ; a line marker controls a number of LSU's depending on the traffic handled by these switching units (maximum 16) ; 3 orders must be sent by the processor to set or release a path in the network : one per type of switching unit. With each line marker is associated a line scanner, the function of which is to detect calling lines or lines going out from the "parking" status. For this purpose, under the processor control, each line scanner tests regularly the line circuits, individual per subscriber, physically implemented in the subscriber switch (A-stage of the network).
The line scanner stops when a significant line status has been detected (calling line for example) or at the end of the scanning of a group of lines.
The group marker also performs the "false cross and ground" test inside the switching network. The operation time of the marker varies from 7.5 ms (usual operation) to 15 ms (set of a path with "false cross and ground" test) ; the line scanner tests the line circuits eight by eight. Each cycle lasts 18 μs.

2.2 The "signalling" section (fig. 2)

It includes all the network terminal circuits : trunk circuits and auxiliary devices (trunk senders and receivers, subscriber receivers, tone senders etc.). It includes also the peripherals associated with these circuits : drivers and scanners.

Junctors and trunk circuits are connected to TSU outlets through an intermediate distribution frame (IDF3). Auxiliary devices are connected to TSU outlets (subscriber receivers for example), or to ISU inlets through the IDF1 (trunk senders and receivers for example).

Relays in network terminal circuits are normally operated or released through slow drivers. A slow driver controls a number of network terminal circuits (maximum 512) according to the traffic handled by these circuits. Its operation time is 25 ms.

All telephonic events (loop closed or open, multifrequency code etc.) are detected by test points implemented in the network terminal circuits.

These test points are tested by an autonomous scanner, under processor control ; during each elementary cycle (22 μs) the autonomous scanner compares the present status of 32 test points, with the previous status, stored in its last look memory. In case of status change, the correspon-

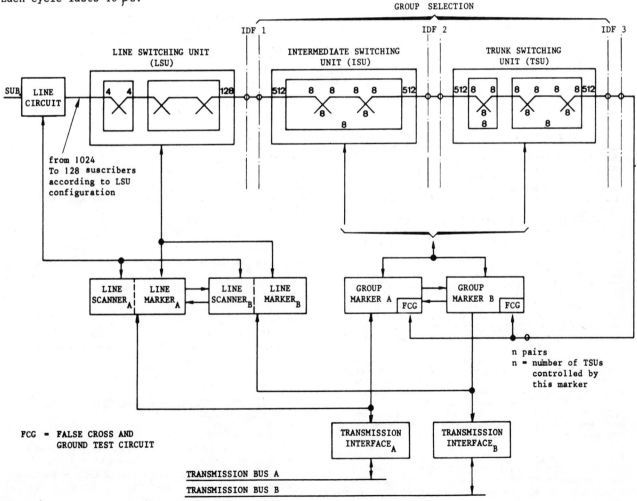

Fig. 1   SWITCHING SECTION

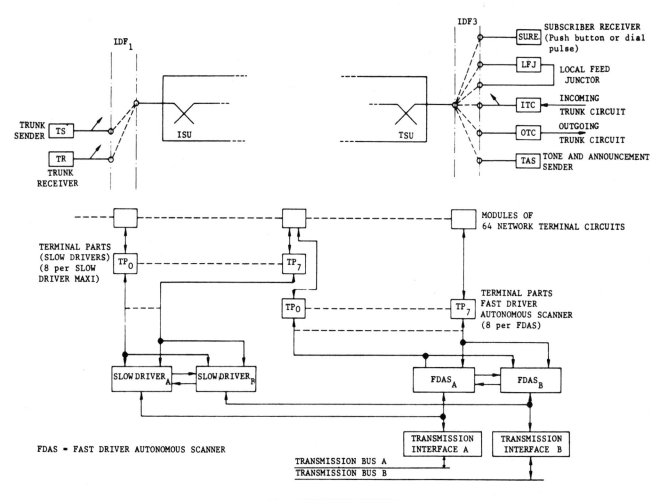

FDAS = FAST DRIVER AUTONOMOUS SCANNER

fig. 2 SIGNALLING SECTION

ding word of the last look memory is updated with the new status and the address of this word is stored in a stack. At each clock interrupt, the processor reads the words of the last look memory in which a change has been detected by the scanner. Afterwards, the processor restarts the scanner, which performs again its autonomous work.

The capacity of a scanner is 2048 test points ; this corresponds, for example to 512 network terminal circuits with 4 test points each.

Relay operation with time constraints (signalling pulses) is performed by a fast driver, a flip-flop being associated in this case to each such a relay. In fact, the fast driver is incorporated in the autonomous scanner, the maximum driving capacity being 1024 driving points per so called fast driver autonomous scanner (FDAS).

The E11 system is designed to process, either classical voice frequency trunks, or PCM channel associated signalling (CEPT specification) or PCM common channel signalling (French specifications) [4] . The same fast driver autonomous scanner is used in all these cases. Only the part which interfaces with the trunk depends on the case.

Fast driving is performed by the processor at the beginning of each clock interrupt, before the treatment of the last look memory words in which a mismatch has been detected by the scanner (fig. 3)

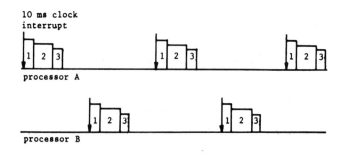

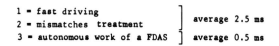

1 = fast driving
2 = mismatches treatment
3 = autonomous work of a FDAS

average 2.5 ms
average 0.5 ms

Fig. 3

2.3. The central control includes two LCT 3200 processors with each :

- one main frame

- a variable number of central memory blocks (each block containing 16384 words , 33 bits 0, 85 μs cycle time), each two blocks being connected to the main frame via a memory controller.

- various peripherals and associated controllers

ISS 74

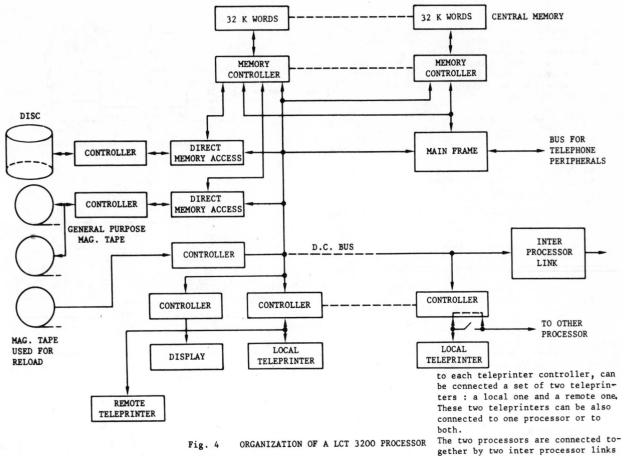

Fig. 4   ORGANIZATION OF A LCT 3200 PROCESSOR

to each teleprinter controller, can
be connected a set of two teleprinters : a local one and a remote one.
These two teleprinters can be also
connected to one processor or to
both.
The two processors are connected together by two inter processor links
(IPL).

teleprinters, displays, disc store, general purpose magnetic tape transports ; one magnetic tape transport is loaded with the master tape for
automatic reload of the system in case of software fault.

- direct memory accesses, that permits direct
data transfer, between the central memory and
some peripherals: mass memory, magnetic tape
transport)

3. DEFENSE STRATEGY FOR TELEPHONE PERIPHERALS.

3.1. "Defense" procedure is an automatic process
by which a processor can remove from service by
hardware or/and software actions a faulty part
of equipment.

In a general way the telephone peripherals have
a matricial access to the non duplicated parts
of the system (switching network and network
terminal circuits). In the markers for example,
all the crosspoint coils are arranged in a matrix according to the fig. 5.

Points P, where both homologous markers are
connected to the non duplicated part of the e-
quipment, are, of course, not realised as simply
as indicated in the figure, in order to avoid
fault propagation from side A to side B.

For economical reasons, the size of the matrix
should be as large as possible. Considering the
group marker, it is, for example, electrically
possible to arrange all the crosspoint coils
of the 8 switching units that it can control, in
a single matrix.

Let us now suppose that a fault is detected by
the marker, in such an arrangement ; it is at

first necessary to determine whether the fault
in located in the duplicated part of the marker
or in the non duplicated part. If the fault is
located in the non duplicated part (faulty
diode, short circuit between X and Y wires of
the matrix...), this fault will be detected also
by the homologous marker. Because of the size
of the switching network which corresponds to
the coil matrix, it is necessary to diagnose
exactly where is the fault (line and column of
the matrix involved), so that the minimum part
of the switching network be removed from service by the defense procedure.

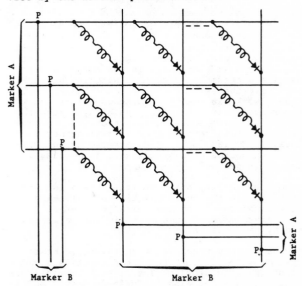

Fig. 5

In any case, in such an arrangement, it is necessary, before taking a defense action, that the processor makes a detailed diagnosis . This method has two main disadvantages : the diagnosis may be wrong ; the diagnosis may be good, but the corresponding defense action not foreseen in the software.

For avoiding this, the telephone periphery has to be arranged in such a way that the defense action can be taken without previous detailed diagnosis : if a fault is detected in a coil matrix, the whole part of the switching network corresponding to this matrix, will be removed from service ; this is possible :

- if the size of the coil matrix is reduced.

- if no fault can propagate from a given matrix to another matrix.

With such an arrangement, a duplex fault (faults detected by both processors) can involve only one single matrix. This matrix is called a "defense unit". Faults involving several defense units are necessary simplex faults (fault detected by one processor). Each processor counts the faults occurring in every defense unit ; the decision of removing from service a defense unit is only based on the fault rate of this defense unit, whatever the faults be. If the fault is located in the part of the marker common to several defense units, all defense units will be successively removed from service, and as already explained, this type of fault cannot be a duplex one.

Fig. 6 summarizes the differences between the two arrangements. In the second configuration there are no connections between TP_0, TP_1 ... of one side ; there are individual connections between a central part and each terminal part.

In case of the group marker, the defense unit is constituted by an Intermediate switching unit or by a Trunk switching unit (a block of 512 inlets and 512 outlets).

3.2 Access of a processor to a non duplicated part of equipment after a defense action

Let us still consider the switching network and the associated markers. Except in case of a duplex failure (in which case only one defense unit can be removed from service), the number of links in the network which can be removed from service after a defense action can correspond to the total capacity of a marker. The blocking in the network, for this processor, should become unacceptable. For avoiding this, a processor for which a simplex fault in the marker decreases its accessibility to the switching network, can, nevertheless, send orders to this part of the network via the inter processor link and the other processor : this is possible, because the number of input/output instructions, in this case, is small (even for the line marker scanner). Thus, a simplex fault of a marker does not prevent the corresponding processor from accessing the whole network.

From the security point of view, there is, therefore, no limitation to the size of switching network which can be controlled by central part of a given marker ; the only limitation is caused by the traffic.

In the network terminal circuits side, the situation is different. For the slow drivers, there is no specific problem. The network terminal circuits are grouped also in "defense units" and in case of a simplex failure on a slow driver, the orders to the concerned network terminal circuits are sent via the interprocessor link and the other processor.

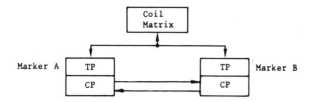

Fig. 6a ARRANGEMENT WITH ONE COIL MATRIX

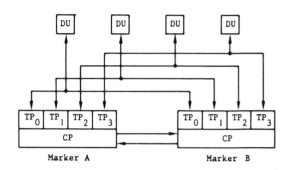

DU : Defense unit (crosspoint coil matrix)
TP : Terminal part
CP : Central part

Fig. 6b ARRANGEMENT WITH SEVERAL COIL MATRICES.

This procedure in not more possible for the fast driver autonomous scanner (FDAS) because of the high number of input/output instructions. Because of that, the number of network terminal circuits controlled by a given FDAS has been limited. Thus in case of a simplex fault, even if a FDAS is completely removed from service for one processor, the blocking for this processor will remain at an acceptable level. The maximum number of network terminal circuits controlled by a central part of a FDAS is 512, these 512 circuits are divided into several groups of 16 circuits of the same type, a defense unit, for the slow drivers,or the FDASs, containing 64 network terminal circuits.

This strategy applies to the automatic defense process ; diagnosis still, of course, remains necessary inside a defense unit, or in the duplicated part of·a network access device, for repair purposes.

4. SOFTWARE STRUCTURE

For a system such as E11, the software consists of some 200.000 instructions, covering multiple functions : call processing, administration(man-machine communications,) maintenance, test and diagnosis , installation table generation, simulation for program debugging. Such a system should live at least for 30 years in an actual and evolving world environment.

Consequently, the major requirements for the system software, are its maintainability and its adaptability to future evolutions such as modifications in network, in technology, in hardware modules and in telephone features specifications.

Functions must thus be as independent as possible one from the others and information interchanges between programs must follow standard interfaces.

ISS 74

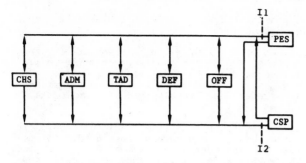

PES : Program Executive Set   DEF : Defense programs
CSP : Common Subprograms   OFF : Off-line programs
CHS : Call Handling Set   I1 : Interface 1
ADM : Administration   I2 : Interface 2
TAD : Test and Diagnosis

Fig. 7 RELATIONS BETWEEN PROGRAM SETS

From these requirements, the French Administration has fixed general principles referring to software security and software modularity, inasmuch as French Administration wants to have the same software structure for both space switching E11 and PCM switching E12 also developed within the SOCOTEL frame [5]

The purpose of software security specifications is to limit fault propagation in order not to disturb telephone traffic. Although call load sharing already reduces considerably the risks of a complete outage, detection means are introduced in programs in order to limit fault propagation and their repercussion on the quality of service ; besides an improved quality of service, fast detection of faults facilitates fault localization and program debugging ; this also improves quality of service.

The purpose of software modularity is to make easier program evolution in the evolving environment and make easier debugging of future program modifications by a limitation of the impact of modifications. In this context several realization constraints are given, the most important ones being :

- function partition.

- program partition into modules and modules linkage at execution time.

- loose relationship between data and programs which have to use them.

- use of tables for decision logic.

- use of programming standards.....

5. FUNCTIONAL PARTITION OF PROGRAMS

5.1 Programs are subdivided into sets which are forming entities relatively independent one from the others. The list of these sets is the following :

- Program Executive Set (PES) ; this set includes the programs which control all input/output operations and other functions with time constraints (e.g. telephone signalling handling). This set constitutes a virtual machine for the other sets which have not to consider real time problems.

- Common Subprograms (CSP) ; this set comprises all the subprograms which may be called by programs of several sets.

- Call Handling Set (CHS) ; this set contains the whole telephone call handling logic.

- Administration (ADM) ; this set includes all the programs which are necessary for the exchange operation (e.g. modification of subscriber class of service).

- Test and Diagnosis (TAD) ; this set comprises all the programs which check the system (preventive action) and locate troubles (corrective action) ; the programs on this set are running on on-line processors.

- Defense (DEF), is the set of programs which provide service continuity in case of fault detection.

- Off-line programs (OFF), are the set of programs which are running on processors handling no traffic, either during the installation period, or for a detailed fault diagnosis.

ADM and TAD programs set interface with the operating personnel via a normalized man-machine language |6| .

The first two sets (PES and CSP) are the service sets, which to the exclusion of all others are in relation with other sets ; consequently two interfaces are defined (fig. 7) :

- the first one , (I1), interfaces programs of the Program Executive Set and programs of the other sets ; this is a bidirectional interface, as PES can receive requests from other sets (e.g. a call handling program can require a path connection in the network) or can initiate a program when a call processing must be continued in another set (e.g. when a new call is detected)

- the second one (I2), interfaces common subprograms and programs of the other sets ; this interface is unidirectional as a subprogram is always called by a program.

5.2 Module partition

Each set is partitioned into several program units which can be written and debugged separately ; such a unit is called "module" and has a length of 100 or 200 instructions.

The independence of modules implies that a unit does not know which module was executed before nor the module which is executed afterwards ; each module has one unique entry and one unique exit.

Module partition is either organic or functional; e.g. a call handling sequence is usually subdivided into (fig. 8) :

- an analysis module (functional)

- a "network" module (organic) - network path search and path marking

- a "signalling" module (functional) - for driving the trunk circuits.

In the Program Executive Set, module subdivision is essentially organic : a module is related to a peripheral type, driver, marker .....

The purpose of this module subdivision is to consider modules as pieces of "meccano" and to constitute an exchange package according to the exchange configuration (signalling types ..), call configurations and service features, by the assembly of modules taken "off the shelves" from the library.

If new signalling types are implemented or if new features are offered to subscribers (e.g. conference call), only modules specific to those new points should be produced, without any modifications brought to the existing modules ;the debugging of the new package should practically be reduced to the debugging of new modules. Similarily, if technological evolution brings new equipment leading to replacements such as of the mass memory, or of a driver by another device, faster or slower, operating more or less relays, only the organic modules related to these devices should be rewritten and none of the call handling sequences should be modified.

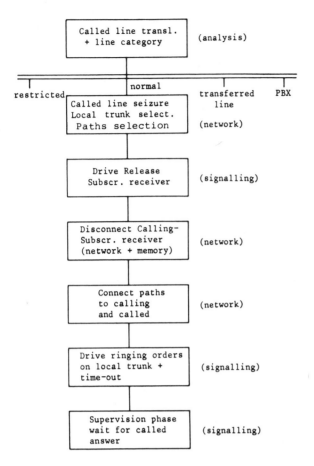

Fig. 8 EXAMPLE OF MODULE PARTITION

6. SOFTWARE SECURITY

The impossibility to have programs written without faults is well known ; besides, program debugging is very expensive in time and manpower, and the resulting package always contains residual faults. Moreover transient hardware faults sometimes appear as software faults. Precautions must thus be taken at every level, system design, program analysis, coding and debugging, to have procedures for decreasing the number of faults appearing in the package and for a fast fault detection, in order, on one hand to facilitate program debugging and on the other hand, that the consequences of a software or pseudo-software fault, on traffic, be as small as possible, for the obtention of a good quality of service.

For program coding, the metasymbol CT assembly language, standardized for the E1 system is used, [7] that allows the use of procedures with several advantages :

- standardization is increased, as every time a programmer uses a procedure, the coding is generated automatically, and trickinesses are decreased, this leads to an improved debugging.

- on the listing, the logical sequence appears more clearly than if everything was coded in machine language, and clearness brings less faults and faults are easier to find.

- procedures allow an introduction of a verification of argument consistancy at assembly time.

Procedures are used as well for data generation as for instructions, and in E11, as much logic as possible lays in decision tables rather than in instructions.

Besides, special off-line programs are foreseen to run on the system source program for verifications such as the application of coding rules (e.g. it is forbidden to write branch instructions referring directly to their own location such as : B $\emptyset$ + n).

For a fast fault detection, fault detectors are introduced in the programs. Some detectors are "natural" and take no additional processor time, e.g. each analysis which leads to a result corresponding to a non-existing or non implemented configuration. Other detectors are introduced in the programs, in spite of an increased execution time, e.g. software key and lock system for mass memory access.

Fault detectors are also introduced in the hardware, such as

- memory lock and key,

- detection of nonexistent operation codes,

- detection of nonexistent operand addresses,

- watch dog timers ...

At the system level, in case **one processor** halts for any reason, hardware or software, call load sharing allows the other processor remaining online to continue the handling of its own calls and also to take over the established calls which were handled by the failing machine. In order that this take over be effective without disturbance of the second machine, special care must be given to interprocessor communications and take over programs. These programs must consist essentially of normal call handling modules and have a minimum of own modules ; they must also have a very careful debugging.

7. PROGRAMS DEBUGGING

For E11 program debugging, environment simulation will be used.
In an actual exchange, many peripheral devices are connected to the processors : telephone devices such as markers and drivers, and data processing devices such as magnetic tape units, teleprinters ...

Environment simulation consists in replacing all these peripherals by one processor which transmits to the system processors via a simulation interface, all signals that the processors would have received from the peripheral devices. (fig. 9)

Principal characteristics of simulation are :

- the whole environment of system processors is simulated : subscribers, network, network access devices, mass memories ...

- real time conditions are kept without real time constraints ; time is counted in a relative manner, thus all non real time functions added for the purpose of simulation can be ignored by not counting the time during the execution of these functions.

- a run repetition always generates the same real time conditions ; this is possible as the three processors are synchronized by a unique clock located in the simulation interface.

Environment simulation has many advantages, among others simulation allows :

- to debug programs without disposing of the complete exchange ; one simulation center allows simulation of programs for different exchanges of different configurations

- to separate hardware and software difficulties as long as they are not mature enough to be put together.

- to generate data corresponding to hardware faults, which otherwise should be introduced into the equipment, at much higher cost and time.

To generate all the data and events in the chronological sequence from natural telephone statements, a special language based on macro-instructions has been developped. Among those data, equipment faults are of prime importance as many residual software errors are due to wrong hardware fault handling.

A new feature has been introduced recently in the environment simulation, it is the SIMAT simulation.

The SIMAT (SIMulation d'Appels Téléphoniques) is a device which can be used with any local exchanges ; it generates calls on different lines, and verifies for each call the reception of dial tone, ringing, continuity calling - called, correct tones in case of abnormalities (as busy tone etc.). The latest simulator version incorporates SIMAT features for testing the system under a traffic of several hundreds simultaneous calls.

In spite of its non negligeable development cost, environment simulation presents a very favorable pay off, as a telephone exchange package is never frozen, it evolves with the introduction of new features, of new signalling types ...; in addition, in the case of the first exchanges production, it is necessary to introduce regularly program corrections. When such modifications are introduced in a package, the package is submitted to simulation with, on one hand, patterns

corresponding to the new call configurations and, on the other hand, recapitulation patterns (e.g. SIMAT) to verify the non contamination of unchanged program modules.

Environment simulation is also used for the evaluation of the system (traffic processing capability etc...).

CONCLUSION

The E11 system design takes into account results from previous SOCOTEL experiences, such as the experimental so called PERICLES exchange [8] and the Roissy airport centrex office [9] , both installed in the Paris network, and also from the Rabat office [10] installed in the Moroccan network and other Metaconta L offices. This must lead to a system capable of meeting the main Administrations requirements : maintainability and ability to evolve, according to technology or specifications changes. The first E11 office will be cut-over un the first half or 1976, at ATHIS-MONS, in the Paris network.

[1] G.YELLOZ, T.CAGNAC, A.LE GALL, C.FRUCHARD.
The 3200 computer. Electrical Communication 1971, volume 46. N° 1

[2] S.KOBUS, A.KRUITHOF, L.VIELLEVOYE.
Central Control Philosophy for the Metaconta L Switching system.
Electrical Communication 1972. Volume 47

[3] A.REGNIER, J.PAYER.
Matrice de points de croisement à contacts scellés et maintien magnétique.
Commutation électronique N° 36. Janvier 1972

[4] P.LUCAS, P.COLLET.
Signalling in digital integrated network
ISS 74 - Munich.

[5] D.LARDY, C.ROZMARYN.
Modularité et Maintenabilité des programmes opérationnels dans les systèmes téléphoniques à programme enregistré.
Commutation et électronique N° 45. Avril 1974

[6] Contribution française au CCITT.
Normalisation d'un langage de relations homme machine. COM 11. N° 15 Période 72.76

[7] Contribution française au CCITT.
Normalisation d'un langage de macroassemblage.
COM 11. N° 14. Période 72.76

[8] L.J LIBOIS, P.LUCAS, J.DONDOUX, J.DUQUESNE.
Les principes de base du système PERICLES.
Commutation et électronique N° 19 Octobre 1967

[9] J. TRELUT
Un central téléphonique électronique à l'aéroport de Roissy en France.
Commutation et électronique N° 40 Janvier 1973.

[10] R.DANIS, J.P.DARTOIS
Field Experience with the first Metaconta L.
Electrical Communication Volume 48 Nber 4, 1973.

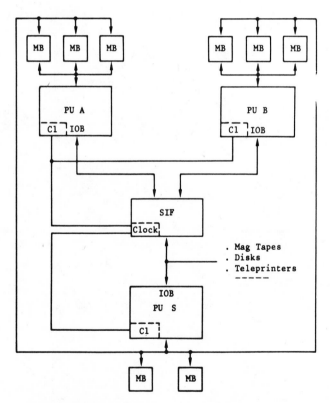

PU : Processing Unit   IOB : Input Output Bus
MB : Memory Block   Cl : Clock
SIF : Simulation Interface

Fig. 9 FUNCTIONAL SCHEMATIC OF ENVIRONMENT SIMULATOR

Supplementary Bibliography for Paper 21

E11

<u>SYSTEM GENERAL</u>

GENERAL STRUCTURE OF THE MAISONS LAFFITTE
ANDRE G + LAMY J
COMMUT ELECTRON NO. 10: 102-12 (OCT 1973)

<u>OTHER</u>

RULES FOR DESIGNING A LARGE SWITCHING NETWORK OF THE E11 TYPE
DARTOIS H + PERROT JJ + SCHULTZ S
COMMUT AND ELECTRON NO. 45: 92-100 (APR 1974)

<u>SYSTEM GENERAL</u>

MAINTENANCE PROCESSES IN THE E11 SYSTEM
TRELUT J + TOURNIER C
COMMUT ELECTRON NO. 48: 58-65 (JAN 1975)

Paper 22

J.-P. COUDREUSE*, P. GRALL* and C. RAPHALEN**

E 10 system : time division tandem exchanges

Time division tandem exchanges are made up by assembling time division exchanges which have been developed in the E 10 system.

This article presents the architectures that have been considered as well as the main working characteristics of such exchanges; finally the organization of their operating and maintenance is specified.

* Centre National d'Etudes des Télécommunications, Lannion.
** Société Lannionnaise d'Electronique (SLE-CITEREL).

Reprinted with permission from *Commutation et Electronique* (Special Issue), pp. 43–56, June 1975.

Introduction

The rapid development of telephone traffic necessitates the creation and operation of even more trunk circuits and, consequently, the necessary tandem exchanges must have ever-increasing traffic-handling capacity [1]. At the same time, digital transmission techniques are rapidly finding application in the telephone network. It is therefore natural to contemplate the use of tandem exchanges directly switching PCM transmission channels. Moreover, it is generally accepted in some countries, such as the USA, that the field of application of TD switching is, par excellence, that of high-capacity tandem exchanges.

Hence, the E 10 system may find a new application there. After the period corresponding to the study of the Platon [2] project, the E 10 TD switching system was used either in the group centres [3, 4], or in the urban or suburban centres.

This paper describes the technical characteristics of a TD tandem exchange established on the basis of E 10 exchanges, the assembly of which enables advantageous capacities to be achieved.

Having examined the various possible structures, we shall study the characteristics of these tandem exchanges from the functional viewpoint with particular reference to the safety rules, and from the operational viewpoint, in particular as regards signalling and translation. We shall then state the rules considered for the extensions. We shall finally explain how the maintenance of these TD exchanges will be carried out. The applications contemplated at present are recalled in the conclusion.

I. Structures of the TD tandem exchanges

I.1. THE BASE MODULE

The fundamental principle governing the study of the TD tandem exchanges was to use the E 10 equipment as it exists in the subscriber exchanges, this in order to reduce the costs of study and development and to permit the manufacture of larger series thanks to the use of equipment which will then be standard.

A tandem exchange will thus be formed by the assembly of a certain number of basic units which we shall refer to as "modules".

The maximum capacity of an E 10 exchange is 3 600 TD paths serving 120 numerical multiplexes TN_1, each of thirty speech paths. The handling capacity of the control units is about 12 calls per second. If we consider a tandem exchange of 1 800 inward and 1 800 outward circuits, loaded with 0.6 E, we obtain a transit traffic of about 1 100 E, corresponding to about 10 calls per second —a capacity generally much too low since, for a tandem exchange, it should normally be between 10 000 and 15 000 E.

Therefore, one base module of 3 600 TD paths is not sufficient. The technically easiest way to increase the capacity is to associate several modules, without altering their control principles, and to keep the connecting network as it is [5]. Other solutions might have consisted, for example, in centralizing the control units and connecting the networks together directly. But this would have meant completely re-arranging the E 10 system, which was quite out of the question.

A TD tandem exchange of the E 10 system therefore consists of several TD exchanges of 3 600 paths, each having its control [6, 7], interconnected by PCM circuit-synchronizing groups [8] using common channel signalling [9]. The various items of equipment are already standardized. The only changes authorized "a priori" are restricted to the switching programming in order to permit internal re-routing.

I.2. DIFFERENT POSSIBLE STRUCTURES

There are many ways of interconnecting the modules; however, it must be remembered that there is no centralized control at the level of the whole of the automatic switching centre. Therefore, exchanges between the registers of the different modules must be effected by signalling on the interconnecting "meshes", which prohibits, for example, too complex selection procedures such as a conjugate itinerary search between the various modules used for a call. However, in all the cases considered, internal re-routing procedures are used to obtain quasi-equivalent accessibility to the whole of the circuits of an outgoing line unit.

I.2.1. Single-train structure

This structure is so called because the majority of the calls are routed through only one module: it therefore uses only a light mutual-aid traffic. The modules of this structure can serve inward and outward line units and are connected to the other modules by internal mutual-aid meshes (fig. 1). The types of traffic carried are the same, irrespective of the module (fig. 2).

It is not necessary to connect all the modules together, provided that each module can serve nearly all the outgoing line units. Indeed, studies carried out by simulation on such a structure have shown that internal re-routings could be limited to two attempts, the third scarcely having a chance to succeed if there have already been three failures on the outgoing line unit. A solution might therefore be to connect the module at position p to those at $p-1$ and $p+1$, modulo n, n being the number of modules; the number of meshes is $2n$, and, since the mutual aid circuits are mixed, the real number of meshes is n.

Besides the all-important advantage of making maximum use of the routing of the calls through a particular module, this solution makes it possible to serve mixed circuits and, what is equally important, PCM links conveying outward, inward or mixed traffic as in the case of junctions between two TD exchanges.

COMMUTATION ET ELECTRONIQUE - JUNE 1975

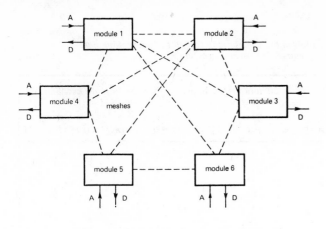

A : incoming line groups
D : outgoing line groups

Fig. 1. — E 10 TD tandem exchange. One-train structure.

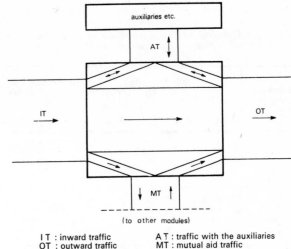

I T : inward traffic   A T : traffic with the auxiliaries
O T : outward traffic   M T : mutual aid traffic

Fig. 2. — Traffics carried by each module of a one-train TD tandem exchange.

If it is desired to limit the mutual aid traffic, it is essential to divide each outgoing line unit over all the modules and to balance the offered traffic on each of the sectors thus realized. This result can be obtained by judiciously distributing the inward line groups on the modules. However, in practice, the realization may be difficult as it necessitates a good knowledge of the traffic matrix of the exchange. This may be altered, either as the result of extensions or by the strategy of use of the tandem exchange. Any noteworthy change in the traffic matrix will involve a redistribution of the inward line units on the modules and hence wiring at the distributor level.

The one-train structure is of interest only if the mutual aid traffic is light. Simulation studies relating to exchanges with 2, 3 and 4 modules have shown that, under the conditions described above, 10% of the traffic carried goes via two modules. If, for safety reasons, 15% of the traffic of a module is reserved for mutual aid, a 4-module exchange could carry 3 700 E for circuits loaded at 0.6 E. Can one go further than four modules?

It seems too soon to answer that question. In the first place, the simulation studies are not yet finished and the corresponding mutual aid traffic is yet to be specified. Moreover, the division of the outgoing line groups into n sections means that these groups must grow with the size of the exchange, an eventuality still to be confirmed. The balancing of the various kinds of traffic on each section of one and the same outgoing line group becomes more difficult to achieve when the size of the exchange increases. It seems therefore that the one-train structure scarcely enables high capacities to be attained.

I.2.2. Two-train structure

This structure is so called because every call is routed *systematically* through two modules.

The first train consists of inward modules serving the incoming line groups; the second train consists of outward modules serving the outgoing line groups.

Each module is divided into two parts: 1 800 inward or outward circuits, 1 800 circuits for the internal meshes. A tandem exchange with $2n$ modules thus comprises n internal meshes each of $1\,800/n$ circuits (fig. 3). The traffic is routed as shown in figure 4.

The essential advantage of this system is to have available internal high-capacity meshes, ranging from 900 circuits in the 4-module exchange to 150 circuits in the 24-module exchange. Working with a loss of 0.1% the circuits have performances ranging from 0.92 E to 0.8 E. It may thus be considered that a two-train tandem exchange works on internal pseudo-expansion.

One sure advantage of the one-train structure is the flexibility of connection of the incoming and outgoing line groups. The constraints of dividing the outgoing and balancing line groups on each of the sections obtained are less severe. One is therefore less dependent on the traffic matrix.

The major disadvantage of this structure is that it necessitates the systematic traversing of two modules, which increases the selection times and is obviously less economical.

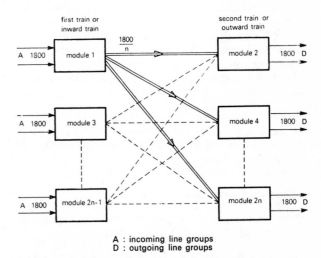

A : incoming line groups
D : outgoing line groups

Fig. 3. — Two-train TD tandem exchange

TABLE I

Overload percentage admissible on the internal meshes for a given blocking probability on the internal meshes.
(parameter: the load on the incoming circuits) (two-train structure).

Blocking probability ($^o/_{oo}$)	4 module exchange ($M = 900$)			10 module exchange ($M = 360$)			20 module exchange ($M = 180$)			24 module exchange ($M = 150$)		
	$C=0,6$ E	$C=0,7$ E	$C=0,8$ E	$C=0,6$ E	$C=0,7$ E	$C=0,8$ E	$C=0,6$ E	$C=0,7$ E	$C=0,8$ E	$C=0,6$ E	$C=0,7$ E	$C=0,8$ E
1	55	33	15	45	25	9	37	17	2,5	33	14	0
5	58	35	19	52	30	14	45	25	9	42	22	6
10	62	38	21	56	33	17	51	29	13	47	26	10
50	70	47	29	68	45	27	65	40	24	63	38	22

C : mean load on incoming (or outgoing circuit) ; M : size of the internal mesh.

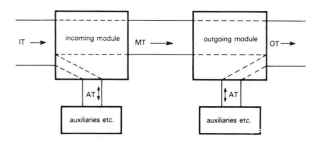

Fig. 4. — Types of traffic routed by a two-train TD tandem exchange.

Another disadvantage is that it is not possible to use mixed circuits as each module handles only one type of traffic.

What are the capacities that can be attained?

For a blocking probability of 1 per thousand, the internal meshes work at 0.8 E in an exchange with 2×12 modules. One can hardly go further than this as it is necessary to retain a safety margin in case of breakdown of a PCM (30-path) multiplex of an internal mesh. Moreover, the two-train structure reacts very substantially on the overloads of internal meshes when this overload exceeds a certain rate, as table 1 shows.

Hence, a maximum capacity of about 13 000 E can be expected, which corresponds to 2×12 modules for circuits loaded at 0.6 E or to 2×10 modules for circuits loaded at 0.7 E.

I.2.3. Other structures

Between the one-train and the two-train structures there is a whole range of intermediate structures.

Hence, in the one-train structure, the use of one or two modules serving specialized "outward" modules

can be imagined; this solution makes it possible to re-group the small outgoing line groups the size of which does not permit division over several modules.

Beginning from the two-train structure, one might imagine the use of outward or inward non-specialized modules, which would introduce a certain flexibility. The 1 800 + 1 800 sharing of the circuits of each module can also be altered. Finally, for a given installation, one might also consider an extension realized by changing over from a one-train structure to a two-train structure.

I.3. SOLUTION ADOPTED : THE TWO-TRAIN TANDEM EXCHANGE

The foregoing critical examination of the possible structures permits us to say, summing up, that below a capacity of the order of 3 500 E, the one-train structure is advantageous, but delicate to use, and that beyond this capacity, the two-train structure is preferable and enables 13 000 E to be attained with 20 to 24 modules.

It was decided to adopt the two-train structure, even for low capacities [21]. This articles is therefore devoted in the main to a description of a TD tandem exchange of this type.

However, in order to allow for all the possibilities, each module of the TD tandem exchange is designed so as to route indifferently outward traffic, inward traffic and mixed traffic. This presupposes that the programs of the control units of each connecting module are not specialized. Now, apart from the technical aspects, it is found that the costs involved by the non-specialization of the modules are relatively negligible.

The rest of the article discusses the two-train structure, but transposition to the one-train structure is possible in most cases.

II. Characteristics of the operation of a TD tandem exchange

II.1. SELECTION PRINCIPLES

In a two-train TD tandem exchange, the inward module directs the selection in the sense that it determines, in the final resort, the destination of the call, taking into account the external events. Several cases are considered, depending on the possibilities of reaching the wanted exchange.

II.1.1. Case of an outgoing line group connected to one module

In this hypothesis, a call presenting itself on a circuit A ending at an inward module i must be routed on one of the circuits B going out via a single outward module j (fig. 5). It is assumed that the distant exchange can only be reached directly.

In module i of the first train, the translation data enables the call to be routed on the whole or part of the interconnection mesh connecting module i to module j. Each interconnecting mesh may be made up of "sections"; each section comprises between 1 and 900 circuits connected to selection units of consecutive numbering (cf. III.2.1.). If module i finds no circuits free on the mesh in question, it initiates a freeing process.

If there is a free circuit, modules i and j dialogue by common channel signalling. When module j has all the necessary elements, it seeks out a circuit on the outgoing line group B. If there is a free circuit, the routing procedure is followed. If not, module j sends to module i the information "line group saturated". Module i then initiates a freeing process.

II.1.2. Case of an outgoing line group distributed over several modules

In this hypothesis, the call presenting itself on a circuit A of a module i can be routed by one of the circuits B of an outgoing line group distributed over several modules j, k, l of the second train (fig. 6). The destination exchange can only be reached directly.

In module i, the translation data indicate a first mesh m_{ij} to the register; if there is no free circuit, the translator then indicates the mesh m_{ik}, and then m_{il}. If no circuit is free, module i initiates a freeing procedure. If module i finds a circuit on mesh m_{ik}, for example, the two modules i and k dialogue as previously. If there is a free outward circuit on module k, the call is routed normally; if not module k sends the information "line group saturated" to module i. The latter then passes on to the following mesh m_{il}.

It should be noted that the method of dividing the internal meshes into segments enables some or all of these meshes to be used. It also permits grading in the order of scanning of the meshes. Moreover, for one and the same outgoing line group, the different routes (ABPQ or PQMC) can go over different sections.

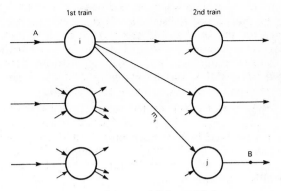

m_{ij} : mesh from module i to module j

Fig. 5. — Routing of a call in the case of an outgoing line group connected to one module.

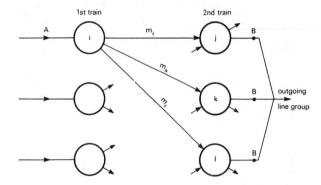

Fig. 6. — Routing of a call in the case of an outgoing line group spread over several modules.

Finally, when the destination exchanges signal the datum "congestion", the outward modules send to the inward modules this information which is different from "line group saturated".

II.1.3. Case of an exchange which can be reached by overflow

The decision to route the call via an overflow line group is only taken by the inward module after exhausting all the possibilities of routing by the direct outgoing line group. In other words, if an outward module finds that the direct line group is saturated, it does not try to route the call to an overflow line group. The inward module receiving the information "line group saturated" explores the other possibilities of direct routing and then, in the event of failure, seeks out the characteristics of the overflow line group and initiates a process similar to that which was described in II.1.1. or II.1.2., but with a special indication to the outward modules: "seizure of the one and only overflow line group". The modules of the second train must then seek out a free circuit on the single overflow line group. The rest of the treatment is as described in II.1.1. and II.1.2. It should be noted that only one possible overflow is provided for.

II.1.4. Selection time

The preselection time, which corresponds to the seizure of a register in the inward module, is a few milliseconds (the time for reception of the dialling obviously depends on the code of the inward circuit).

The selection time which elapses between the moment when the inward register has all the elements necessary for the routing and the seizure of an outward circuit is essentially variable, depending on whether or not the outgoing line group is distributed over several modules, on the congestion of the internal meshes and on the existence of an overflow.

In the case of a call routed successfully by the first outward module chosen, the mean selection time is 1.8 s which breaks down into 80 ms of exchange between units and 1 720 ms of treatment (214 phases of the program of the registers). Table II gives the details of this treatment.

TABLE II

Treatment of selection effected by the two registers
of a two-train tandem exchange.

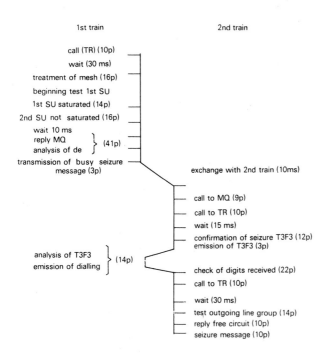

II.2. RELIABILITY OF OPERATION

II.2.1. Reliability at the tandem exchange level.

The modules are totally independent. They are only connected by the interconnecting PCM circuits. A serious accident at the level of a module does not cause any disturbance to the operation of the others. However, there is a degradation of the service quality.

II.2.2. Reliability at the level of the line groups

As already explained (II.1.), the internal re-routing procedures permit great flexibility as to the means of connecting the line groups.

The LF inward or outward line groups can be distributed over several outward modules. The outward or inward numerical line groups may be divided as soon as they exceed 30 paths.

However, it is necessary to strike a compromise between reliability and degradation of the traffic flow; actually an ill-conceived spread of one line group over several modules involves an increase in the selection time (too many internal re-routings). In practice, an outward line group will not be divided over more than three modules. On the other hand, the inward line groups will be able to be distributed over any number of modules.

II.2.3. Reliability of operation of the module

The central units of each module are either duplicated or organized in independent units [6, 7]. The same applies to the connecting network [5].

Each circuit-synchronization group [8] provides the management of 8 multiplexes (240 paths). To ensure the reliability of operation of the interconnecting meshes, the multiplexes connecting an inward module to an outward module will be connected on different synchronization groups.

Similarly, the inward and outward circuits connecting a distant exchange to the tandem exchange will, as far as possible, be connected to different synchronization groups.

III. Operating characteristics of a TD tandem exchange

The operating characteristics described in this chapter concern the types of signalling treated, the translation possibilities and the connection of various devices.

III.1. SIGNALLING TREATED

III.1.1. General

The TD tandem exchange deals only with circuits. In particular, there is no provision for connecting subscribers' units permitting the treatment of operators' positions for various special services. Signalling of subscribers of the dial or keyboard type is not envisaged, except in very special cases (*cf.* V.3).

III.1.2. The provincial TD tandem exchange

The signalling codes treated in a provincial tandem exchange are :

- the trunk decimal code with pulses transmitted by TIP-RING wires or by 50 Hz current;

- the Socotel MF code with pulses transmitted on TIP-RING wires;

- the Socotel MF code with changes of state;

- the Socotel MF code permitting direct selection at the receiving end for private installations (code with pulses or changes of state);

- the MF code of the information centres;

- a special MF code reserved for the outward hypsometers (*cf.* V.3);

- the common signalling channel E 1.

In the two-train structure, there is always a change of signalling code as there is obligatory passage through the internal common signalling channel connecting each of the registers involved in the two trains. One might then think that only tandem treatments are accepted, which would not conform to the evolution at present foreseen, resulting from the intensive use of MF signalling. In fact, this is not the case. The operation of the MF signalling will take place in transit whenever the transmission conditions so permit, thanks to the abundance of the common signalling channel which makes it possible to indicate to the registers concerned the nature of the inward and outward circuits.

However, it should be noted that, for the TD exchange, the only advantage of operation in transit is shorter occupancy of the MF receivers; the registers, interpreting the line signatures are, in any case, occupied as long as in tandem working.

In the present state of tone and auxiliary equipment [10], the maximum number of MF receivers is 120, i.e. 90 in degraded working. The works of Mr. Le Gall [11] on traffic with waiting periods, constant service time (10s) and random choice (independent of the order of arrival), show that the 90 MF receivers can carry 72 E, i.e. a load of 0.8 E per receiver with a waiting probability of 2×10^{-2}, a mean waiting time of 11 ms and a probability of less than 10^{-4} that the waiting time will exceed 10 seconds.

If we consider circuits carrying 20 calls per hour and seizing a receiver for 10 seconds per call, it is possible to serve about 1 300 MF circuits in degraded working. When the 120 MF receivers are in service, the waiting probability becomes almost zero.

In a two-train structure, the number of inward (or outward) circuits is 1 800 per module; one can therefore see the necessity for increasing the capacity of the tone and auxiliary equipment. It is contemplated at present to double the number of receivers. However, the urgency may not be as great as it seems: on the one hand, there are still many circuits with decimal signalling and, on the other hand, one can foresee the development of electronic switching and the common signalling channel will compete advantageously with a signalling code, the application of which seems to pose a number of transmission problems.

III.1.3. The Paris local tandem exchange

This type of exchange is only in the stage of being studied. However, Rotary signalling treatment is contemplated. A later article will pinpoint the problems encountered.

III.1.4. Charging

No charging unit is provided at a TD tandem exchange. In particular, the connection of the sector centres and sub-centres is not contemplated.

III.1.5. International traffic

At present, the possibility of establishing an access chain to the international network is contemplated. Besides the problems inherent in the retransmission of the dialling to the downstream exchanges, the problem of retransmission back of the charging pulses still remains. In an E 10 exchange, this constraint necessitates the presence of registers and, for the case of electromechanical exchanges connected directly to the transit centres, the presence of a pulse generator situated in the charging unit [12]. The solutions under consideration show clearly that, at present, it is only possible to carry a very marginal international traffic (a few per cent of the total traffic).

III.2. TRANSLATION POSSIBILITIES

The case of a Paris local tandem exchange is not considered here.

For the provincial exchanges, the translation units [7] have a single translation program independent of the nature of the exchange and translation tables of the same format, but of different volumes and contents.

III.2.1. Capacities of the translation units

All the PQM's and all the ABPQ's form the subject of a validity criterion (refusal or acceptance).

The analysis of routes, characterized by a group of circuits and a charging rate, rests on AB, ABP, ABPQ in national dialling and on PQ, PQM and PQMC in regional dialling. The charging rate permits, if desired, the transmission of charging scale levels.

The maximum number of direct and overflowed routes is 1 275. However, an alteration to the rear wiring of the translation units would enable 2 295 analysed routes to be attained. These characteristics are valid for each of the modules. The analysis data will be the same for all the inward modules, but this will no longer be the case for the second train.

A group of circuits, internal or outgoing, may consist of one or more sections linked-up unidirectionally; a section consists of 1 to 900 circuits. Each module may have 510 sections. A given route uses a line group consisting of interconnected sections. Two line groups may thus have in common the same chain, explored in the same direction but begun at different positions.

The routes of the first train go via the internal meshes. The routes of the second train go via the outgoing circuit groups.

The different combinations between the routes and the line groups enable the internal mesh traffic to be balanced against that of the outgoing line groups.

Overall, considered at the outlet of the second train, there can be $n \times 510$ outgoing line group sections (n being the number of modules of the second train). These sections may attain p exchanges, p varying from 1 to $n \times 150$.

III.2.2. Diallings treated by the provincial tandem exchanges

The diallings treated by the provincial tandem exchanges are the following:

- 1 X preceded by an access code, if any ($a5$ in MF, $T1$, $F1$ in common signalling channel (CS));

- $AB1Q$ preceded by the national access code ($a3$ in MF, 12 in decimal, $T1F3$ in common signalling channel);

- $PQMCDU$ preceded by a regional access code, if any ($a1$ in MF, 11 in decimal, $T1F4$ in common signalling channel);

- $ABPQMCDU$ preceded by a national access code, if any ($a3$ in MF, 12 or 13 in decimal, $T1F6$ in common signalling channel)

- 777,999,7777,9999 (preceded by $a1$ in MF and $T1F3$ in common signalling channel);

- 7798 or 9988 (preceded by $T1F3$ in common signalling channel);

- $77MCDU$ or $99MCDU$ ($M \neq 9$) for calling inward robots;

- $11X$ (in decimal or in common signalling channel with $T1F2$; in particular 118 for the outward hypsometers (cf. V.3)).

The tandem exchange can transform a national dialling into a regional dialling by elimination of the AB's involved.

The "regional rerouted" and "national rerouted" access codes are "absorbed".

The translation units permit the alteration of any number of from 2 to 4 digits into numbers of from 2 to 6 digits.

III.3. CONNECTION OF VARIOUS DEVICES

The various maintenance devices and the connecting units for talking machines can have two interfaces with the exchange: one, a switching interface for the exchange of analog signals and the other a management interface for any necessary exchanges with the data processing centre (CTI) [13].

Generally speaking, the receiving devices are connected downstream with respect to the first train and the transmitting devices upstream with respect to the second train. They are connected to GSM's [8] and treated as special circuits (cf. V.3), which constitutes an exception to the specialization of the two trains. The disadvantage of this organization is that it necessitates as many units as there are modules ; no benefit is gained from the grading of the internal meshes and there is a type of supplementary transit for each module. But the advantages are numerous:

● in the case of the talking machines, the first train remains in control of the routing of the calls shunted on to them;

● the internal meshes are relieved on not specifically telephone traffic (which is advantageous for the talking clock and spoken information);

● the treatment of the dialling in the outward and inward hypsometers is simplified, both for the data processing centre and for the registers.

This method assumes non-specialized connecting networks. Figure 7 summarizes the organization adopted for the connection of the various devices.

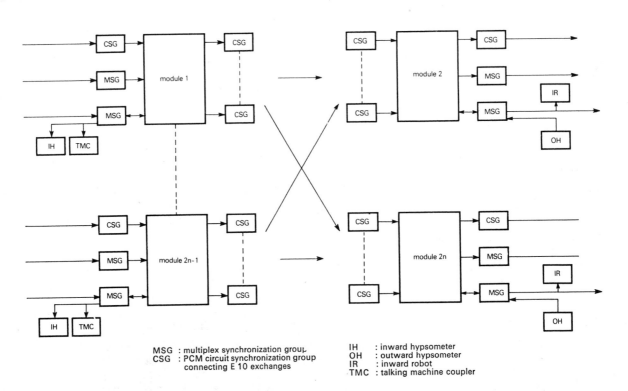

MSG : multiplex synchronization group
CSG : PCM circuit synchronization group
     connecting E 10 exchanges

IH : inward hypsometer
OH : outward hypsometer
IR : inward robot
TMC : talking machine coupler

Fig. 7. — Connection of various devices over a two-train tandem exchange.

COMMUTATION ET ELECTRONIQUE - JUNE 1975

IV. Realization of extensions

Extensions can be made in two different ways depending on the equipment of the modules at the time of the extension. If these are incomplete, the extension is effected by completing each module up to 64 selection units. If not, the extension is effected by adding $2n$ modules, n varying with the volume of the extension. In what follows, we shall only assume this latter case.

IV.1. INTERVENTION ON THE INTERMEDIATE DISTRIBUTOR

Each module comprises a PCM circuit distributor in the form of two levels of connecting blocks. The first level comprises a fixed number of blocks to which the multiplexes coming from the module (2×60) are connected. The second level, effecting interconnection of the distributors comprises a number of connecting blocks which depends to a certain extent on the number of modules. The grading of the multiplexes is effected between the two levels of connecting blocks in each distributor by shielded pairs.

The links between distributors are effected by shielded 8-pair cables (four two-way multiplexes).

The connecting blocks used are of the "Pouyet RBS" type, with 6×32 points and they are installed in the end racks of the bays.

Depending on the maximum extension contemplated, the number of connecting blocks initially installed varies from 4 to 7 (2 in inlets and 2 to 5 in outlets), as table III shows.

Extensions during the life of the exchange are effected by the addition of cables, the dismantling of unused cables and the resumption of the grading between the inward and outward connecting blocks at the level of each repeater.

TABLE III

Characteristics of the intermediate distribution frame of each module.

Number of modules in the final phase	Number of connecting blocks	Number of cables between distributors
2 + 2	4	8
3 + 3	5	5
4 + 4	6	4
5 + 5	6	3
6 + 6	6	3
7 + 7	6	3
8 + 8	6	2
9 + 9	7	2
10 +10	7	2

IV.2. MODIFICATIONS OF THE TRANSLATION DATA

The translation data are contained in three types of stores: line group number stores, line group address stores and circuit discrimination stores. The data of the first type evolve when new outward routes are created. The data of the second type evolve when new outward or interconnecting circuits are introduced. The data of the third type evolve as soon as new outward, inward and interconnecting circuits are connected.

When an extension is made, it is usually essential to modify the circuit lines and group address lines. Repetition of the contents of the group address stores may involve work on the general distributor.

The preparation of the new data enables rapid modification, as from the data processing centre, of the translation stores of each module considered individually. Moreover, the data processing centre can isolate a module from the rest of the exchange by putting the common signalling channels and the corresponding circuit synchronization groups out of action.

The procedure of an extension may be as follows:

- isolate the module,
- intervene on the general distributor on the circuits relative to the isolated module,
- charge (load) the new translation tables,
- intervene on the intermediate distributors concerned by the module,
- restore the module to service,
- repeat the foregoing operations for all the modules.

V. Organization of operation and maintenance in a TD tandem exchange

The TD switching E 10 integrated network consists of two levels: the first carries out the switching functions and the second the operational and maintenance functions. This organization has been preserved in a TD tandem exchange. Actually, the structure with several interconnected modules for establishing a tandem exchange is exactly equivalent to that of several TD exchanges situated in different places. These latter are connected to a data processing centre [13] which centralizes the maintenance and operation functions. In the TD tandem exchange, this same articulation re-appears: the first level consists of the various modules, the second of the data processing centre.

For operating facilities, it is preferable to have a single computer managing all the modules and not managing other types of exchanges. However, if the respective powers of the tandem exchange and the data processing centre so require, one could consider the possibility of connecting several data processing centres (DPC) to the same tandem exchange. Two solutions are feasible: either traffic-sharing, each computer serving only a certain number of modules, or function-sharing, each computer only performing certain functions. The second solution is more satisfactory for operation, but it involves a considerable reorganization of the programming of the centre as it functions at present.

In what follows, we shall consider only the use of one data-processing centre.

V.1. LINKS BETWEEN THE DATA PROCESSING CENTRE AND THE MODULES

The links between the DPC and the modules are identical with those which are used between the subscribers' exchanges and their DPC [14]. For each module, a time interval is used (8 bits every 125 µs which corresponds to an output of 64 000 bits per second) taken on one or more multiplex links connecting the computer to the check unit [15]. The transfer of this management channel from one multiplex to another can be effected either by permanent connection in a TD connecting network, like a speech path, or by a special device used in data transmission and known as transfer equipment (TRE). In a two-train structure, the modules of one and the same train are not interconnected. Therefore, the connection of the modules to the data processing centre is effected as shown in figure 8:

- the management paths of the inward modules are grouped on a single multiplex of an outward module (by permanent connections);

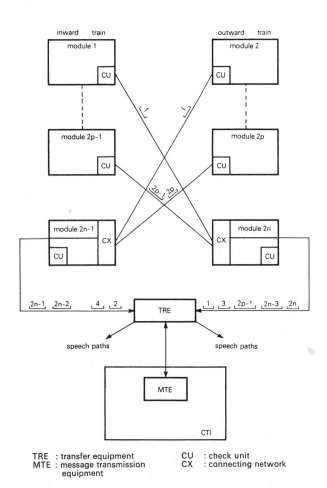

TRE : transfer equipment
MTE : message transmission equipment
CU : check unit
CX : connecting network

Fig. 8. — Connection of the modules to the DPC.

the management paths of the outward modules are grouped on a single multiplex of an inward module;

- the two multiplexes thus constituted are combined by means of an equipment for transfer to the multiplex serving the data processing centre.

A variant can be used when the connecting networks so permit. It consists of using for one of the grouping multiplexes that which connects the modules $2n-1$ and $2n$ (fig. 8). The transfer equipment is thereby eliminated. This solution may be advantageous in certain cases; this depends on the additional cost of the switching equipment immobilized by the reservation of a multiplex for the link with the data processing centre.

The modules $2n-1$ and $2n$ insert their management paths directly on the grouping multiplexes, which makes it possible to reconstitute, as from the data processing centre, any permanent connections which might have been disturbed.

V.2. OPERATION AND MAINTENANCE OF THE MODULES FROM THE DATA PROCESSING CENTRE

Each module is treated by the DPC as an independent exchange. In particular, the signalling of faults, the transmission of alarms and the test programs [16] are effected by the DPC under the usual conditions. Interventions and reconfigurations of the devices are effected by the operating personnel using teleprinters. As regards supervision of the circuits, the cases of failure to invite transmission and to signal end of selection are totalled for each circuit and submitted to the operating personnel when they so request.

The management of the translation data is carried out by the data processing centre. There are four categories of information:

● the data concerning the circuits;

● the data concerning the line groups which describe the constitution of the groups in sections and circuits;

● the data on the routes which concern the outgoing line group, a charge level and a possible overflow;

● the data concerning the dialling analysis fields.

The operating personnel may, through the intermediary of the teleprinter, write, amend, read, check and cancel these various translation data. For each module, the DPC checks the coherence of the data introduced. Subsequently, this coherence check will be able to be extended to all the modules of the two trains. For example, one may contemplate automatic checking of a routing indicated by a module of the first train and which must exist in the indicated module of the second train. This presupposes that one data processing centre carries out the management of the translation tables.

Finally, a routine program of the DPC systematically checks the identity of its translation data with those of the two translators of each module; a majority comparison between the contents of the data of the 3 devices enables any faults to be corrected.

COMMUTATION ET ELECTRONIQUE - JUNE 1975

V.3. MAINTENANCE OF CIRCUITS

The principles of maintenance of incoming and outgoing circuits of a TD tandem exchange are the same as those applied in the subscribers' exchange. For the outgoing circuits, outward hypsometers are available [17]. The latter are remote-controlled by the data processing centre via the multiplex synchronization group to which they are connected [18]. The service quality is determined by the "callers" of inward robots.

The outward hypsometers are those which are used in the subscribers' exchanges. Besides the adapters of subscriber line signals to the line signals of the continuous MF code (table IV), their connection necessitates the use of keyboard dialling receivers. For safety reasons, two receivers are provided for each outward module. The same applies to the inward modules to which are connected callers of inward robots which make it possible to supervise the correct operation of the transit centre as a whole and more particularly, of the internal meshes. Moreover, the internal common-channel signalling provides for management signals (T7F3) remote-controlled by the data-processing centre which check the proper operation of the management units of the common signalling channel.

V.4. TRAFFIC OBSERVATIONS

An article in a previous issue of this review [19] describes, in a general way, the principles and means of observing traffic which are employed in the E 10 system.

The aims of traffic observation are:

- general supervision of the traffic carried by the tandem exchange ;
- measurement of the loads on the control units and line groups ;
- the statistical distribution of the traffic (traffic matrix, mean duration of characteristic events, efficiency rate, etc.);
- supervision of the operation of the circuits.

TABLE IV

Line and register signals of testing equipments and of connecting units fort talking machines.

LINE SIGNALS				
Functions	RING wire	TIP wire	Adaptor	Inward unit
Availability	⏚	⏚	A ∞ on wire C	
Seizure	∞	⏚	A' ⏚ on wire C	
Reply DE	∞	∞	A' ⏚ on wire C	Loop ab ←
Hang-up DE	∞	⏚	A' ⏚ on wire C	Elimination of loop ab ←
Release	⏚	⏚	A ∞ on wire C	
Functions	RING wire	TIP wire	Adaptor	Outward unit
Availability	⏚	⏚	A	
Seizure	⏚	∞	A	Loop ab ←
Reply DE	∞	∞	A'	Loop ab ←
Hangup DE	⏚	∞	A	Loop ab ←
Release	⏚	⏚	A	Loop cut off ab ←

A : ⏚ on wire a, battery on wire b.   A' : battery on wire a, ⏚ on wire b.

REGISTER SIGNALS (outward device)	
Dial tone	450 Hz tone
Dialling	Keyboard code
End of selection	Return of call or busy state (audible signal)

The first two types of results are obtained by permanent sampling, at a slow or fast rate, of traffic counters in each of the modules, of the occupancy stores of the circuits of the outgoing line groups and of the stores of the connections effected in the networks [5].

The last two types of results are obtained by temporary discrimination of the circuits and of the line groups, which enables the registers to transmit observation messages to the data processing centre;

TABLE V

Traffic counters in the two-train time-division tandem exchanges.

Name of the counter	Events counted (in a module)
AR1 or DP1	New calls
AR2 or DP2	Successful calls (handset replacements)
AR3 or DP3	Seizure of translators
AR4 or DP4	Calls not routed
AR5	Internal re-routings
AR6 or DP6	Special translations
AR7	Changes of internal meshes

AR: Counter in an inward module
DP: Counter in an outward module

TABLE VI

Observation of traffic load.
(Overall results for a two-train tandem exchange.)

Number of calls	$\Sigma(AR1)$
Number of successful calls	$\Sigma(AR2)$
Efficiency rate	$\dfrac{\Sigma(AR2)}{\Sigma(AR1)}$
Blocking rate	$\dfrac{\Sigma(AR4)}{\Sigma(AR1)}$
Internal blocking rate	$\dfrac{\Sigma(AR4)+\Sigma(AR5)-\Sigma(DP4)}{\Sigma(AR1)}$
Blocking rate by congestion of outgoing line groups	$\dfrac{\Sigma(DP4)-\Sigma(AR5)}{\Sigma(AR1)}$
Internal re-routing rate	$\dfrac{\Sigma(AR5)}{\Sigma(AR1)}$

Σ: sum of the counters concerned on the modules of a train

the latter can thus reconstitute the characteristics of each call observed.

The results supplied by the centre are described in [19]. As regards more particularly a two-train TD tandem exchange, the events counted systematically in each outward and inward module are shown in table V. The counters marked DP4 add up the saturations of the outgoing line groups; the counters marked AR4 add up all the events causing the upstream transmission of signalling equivalent to "congestion". The whole of the counters of table V enable the centre to obtain, for the whole of the tandem exchange, valid synthesis results summarized in table VI. This obviously presupposes that one and the same DPC manages the counters of the different modules.

As regards the countings of the numbers of successful and unsuccessful calls by prefixes (*AB, ABP, ABPQ, PQ, PQM, PQMC*), it is proposed to carry them out at the request of the operators on a limited number of prefixes and for a limited period; to this end, the discrimination is allocated to each of the directions and, for each call, messages are sent to the data processing centre which totals them for each direction.

Should it be found that the operating needs so require, one might contemplate carrying out these countings permanently and for all the prefixes, but it would then be necessary to make substantial alterations to the translation units of the various modules.

VI. Establishment of a TD tandem exchange

Each E 10 module consists of three bays of 12 racks of low height Socotel [20]. As figure 9 shows, the central bay comprises the central control and connection units; the other two bays comprise the circuit connection units. The interval between the bays is 1.30 m the length of one bay is about 9.40 m and the surface on the floor is about 40 m². It should be remembered that the intermediate distributor effecting the interconnections between the modules is situated at the end of the bays. The mean consumption of a module is about 450 A under 48 V; this energy forms the bulk of what has to be absorbed by air-conditioning.

The data processing centre, constructed with a different technology, may be situated in another room. It takes up as much space as three Socotel racks and its consumption is about 20 kVA.

The TNE 1 equipement may be distant or local. In the latter case, it is usually situated in the same room as the main distribution frame. It is set up in Socotel racks with 6 TNE1s per rack.

The links between the modules are formed by standardized multiplex links terminated by two transcoders. They can thus attain a length of 1 800 metres without regeneration, and possibly more if repeater/regenerators are used.

The space requirement of a two-train TD tandem exchange is about 220 m² for 4 modules and 1 200 m² for 20 modules, which corresponds respectively to 2 500 E and 13 000 E.

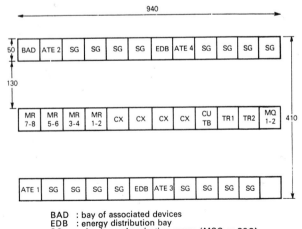

BAD : bay of associated devices
EDB : energy distribution bay
SG : circuit synchronization group (MSG or CSG)
ATE : auxiliary and tone equipment
CX : connecting network
TR : translator
MQ : marker
MR : multiregister
CU : check unit
TB : time base

Fig. 9. — Setup of a module of a tandem exchange.

COMMUTATION ET ELECTRONIQUE - JUNE 1975

VII. Conclusion

The construction of TD tandem exchanges from E 10 basic modules thus seems relatively easy. The widespread use of these basic modules is also obviously advantageous from the viewpoint of manufacture, as has already been pointed out.

Moreover, the exchanges are also connected by electro-mechanical means in order to increase the capacity of a complex. However, it should be noted that an electronic system is favourable for these groupings from various viewpoints:

● the use of multiplex links for interconnection of the various modules makes these connections very economical; in particular, common channel signalling for line groups of this size requires equipment which is very small in relation to what is required by the electro-mechanical system in which one junctor per circuit is needed;

● the common channel signalling also provides flexibility of use and rapid exchanges which permit more elaborate working than is possible with the electro-mechanical system, for example by trying several successive re-routings in the event of a load without prohibitively increasing the trunking times; the traffic flow is therefore comparable to that which would be obtained electro-mechanically, if there were conditional selection between the modules constituting the exchange.

The most delicate problem is the choice of the structure.

In the case of a tandem exchange with a capacity of below 3 500 E, which it seems possible to attain with the one-train structure, and the future evolution of which is not expected to exceed this figure, its growth being limited to an increase in the magnitude of the outgoing line groups, the one-train structure is to be chosen.

On the other hand, if it is a high-capacity exchange, the two-train structure, which enables about 13 000 E to be attained, will be chosen. It is obviously more expensive and serves only specialized inward or outward circuits.

It should also be noted that the choice of the basic module, as its connecting network is not specialized and as its switching program is independent of its function, can make it possible, if required by the operating conditions, to change over from the one-train structure to the two-train structure or vice-versa.

Originally intended to serve only trunk circuits, the tandem exchange could also switch circuits of sector exchanges or sub-exchanges, but charging equipment would then have to be added to them.

The first two-train tandem exchange was set up in July 1974 in Saint-Brieuc. This exchange will consist of 4 modules and, in its first phase, is serving about 1 800 inward and 1 800 outward circuits.

A second exchange is contemplated for Paris. This is a local tandem exchange with a final capacity of about 5 000 E. It is proposed to bring it into service in September 1975 in the Tuileries telephone complex.

These two installations will make it possible to check the validity of the principles underlying the design of the TD tandem exchanges built with the basic modules of the E 10 system.

Acknowledgments

It is our wish to acknowledge the collaboration of the Research Laboratories of the Australian Post Office in Melbourn for the translation of this paper.

BIBLIOGRAPHY

1 DURAND (M.), DESPLANQUES (M.), HOURMILOUGUÉ (A.), — Les grands centres interurbains Pentaconta (GCI). (The large Pentaconta trunk exchanges (GCI)). *Commutation & Electronique*, n° 39, octobre 1972, pp. 34 à 51.

2 LIBOIS (L.J.), LÉGARÉ (R.), PINET (A.), BODIN (P.). — Expérimentation d'un système de commutation électronique intégrée dans la zone de Lannion. Le projet Platon. (Experiments with an integrated electronic switching system in the Lannion district. The Platon project). *Commutation & Electronique*, n° 20, janvier 1968, pp. 7 à 16.

3 MEREUR (J.-N.). — L'automatisation des groupements de Guingamp et Paimpol. (The automatization of Guingamp and Paimpol networks). *Commutation & Electronique*, n° 33, avril 1971, pp. 5 à 15.

4 MENET (R.), MEREUR (J.-N.). — Automatisation des groupements de La Flèche et Sablé. (Automatization of La Fleche and Sable networks. See in this issue pp. 57 to 66). *Commutation & Electronique*, n° 41, avril 1973, pp. 17 à 27.

5 POSTOLLEC (J.). — Le réseau de connexion du système E 10. (The connecting network of the E 10 system). *Commutation & Electronique*, n° 40, janvier 1973, pp. 14 à 40.

6 HARDY (D.), GOBY (D.), JACOB (J.-B.), BAUDIN (J.). — Organes centraux dans un système de commutation temporelle. Projet Platon — Première partie : les organes de commande. (Central equipments in a time-division switching system. The Platon project — Part one : the control equipments). *Commutation & Electronique*, n° 25, avril 1969, pp. 24 à 38.

7 LE BELLEC (C.), LE POLLES (Y.). — Organes centraux dans un système de commutation temporelle. Projet Platon — Deuxième partie : organe de traduction. (Central equipments in a time-division switching system. The Platon projet — Part two : the translating equipments). *Commutation & Electronique*, n° 26, juillet 1969, pp. 25 à 48.

8 FEUERSTEIN (D.), JACOB (J.-B.), RENOULIN (R.), GUEZOU (J.) — Groupes d'équipements de synchronisation du système de commutation temporelle Platon (E 10). (Synchronization units in the Platon time-division switching system). *Commutation & Electronique*, n° 34, juillet 1971, pp. 7 à 24.

9 LUCAS (P.), HARDY (D.), PENNANEC'H (J.-C.). — Signalisation par canal sémaphore dans le système E 1. (Common channel control signalling in the E 1 system). *Commutation & Electronique*, n° 41, avril 1973, pp. 7 à 16.

10 (1) Revel (M.), Postollec (J.), Guezou (J.). — Dispositifs annexes dans un centre de commutation temporelle de type Platon. (Associated units in a time-division switching centre of the Platon type). *Bulletin technique d'information* Socotel, janvier 1970.

11 Le Gall (P.). — Les systèmes avec ou sans attente et les processus stochastiques. (Systems with or without waiting time and stochastic processes). Tome 1, Dunod.

12 Le Bellec (C.), Le Polles (Y.). — Organes centraux dans un système de commutation temporelle Système Platon. — Troisième partie : organes de taxation. (Central equipments in a time-division switching system The Platon system. — Part three : the charging equipments). *Commutation & Electronique*, n° 28, janvier 1970, pp. 40 à 65.

13 Grall (Ph.). — Le centre de traitement des informations du projet Platon. (Platon Project : the processing equipment). *Commutation & Electronique*, n° 27, octobre 1969, pp. 38 à 46.

14 (1) Queffeulou (J.-Y.), Tanguy (R.). — Liaison entre centraux et CTI. (Connection between exchanges and the DPC). *Bulletin technique d'information* Socotel, avril 1973.

15 Simon (Y.), Guezou (J.), Jacob (J.-B.). — L'organe de contrôle dans un centre de commutation temporelle (système Platon). (Monitor apparatus in a time-division switching centre (the Platon system)). *Commutation & Electronique*, n° 29, avril 1970, pp. 45 à 51.

16 Hollocou (E.). — Système E 10. Test automatique des organes. (E 10 system. The automatic testing of the equip-ments). *Commutation & Electronique*, n° 42, juillet 1973, pp. 35 à 39.

17 Fichaut (J.), Gouttebel (R.). — Maintenance des circuits et essais de qualité de service dans les réseaux intégrés de commutation électronique temporelle. Système E 10. (Trunk maintenance and quality of service monitoring in time-division electronic switching integrated networks. E 10 system). *Commutation & Electronique*, n° 39, octobre 1972, pp. 7 à 23.

18 Coudreuse (J.-P.), Le Drezen (P.). — Système E 10. Procédures de maintenance des lignes et des circuits. (E 10 system. Lines and trunks maintenance procedures). *Commutation & Electronique*, n° 42, juillet 1973, pp. 40 à 47.

19 Coudreuse (J.-P.). — Système E 10. Observation de charge et de trafic. (E 10 system. Load and traffic observation). *Commutation & Electronique*, n° 43, octobre 1973, pp. 86 à 93.

20 Simonneau (R.). — Normalisation des bâtis Socotel. (Standardization of the Socotel racks). *Commutation & Electronique*, n° 21, avril 1968, pp. 44 à 57. Brevet n° 72. 10448 du 24 mars 1972.

21 Libois (L.J.), Duquesne (J.), Pinet (A.), Fortin (P.). — Systèmes de centraux électroniques de commutation temporelle extensibles pour centres de transit et autres. (Systems of time-division electronic switching centres extensible for tandem and other exchanges). Brevet n° 72.10448 du 24 mars 1972.

(1) Internal, non published document.

Paper 23

Automatic Code Switch Electronic System No. 13 (AKE 13)

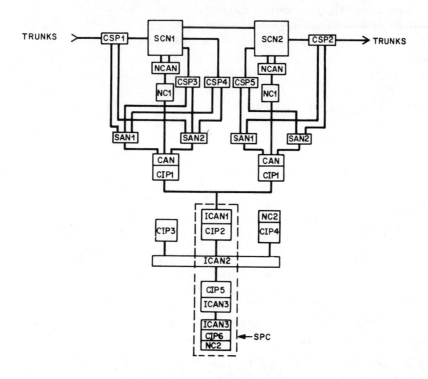

SCN1 = INCOMING SWITCHING STAGE	CSP3 = TONE RECEIVER
SCN2 = OUTGOING SWITCHING STAGE	CSP4 = CODE RECEIVER
CIP1 = TEST AND OPERATIONS GROUP	CSP5 = CODE SENDER
CIP2 = TRANSFER CONTROL BLOCK	ICAN2 = MULTIPLEXER
CIP3 = COMMON PROGRAM STORE	NC1 = SWITCH OPERATING UNIT
CIP4 = DATA STORE BLOCK	NC2 = NETWORK MAP
CIP5 = CENTRAL PROCESSOR	SAN1 = OPERATION AND DECODING UNIT
CIP6 = INTERNAL PROGRAM STORE	SAN2 = TEST UNIT
CSP1 = INCOMING JUNCTION CIRCUIT	SPC = DATA PROCESSING BLOCK
CSP2 = OUTGOING JUNCTION CIRCUIT	

THE L M ERICSSON TRANSIT EXCHANGE SYSTEM AKE 13

Kurt Katzeff and Ulf Jerndal

Telephone system AKE 13 is a system developed for transit exchanges with a very large volume of traffic. When designing the system consideration has been given to the requirements concerning national and international transit or trunk traffic and traffic to special facilities (operator etc.). The system is suitable for all the signalling systems existing today. Normally only signal transmitting and receiving devices are found in the telephony unit while all the logic functions are concentrated in the data processing unit. Consequently the system is very flexible with regard to the introduction of new signalling systems and modifications to the existing systems. The requirements imposed by CCITT signal systems No. 4, 5 and 6 can be met without difficulty. A standardized connecting equipment for data transmission channels is under development and will come into use when the signal channel in system No. 6 is connected. The system is very flexible with regard to numbering and alternative routing. An extension of the exchange will not disturb its operation. Rerouting of special facilities from one exchange to another presents no problems. A fault in an outgoing line can be overcome by blocking the line and routing the traffic over alternative routes. With respect to metering and billing it can be mentioned that automatic toll-ticketing can be arranged, transfer of rates to a subordinate station can be made and also automatic metering of calls connected by the operator. A queue can be arranged with respect to operator´s positions.

In the areas of traffic supervision and statistics the following functions are included in the system: Traffic measurement, traffic supervision, call counting, congestion counting and congestion supervision. These measurements can either be made continually or carried out on particular occasions. From this it is apparent that the system offers telephone administrations many new possibilities.

It would take far too long to describe here in detail the structure of the system, but a general picture is given below.

The system is built up on the same basic principles as the AKE 12 system, characterized by an extensive modular construction of both hardware and program. In contrast to the AKE 12 system we have presented up to now the AKE 13 is a multi-processor system. Consequently, should the capacity of a processor be insufficient to cope with the traffic at an exchange, one or more processor modules can be added to the system. In cases where the traffic is calculated to reach 2400 Erlangs or more, a multi-processor system is recommended.

The AKE system can be functionally divided into three main parts, namely the telephony, transfer and data processing units. See figure 1.

Kurt Katzeff is chief engineer at the L M Ericsson Telephone Company, Stockholm, Sweden.

Ulf Jerndal is with the L M Ericsson Telephone Company, Stockholm, Sweden.

Reprinted with permission from *IEE Conf. Publ. 52, Switching Tech. Telecommun. Networks*, Apr. 21-25, 1969, pp. 230-234.

Telephony unit

The telephony unit consists of a 4-wire network built up of code switches and relay sets for signal, transmitting and receiving functions. The grouping of the switching network is arranged with a number of incoming and outgoing group selector units with 600 inlets, 800 A-links and 1640 outlets. Since only speech wires are required the multiple capacity of the selector can be completely utilized. A completely built up switching network with 51 incoming and 51 outgoing group selector units gives a maximum of 30,600 incoming and 30,600 outgoing lines, and a traffic capacity of approximately 23,000 Erlangs.

Transfer part

The transfer part does not differ from that of the AKE 12.

The data processing unit

The data processing unit consists of a processor group, a transfer control with associated multiplexor and a data memory with associated multiplexor. See figure 2. The processor groups can consist of up to eight processors each containing two central processing units, two program memory units and a supervisory unit. The central processing units function synchronously and each normally fetch instructions from the respective program memory unit in parallel.

There are in the supervisory unit the comparison circuits which check that there is a continuous parallelity between data in both the central processing units. These circuits, together with other control functions in the system, originate alarms when faults occur. The data memory consists of up to 14 data memory blocks and two spare memory blocks in which each block consists of two data memory units of the ferrite core type.

The transfer control in the data processing unit consists of up to 16 transfer control blocks, each one built up of two identical units. Each one of these units contains an address and data register as well as control and supervisory functions.

The transfer groups in the transfer unit are connected to the transfer control. Input and output units are also connected to the transfer control.

The data memory multiplexor consists of up to 8 data memory channels, each channel consisting of two units. Each channel unit is connected to its data memory unit via a bus. The transfer multiplexor is built up in a corresponding way.

The task of the input-output units are to make possible the connection of different numbers and types of external units to the data part. Data transmission between an external unit and the system is always initiated by a program, but on the other hand, guidance and control can either be carried out by a program or by circuitry. Connection of low-speed external units such as typewriters, tape punch and tape reader are characterized by program guidance and control, while the connection of high-speed external units such as drum memory, disc memory and magnetic tape station is guided and controlled by circuitry which is carried out by a special processor IOP with direct access to the data memory.

Program

The structure and dynamic behaviour of the programs in the multi-processor system cannot be considered separately from the systems hardware configuration, operational security or maintenance viewpoints, for which reason the program system has been designed so as to satisfy all the various conditions that are placed on these integrated functions. The program system has a modular construction so that it can be applied easily to different applications, customer requirements and markets. This modularity also implies that extension, insertion of new facilities and changing of programs can be easily carried out in an existing system. This basic philosophy, which is valid for both hardware and software, makes the system extremely flexible and applicable to all possible changes that can be thought to apply to a modern telephone exchange.

This program system modularity implies that the total work to be performed by the processing system has been divided among a number of interworking programs, where each individual program is relatively small. Each program belongs to one of the four organizationally separate base systems, namely the Operating System, the Standard Functions System, the Application System and the Market Dependent System.

The Application System and Operating System are about the same size and together make up 80 % of the total program volume.

Applications

A very short account will now be given of a couple of applications, viz. Rotterdam DC II and Copenhagen Nc.

Rotterdam DC II will, in the first stage, have a capacity of about 2200 incoming lines and 2300 outgoing lines. The traffic is to and from local exchanges in Rotterdam city, terminal exchanges, and group exchanges in the Rotterdam district, other district exchanges in the Netherlands and international exchanges abroad.

Traffic per line has been estimated to between 0.65 Erlang and 0.75 Erlang. The exchange will in the first stage be built up with one processor.

Copenhagen Nc

From the trunking diagram, figure 3 for Copenhagen Nc it can be seen that, already at the first stage, this exchange is considerably larger than Rotterdam DC II. The number of inputs in the incoming group selector stage is about 9400 and the outgoing group selector stage is of roughly the same size. There are places for no less than 124 international operators. The requirements for adaption to different signal systems, numbering and directing, extension of exchange capacity, metering and billing, traffic supervision etc., are especially rigorous. The advantages of the stored program controlled system can be clearly seen here. In this case the exchange will be built up with 3 processors in the initial stage.

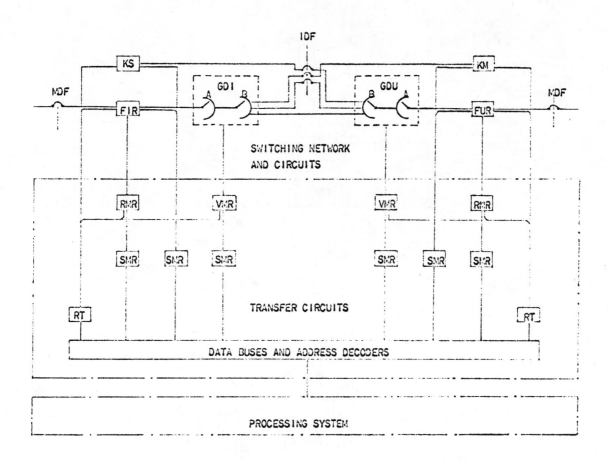

FIR	Incoming Trunk Circuit	VMR	Switch Operation Unit
FUR	Outgoing Trunk circuit	RMR	Relay Operation Unit
KM	Code Receiver	SMR	Fast Relay Operation Unit
KS	Code Sender	RT	Relay Test Unit
GD	Group Selector Stage		

<u>Fig. 1</u>   SYSTEM AKE 13   TRUNK EXCHANGE

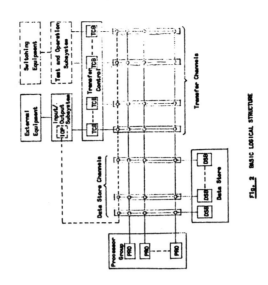

Fig. 2 BASIC LOGICAL STRUCTURE

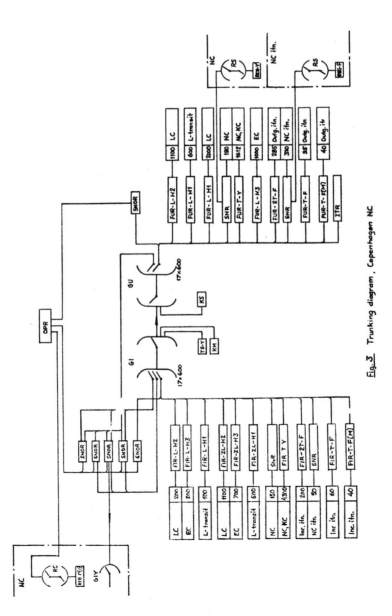

Fig. 3 Trunking diagram, Copenhagen NC

198

Supplementary Bibliography for Paper 23

AKE-13

SYSTEM GENERAL

INTERNATIONAL STORED PROGRAM CONTROLLED TRUNK EXCHANGE (AKE-13)
ALLEN P F + SINDEL P. J.
TELECOMMUN J AUSTRIALIA 25 (1): 34-43 (1975)

STORED PROGRAM CONTROLLED TRANSMIT EXCHANGES TYPE AKE-13 IN
STOCKHOLM AND GOTHENBURG
REHNBERG E + WIEZELL CJ
TELE (ENG ED) 26 (NO. 1: 17-26, 34 (1974)

SWITCHING EQUIPMENT OF THE AKE-13 EXCHANGE
ZWEEDIJK M
PTBDA8 P221-8 OF AKE-13 SEMINAR, ROTTERDAM, NETHERLANDS, OCT 1972

AKE-13 - FURTHER DEVELOPMENT
SUNDSTROM S
PTBDA8 P286-6 OF AKE 13 SEMINAR, ROTTERDAM, NETHERLANDS, OCT 1972

AKE-13 - SYSTEM ARCHITECTURE
NOREN LO
PTBDA8 P229-32 OF AKE-13 SEMINAR, ROTTERDAM, NETHERLANDS, OCT 1972

TRANSIT EXCHANGE SYSTEM -AKE 13
MEURLING J + NOREN LO + SVEDBERG B
ERICSSON REV 1973 (2): 34-57 (1973)

SOFTWARE

SOFTWARE SYSTEM FOR AKE-13
NOREN L + SUNDSTROM S
ERICSSON REV (ENG ED) 51 (2): 34-47 (1974)

EDP ADMINISTRATION OF EXCHANGE DATA FOR COPENHAGEN AKE (KHNC)
RISBAK L
TELETEKNIK 18 (1): 1-10 (1974)

AKE-13 - SOFTWARE RELIABILITY ASPECTS
NOREN LO + SUNDSTROM S
P133 OF INT SWITCHING SYMP RECORD MUNICH 1974 (621.381537/159)

SOFTWARE ORGANIZATION IN AKE-13
SUNDSTROM S
P301 OF CONF SOFTWARE ENGRG FOR TELECOMMUN SWITCHING SYST APR 1973
INT ELECT ENG (LONDON) CONF PUB 97

EQUIPMENT

THE POWER SUPPLY OF AKE-13 EXCHANGE IN ROTTERDAM
WILLEMSE A
PTBDA8 P271-6 OF AKE-13 SEMINAR, ROTTERDAM, NETHERLANDS, 9-13
OCT 1972 CONF PROC

FIELD EXPERIENCE AND MAINTENANCE

THE AKE-13 EXCHANGE-TESTING AND PUTTING INTO SERVICE
BAL LM
PTBDA8 P251-6 OF AKE-13 SEMINAR, ROTTERDAM, NETHERLANDS,
9-13 OCT 1972

SOME MAINTENANCE ASPECTS OF THE AKE-13 IN ROTTERDAM
SPOORENBERG HJ
PTBDA8 P247-50 OF AKE-13 SEMINAR, ROTTERDAM, NETHERLANDS, OCT 1972

COMMANDS AND OUTPRINTS IN THE AKE-13 SYSTEM
TROMMELEN LG
PTBDA8 P241-6 OF AKE-13 SEMINAR, ROTTERDAM, NETHERLANDS, 9-13
OCT 1972

FIELD TRIAL OF CCITT SIGNALING SYSTEM NO. 6 USING AKE-13
HINWORD J + CLARK L
ERICSSON REV (ENGL ED) 49 NO. 4: 124-38 (1972)

AKE-13 ROTTERDAM EXCHANGE AND EXPERIENCE FROM FIRST YEAR OF
OPERATION
HAMSTAND O + NOREN LO
ERICSSON REV 1973 (2): 58-64 (1973)

———————————————

Paper 24

Automatic Electronic Register Crossbar System No. 11 (ARE 11)

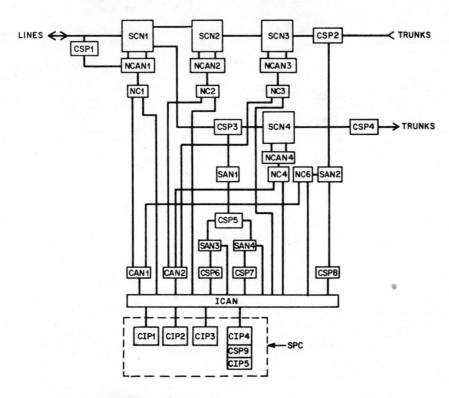

SCN1 = SUBSCRIBER STAGES A & B
SCN2 = SUBSCRIBER STAGES C & D
SCN3 = COMBINED SECOND AND INCOMING GROUP SELECTOR STAGE
SCN4 = FIRST GROUP SELECTOR STAGE
CAN1 = SUBSCRIBER IDENTIFIER
CAN2 = GROUP IDENTIFIER
CIP1 = TRANSLATION STORE
CIP2 = SUBSCRIBER STORE
CIP3 = ABBREVIATED DIALING STORE
CIP4 = CENTRAL PROCESSOR UNIT
CIP5 = PROGRAM STORE
CSP1 = LINE CIRCUIT
CSP2 = INCOMING JUNCTION LINE RELAY SET
CSP3 = CORD CIRCUIT
CSP4 = OUTGOING JUNCTION LINE RELAY SET
CSP5 = SIGNALING TRANSFER UNIT - ORIGINATING TRAFFIC
CSP6 = CODE RECEIVER (FOR PUSHBUTTON DIALING)
CSP7 = CODE SENDER
CSP8 = SIGNALING TRAFFIC UNIT - INCOMING TRAFFIC
CSP9 = DATA STORE
SAN1 = FINDER FOR ORIGINATING SIGNALING TRANSFER UNIT
SAN2 = FINDER FOR INCOMING SIGNALING TRANSFER UNIT
SAN3 = SENDER FINDER
SAN4 = SENDER FINDER
SPC = TRAFFIC CONTROL PROCESSOR

ARE - A DUAL PURPOSE SWITCHING SYSTEM FOR NEW INSTALLATIONS AND FOR UPDATING OF EXCHANGES IN SERVICE

John Meurling and Rolf Eriksson
Telefonaktiebolaget L M Ericsson
Stockholm, Sweden

ABSTRACT

The paper discusses the background to the development of the ARE switching system. This development has been carried out with the dual purpose of modernizing the family of L M Ericsson crossbar systems for new exchanges and of creating a subsystem to be used for the updating of exchanges in service. The ARE system is described with the focus of interest on the register subsystem, which uses stored program control. Reference is made to results from a field trial and further developments are indicated.

The full advantages of SPC have been utilized with the moderate volume of some 10 000 traffic handling program instructions. This has resulted in a system of small complexity; it is easy to learn and maintain and requires moderate volumes of documentation.

1. INTRODUCTION

There is an ever-increasing demand for new facilities in telephone switching systems. These facilities fall mainly in two areas - improved administrative services and new subscriber services. The reasons for the demand are to be found in many developments as for instance changes in social structure, introduction and development of new business practices and of course the need to mechanize and centralize the functions within the telephone administration. The new ARE switching system has been developed with particular attention paid to the provision of this type of facilities. The ARE system uses a stored program control register subsystem, ANA 30.

One problem being encountered when introducing SPC technique, or rather a switching system offering a large range of modern facilities, into a network is that it creates a disparity in capability level - for example in the form that subscribers connected to exchanges of an old type cannot be offered certain new facilities. In this particular example the problem might be overcome by installing new exchange equipment adjacent to the existing and connecting such subscribers that require added facilities to this new part, accepting of course the necessary number changes. However, in the area of administrative functions, such as for example subscriber meter reading, traffic recording, supervision of traffic, procedures for adding or changing subscriber categories and procedures for changing analysis data (route translations), the disparity in capability level and thus often also in the methods to be used can create serious administrative problems and cause additional costs.

With present day growth figures the average age of equipment is around 6 to 7 years, i.e. 50 % of the plant is less than 6 to 7 years old. Under these circumstances the total replacement of existing exchanges in order to reach the desired level is unthinkable. Instead, the preferable solution is to seek a means for the updating of existing conventional exchange equipment.

The development requirements for the ARE system therefore specified that the register system, ANA 30, be designed with the dual purpose of also being employed for the updating of equipment in service. The first object for updating would be the LME local crossbar exchange equipment, ARF.

When analysing the functions desired in a new system the need for flexibility is obvious - especially it is important to provide changeability. Today stored program control offers the best means for this. Further analysis shows that the functions which offer the best advantages when executed in SPC are located mainly in the register organization and that the updating requirements can be fulfilled here.

One further objective in designing the ARE system has been to utilize the advantages of stored program control while minimizing the complexity. SPC system complexity may be expressed in the number of instructions or program store capacity. The aim was set to design a system with a maximum of some 10 000 traffic handling instructions as compared to the 100 000 or more to be expected in a full SPC system.

From a technical point of view crossbar systems using register control, offer a ready area in which to set in stored program control - the functions offering the most interest are practically all to be found in the registers. By concentrating on the registers the natural interfaces become few and well defined and thus simple ways of updating exchange equipment in service are readily available. Some 10 % saving in floor space is obtained with ARE compared to conventional crossbar.

Further consideration showed the advantages to be gained in different ways by continuing the production of the family of LME crossbar systems. A system based to a large degree on the well established crossbar systems would prove advantageous both from a production point of view (LME crossbar production now takes place in some 25 different countries) and from an operation point of view by in its greater part being familiar to maintenance personnel, by needing less new, and unfamiliar, documentation and by requiring relatively few new spare parts.

In the ARE system the SPC register system accounts for roughly 20 - 25 % of the total cost. This fact is naturally also reflected in production and of special importance in the many areas where local manufacture is carried out. The switch-over to ARE production will affect only the part of the production process corresponding to the new register system while the bulk of production consisting of switches, relay sets, markers, etc. is not affected.

This technical policy thus results in a situation where an administration may acquire a system with a high facility level and using SPC but requiring only moderate efforts in re-training and operational handling. If the administration already has crossbar exchanges in service these may be updated with ANA 30 equipment and reach parity with the new exchanges and thus a homogeneous facility level is obtained in the whole network at a cost considerably below that to be expected for total replacement.

2. BRIEF DESCRIPTION OF THE ARE SYSTEM

The main philosophy has been to use the existing crossbar systems as a base for the new system and to modernize only those parts of the system necessary to obtain a larger range of subscriber services and administrative functions. This is achieved by introducing new equipment in those parts of the system in which the functions of receiving, storing, analysing and retransmitting the called subscriber s number are carried out. All these functions are found in the register organization including local registers and incoming registers.

The register organization offers the advantage that it can easily be replaced and modernized without affecting the other subsystems of the exchange. The subscriber stage, the group selector stage and the junction circuits have to a large extent been kept unchanged except that direct processor control of the switching stages have been included. The requirement that it must be possible to introduce the new equipment in an exchange in service without interruption of service has been fulfilled.

The new equipment ANA 30 is basically an electronic register organization utilizing SPC technique.

The first application of ANA 30 is for register-controlled local crossbar exchanges called ARE 11.

ANA 30

Traffic Handling

All the traffic handling functions in ANA 30 have been

Reprinted with permission from *1974 Int. Switching Symp. Rec.*, Sept. 9-13, 1974, pp. 445/1-445/4.

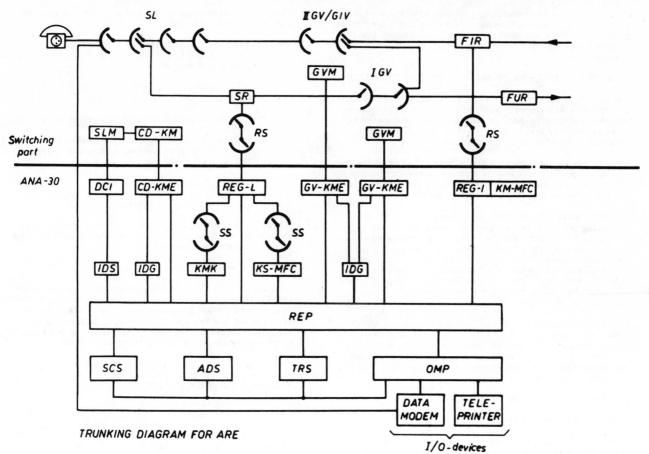

TRUNKING DIAGRAM FOR ARE

I/O-devices

located in a number of register processors which each can control up to 60 registers, local and incoming. For normal traffic intensity 2 - 3 register processors are required for a 10 000-line exchange. The register processors contain programs for the control of registers (REG), code receivers and senders (KMK, KS-MFC), selector stages (SL, GV), analyses of calling and called subscribers number, interpretation of register signals as well as programs for interworking with the operation and maintenance processor.

To simplify the program handling a register processor works with only one specific register during a specified time. The primary interval of 8 ms has been divided into 60 so-called time slots, each 120 µs long (800 µs is reserved for operation and maintenance).

Data, common to all processors such as subscriber data, analysis data and abbreviated dialling data are located in central stores.

The subscribers´ store (SCS) contains information about categories for calling and called subscribers such as restrictions for certain traffic, interception service etc. The analysis store (TRS) contains data for the calculation and directing of routing, alternative routing, type of signalling etc. The abbreviated dialling store (ADS) is used to translate one- or two-digit abbreviated numbers to full national or international numbers.

Operation and Maintenance

Supervision

Supervision of all devices in ANA 30 is taken care of by a common operation and maintenance processor which also handles the I/O functions. Supervision takes place of call congestion per route, fault rate per individual device within ANA 30 and fault-rates per route. The need for supervision tests with artificial traffic is thus considerably reduced, especially in an area containing solely ARE exchanges or exchanges using a similar maintenance philosophy.

Because disturbance occurrences are indicated per individual device, direct indication of a faulty device is obtained; this considerably facilitates fault tracing.

In case of failure in the system there is always an automatic adaptation of the system to the changed situation in order not to impair the traffic handling capacity. For instance the register processors normally work in a load sharing mode but in case of a failure in one, one of the other processors takes over the control of the registers of the faulty processor.

Fault localization

Fault localization in devices in ANA 30 can be remotely controlled as each device is provided with an electronic disturbance counter in the data store which is remotely read-off when a command is issued.

When a previously decided acceptable fault level for an individual device is exceeded, an alarm is issued in the exchange and transferred to e.g. an Operation and Maintenance Centre as an indication that a fault must be investigated.

When such an alarm is received an operator sets up a connection to the operation and maintenance processor in the exchange in question via his data terminal. He then requests a printout of the cause of the alarm; this is done in the form of the alarm device identity and fault type.

Changes in Exchange Data

Changes in exchange data, such as changes in routing information, the introduction of new signalling schemes, changes of numbering plans, changes of data for subscribers (barring from service, rerouting) may also be directed from a remote point. For instance barring of a subscriber from service is controlled from a remote point by first setting up a call to the operation and maintenance processor via a modem and then sending a command and the subscriber´s number. The command is received and analysed by the processor and is later executed by changing the data in the subscriber´s store. The setting of interception service category is done in a similar way.

Statistical Network Data

If the network is complex and/or if the fault frequency in the network as a whole exceeds the normal level, ANA 30 offers facilities for collecting valuable statistics which, after data processing, can provide important information about difficulties encountered in other exchanges (call congestion per route, fault-rate per route, traffic dispersion etc.).

3. INTRODUCING ANA 30 INTO EXISTING EXCHANGES

When an area is provided with new exchanges of the ARE system or a system with similar facilities, it is important that existing exchanges can be smoothly updated to an equal facility level. Also in other situations, such updating possibility is of great value.

ANA 30 can be introduced without causing service interruption. Upon installation the system is tested, partly with the help of simulators, before it is cut into service and the existing registers are taken out of operation.

The necessary changes and additions in the markers (including the code receivers) are carried out with corresponding modifications to the rack cabling. The work is always carried out so that only one device is taken out of service at a time. After this, the device is reconnected with its function retained. If additions have to be made to any relay set, this is done so that the set will function both in its original environment and when interworking with ANA 30.

As an additional safety factor, when ANA 30 has been completely tested, the new registers are connected in one by one in joint operation with the existing registers. New relay sets are plugged into the prepared positions in the marker racks and surplus ones removed according to a predetermined plan.

4. EXPERIENCE FROM FIELD TRIAL

In November 1973 a field trial with the new system ANA 30 was started in Mundelstrup, a suburb to the city of Aarhus, Denmark. In the Mundelstrup exchange, which is a public local exchange having 3 000 lines, a fourth 1000-group has been installed, containing the register organization ANA 30. Approximately 900 subscribers have been connected to this 1000-group.

Several of the new services for subscribers and administration have been introduced in this first installation and so far the exchange has worked very well.

Although the ANA 30 part of the exchange has only been in service some months it has been possible to use some of the new facilities also for tracing faults in other exchanges connected to Mundelstrup with the help of e.g. programs for traffic dispersion measurements.

During the trial there have been some hardware failures also in one of the register processors, but as the system supervises itself and has built-in recovery, this has only resulted in switch-over of the traffic to the non-faulty processor and no traffic degradation has occured. Most of the failures that have been detected so far are due to design faults in the programs and in the hardware.

5. CONTINUED DEVELOPMENT

Transit exchange

The ANA 30 principles are now also being applied to the crossbar 4-wire Transit System, ARM 20, using identical hardware with some additional interface equipment.

The most outstanding characteristics of this system, designated ARE 13, are:

- Centralized and increased operation and maintenance functions in the areas of supervision, fault diagnosis and statistics.

- Exchange data may be remotely controlled thus preparing for network management.

- ANA 30 used for updating of equipment in service.

- Increased call handling capacity in the markers and increased maximum exchange capacity, up to 12 000 inlets/12 000 outlets.

- Considerable floor space saving.

Updating of direct control systems

At the present time investigations are under way to determine the feasibility of using ANA 30 for updating of non-register systems.

CCS, Common Channel Signalling

The use of CCS is expected to have great impact upon the development of future telephone networks. The ARE system and also the updated versions of older systems is prepared for the introduction of common channel signalling. Such requirements as providing the identity of incoming and/or outgoing trunk circuit are fulfilled.

A field trial of CCS for register signalling is at present being set up in cooperation with the Jutland Telephone Company in Denmark.

Network Management

Pertinent exchange data in the ANA 30 system are changeable by remote control. Typical examples in this context are translation data for route numbering and setting of time supervisions. Thus a strategy for network management may be carried out either by direct data link access via the operation and maintenance processor or using the common channel signalling system as a network management distribution media.

Centralized PABX

A further development will be the introduction of centralized PABX (Centrex) facilities in the ARE system based on the use of ANA 30. With centralized PABX all extensions of a group (subscriber, firm) are connected directly to the public exchange but retain all the facilities normally found in a PABX such as call transfer, inquiry, rering on busy etc. The operator's position equipment will in the normal case be situated on the subscriber's premises and connected to the public exchange over a 4-wire circuit.

Conclusion

The ARE family of switching systems is a logical extension of the earlier range of crossbar systems, exploiting the benefits provided by even a moderate integration of stored program control. In addition, the ANA 30 subsystem offers an economical means of updating different types of exchange equipment in service, expecially register control systems.

Reference: Ellstam, S & Mannby, P-A: Stored program control register system ANA 30 for crossbar exchanges. Ericsson Review 50 (1973) : 4.

Supplementary Bibliography for Paper 24

ARE

STORED PROGRAM CONTROLLED TRANSIT EXCHANGE ARE 13 WITH CONTROL SYSTEM ANA 302
BY - STIG ELLSTAM AND BENGT OLSSON
ERICSSON REVIEW 3/4 '75 - P116-127

Paper 25

SPC Telephone Switching System (AXE)

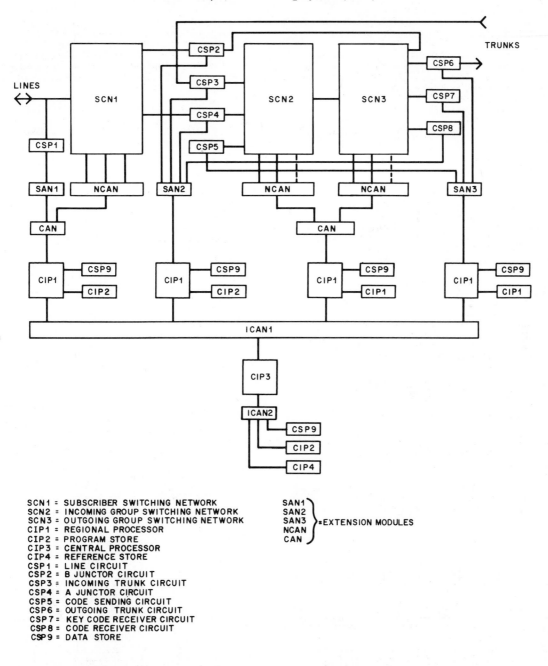

SCN1 = SUBSCRIBER SWITCHING NETWORK
SCN2 = INCOMING GROUP SWITCHING NETWORK
SCN3 = OUTGOING GROUP SWITCHING NETWORK
CIP1 = REGIONAL PROCESSOR
CIP2 = PROGRAM STORE
CIP3 = CENTRAL PROCESSOR
CIP4 = REFERENCE STORE
CSP1 = LINE CIRCUIT
CSP2 = B JUNCTOR CIRCUIT
CSP3 = INCOMING TRUNK CIRCUIT
CSP4 = A JUNCTOR CIRCUIT
CSP5 = CODE SENDING CIRCUIT
CSP6 = OUTGOING TRUNK CIRCUIT
CSP7 = KEY CODE RECEIVER CIRCUIT
CSP8 = CODE RECEIVER CIRCUIT
CSP9 = DATA STORE

SAN1
SAN2
SAN3 ⎫=EXTENSION MODULES
NCAN
CAN ⎭

AXE, A FUNCTIONALLY MODULAR SPC SYSTEM
SYSTEM STRUCTURE AND OPERATION AND MAINTENANCE FEATURES

Kjell Sörme,
Ellemtel Utvecklingsaktiebolag

Inge Jönsson,
Telefonaktiebolaget L M Ericsson

Stockholm, Sweden

INTRODUCTION

AXE is a new SPC-system for telephony. AXE can cater
for different applications up to about 40,000 subscribers. (With a traffic of 0.10 erlangs/subscriber and
an average holding time of 100 seconds.)

AXE is developed jointly by Ellemtel Utvecklingsaktiebolag, Telefonaktiebolaget L M Ericsson and the Swedish
Telecommunications Administration. (Ellemtel Utvecklingsaktiebolag is a development company owned jointly by
Telefonaktiebolaget L M Ericsson and the Swedish Telecommunications Administration.)

AXE is marketed and manufactured by Telefonaktiebolaget
L M Ericsson.

AXE OBJECTIVES

When introducing a new telephone system into a network,
it is essential that it meets the demands which will be
made upon it during its life time, both as a product
and as an exchange in operation. The AXE system is based
on extensive investigations of the expected developments
in switching technology and in the areas of subscriber
services, telephone networks and operation and maintenance.

The AXE system is designed to live in the telephone
networks both of today and of the future.

The introduction of a new telephone system necessitates
the training of staff, the introduction of new documentation and of new aids and support systems. Great emphasis has been put on the development of the AXE system in
order to simplify administrative routines.

The AXE system is designed to be easy to understand and
to handle.

AXE. SYSTEM SURVEY

The AXE system structure is characterized by a pronounced
modularity in both hardware and software. The structure
is formed by a strict hierarchy in four levels: system,
subsystem, function block and function unit.

Subscriber functions, trunk switching functions, signalling functions, charging functions, operation and maintenance functions, each form carefully separated subsystems.

This modularity provides for:

- Great freedom to engineer each exchange individually,
  with regard to application, size and functional
  requirements.

- A system easy to understand and to handle. Such handling
  as training, planning, fault finding etc. can be treated
  in one subsystem at a time.

- A system which can live in a future environment. The
  introduction of common channel signalling, digital
  switching networks, centralized subscriber functions,
  remote controlled subscriber switching networks etc. is
  made easy.

- Possibility to introduce new technology without
  changing the basic system structure e.g. new types of
  memories, electronic switching matrixes.

In order to cover a broad field of application, the AXE
system has a pronounced separation of subscriber switching networks from group switching networks. The AXE
system has a collection of different types of subscriber-
and group switching networks from which a suitable combination can be chosen for each specific exchange.

The control system is a data processing system with
partially decentralized logic. There is one central
duplicated processor working in the synchronous mode
and, depending on the exchange size, a number of small
regional duplicated processors working in the active/stand
by mode.

By decentralizing the data processing system, a system
structure has been created which is economical for small-
scale applications while at the same time meeting the
requirements for high maximum capacity.

The AXE system is designed throughout with printed board
assemblies and uses a new mechanical design, in which
the board magazines form the largest wiring unit.

The AXE system uses reed switches, but it can also be
equipped with digital group switching networks for PCM
switching.

Figure 1 gives a general picture of the hardware structure of the system.

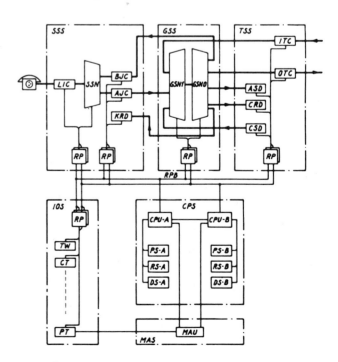

Fig.1 AXE Hardware structure

Reprinted with permission from *1974 Int. Switching Symp. Rec.*, Sept. 9–13, 1974, pp. 411/1–411/7.

The figure shows the hardware of some of the subsystems, for example the subscriber switch subsystem (SSS) which contains the subscriber line circuits LIC, the subscriber switch network SSN, the A-side and B-side junctors, the key set receiver device KRD and the corresponding regional processors RP. The group switch subsystem GSS contains only the group switch network GSN and its regional processors RP. The feeding and the ringing functions toward the subscribers are placed in the SSS in such a way that no d.c. or ringing current passes through the group switch network GSN. This makes it possible to use either a reed network or an electronic network for the GSN. The trunk signalling subsystem TSS, contains the trunks and the signalling devices and their regional processors. The number of regional processors depends on the number of devices in the different subsystems.

In the lower part of the figure both sides of the duplicated, synchronous-mode central processor can be seen, viz CPU-A and B. Each side has a complete set of program store, data store and reference store. The maintenance subsystem, MAS, supervises both CP and RP. Finally the input/output subsystem is shown with some typical I/O devices such as teletypewriters and magnetic tape cartridges.

The AXE project also includes the development of a large number of support systems in the form of programming systems, computer-based design aids, carefully designed documentation structures, testing systems etc. All these provide for system economy in all stages (design, production, installation and operation). The AXE system should be regarded as a telephone exchange system inclusive of support and back-up systems.

AXE. FUNCTIONAL STRUCTURE

For a closer understanding of the AXE system it is necessary to describe the system from its characteristic and specific angle, namely its functional structure. The hardware structure description of the previous chapter gives only an incomplete picture. The functional structure includes both the software and the hardware, and it is therefore possible, in this structure, to describe a complete function regardless of if the function is implemented by software and/or hardware.

The AXE system structure is formed by a strict hierarchy in four levels: system, subsystem, function block and function unit. Figure 2.

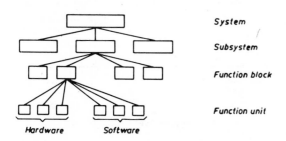

Fig. 2   AXE.   System structure levels

The system, subsystems, function blocks and function units are for all handling purposes considered as "black boxes" on their own level of the system hierarchy with defined interfaces toward the other "black boxes" on the same level. This implies that, when handling function blocks, for instance, no need exists to examine the

function unit structure within the block. The function blocks constitute the normal handling objects, regardless of which combination of hardware and software they are implemented by. A function block is, for example, an incoming trunk function block, which consists of the hardware and the regional and central software that is needed in order to take care of the complete function of the incoming trunk.

At the system level, AXE consists of the switching system APT 210 and the data processing system APZ 210. The block diagram in figure 3 shows this division and the two systems' associated subsystems.

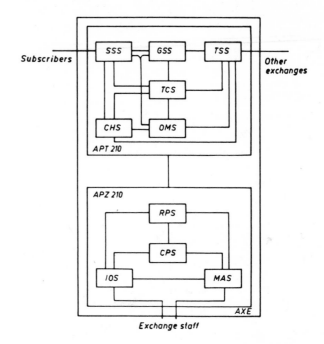

Fig.3   Block diagram

Switching system APT 210

The division of APT 210 into subsystems is determined by the conditions and requirements from the traffic handling and operation functions. These subsystems are implemented partly with hardware and partly with software. The APT hardware handles for example, electrical adaptation to the lines and some simple functions.

The APT software is divided into simple, routine, high-capacity-requirement functions on the one hand and complicated executive functions on the other.

In order to reach a high level of optimization in the control system requirements for large capacity and low cost, the executive functions are performed centrally by the central processor subsystem while the routine, high-capacity-requirement functions are carried out as a preprocessing stage in the regional processor subsystem comprising a number of small simple processors. APT software is thus divided into regional software and central software.

Figure 4 on the next page shows the general distribution between the hardware and the regional and central software for the various subsystems in APT.

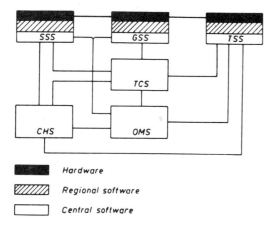

Fig. 4   APT 210. Distribution of hardware and software

Subscriber switch subsystem SSS

Consists of both hardware and software and has the task of supervising the state of connected subscriber lines, setting up and releasing connections in a subscriber switch network, and sending and receiving signals to and from subscribers.

Trunk signalling subsystem TSS

Consists of both hardware and software and has the task of supervising the state of trunk lines to other exchanges and sending and receiving signals to and from other exchanges.

Group switch subsystem GSS

Consists of both hardware and software and, controlled by the traffic control subsystem TCS, has the task of setting up a path through a group switch network between any device in SSS and TSS.

Traffic control subsystem TCS

Consists of software and has the task of controlling and supervising the setting up and releasing of speech connections. TCS stores and analyzes digits received from SSS and TSS and, based on stored information about subscriber categories, routes, tariff classes etc., decides how the call is to be handled.

Charging subsystem CHS

Consists solely of software and has the task of charging for the call. When pulse charging is used, CHS sends charging signals, based on the tariff for each call, via TCS to the subscriber connection or junction line in question or to an internal call meter. When toll ticketing is used, CHS collects the necessary charging information for each call and issues it, for example on a magnetic tape unit in the input/output subsystem IOS.

Operational and maintenance subsystem OMS

Consists mainly of software and has the task of supervising the operation of APT and to take suitable measures if faults occur. OMS also collects traffic statistics etc.

Data processing system APZ 210

APZ 210 has both a central and a regional processor subsystem. In addition, APZ 210 contains an input/output subsystem and a maintenance subsystem. The central software for APT is stored in and executed by the central processor subsystem CPS, while the regional software for APT is stored in and executed by the regional processor subsystem RPS. See fig. 3.

Regional processor subsystem RPS

Consists of both hardware and software and carries out simple, routine, high-capacity-requirement functions. The regional part of the software for APT is stored in and executed by RPS. RPS is divided up into a number of regional processors RP, each of which controls its part of the hardware for APT.

Central processor subsystem CPS

Consists of both hardware and software and carries out the more complex control functions. The central part of the software for APT is stored in and executed by CPS. CPS consists of one duplicated central processor which is working in synchronous mode.

Input/Output subsystem IOS

Consists of both hardware and software and handles man-machine communication in the form of commands and print outs as well as input and output of large amounts of data.

Maintenance subsystem MAS

Consists of both hardware and software and has the task of supervising operation in APZ as well as taking suitable action if faults occur.

AXE SOFTWARE STRUCTURE

The software structure of the AXE system follows the black-box principle, both for central as well as for regional software (software stored and executed by the central and regional processors respectively). The hardware structure of the APZ 210 system is designed to enforce this black-box structure. This necessitates that the structure of the function block software (program and data) is completely internal within both the regional and the central software part of the function blocks.

When discussing software structures there are three essential characteristics: program interfaces, data structures and addressing methods. Interworking between function blocks can only be done between the program parts performed by specific software signals, as shown in fig. 5.

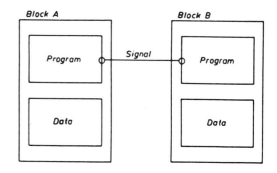

Fig. 5   Interworking between function blocks

Only one function block is active at a time in the central processor. This is accomplished by assigning a unique block number to every function block and in order to gain access to the central software of a certain function block, the block number of this function block is activated. Transfer of control between function blocks by means of the defined software signals is implemented by specific control transfer operations. A consequence of the hardware enforced black-box structure in the software is that no access can be obtained to the program and data of another function block other than by transferring of control to this function block by means of a software signal.

ISS 74

A further objective of the APZ 210 system structure is to facilitate programing in a high level programing language. For this reason addressing and accessing of data are performed with a base address method, the base address containing all the information needed to address and access a single data item. Thus only the location of the base address needs to be given in a machine operation in order to access any piece of data. Every function block has its own set of base addresses only accessible by the program belonging to the same function block.

Figure 6 gives the principal structure of the central software.

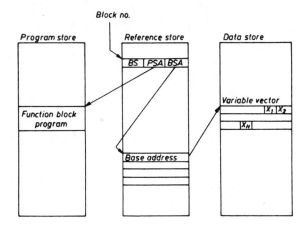

BS = Block state

PSA = Program start address

BSA = Base start address

Fig. 6   Central software structure

The block number for a particular function block defines a reference area in the reference store containing the start address to the program area in the program store and the start address to the base address table in the reference store. The APZ 210 central processor is designed so that all locations given as parameters in the machine operations always refer to the program start address for program locations, respectively to the base address table for base addresses.

Thus the black box principle is upheld while at the same time the machine coded programs and data are completely relocatable.

The design, production, testing and installation of the software is thus greatly facilitated and may in fact be performed on a function block basis controlled by simple commands without the help of a sophisticated on line programing system.

The software structure for the regional software follows the same principles as the central software, but the regional processors are much simpler in their design. The basic principles are however valid, i.e. interworking by means of software signals and no possibility to address and access data outside the own function block.

OPERATION AND MAINTENANCE

By operation and maintenance is meant the supervision of the traffic handling process and all the measures that have to be undertaken in an exchange after cut-over.

Guidelines for AXE operation and maintenance have been:

- the exchanges must be easy to handle

- live traffic is used to supervise the traffic handling process
- faulty units are identified automatically

Routines influenced by the AXE structure

The aim in making the system easy to handle has had a decisive influence when determining the AXE system structure. The following examples of handling show how the operation and maintenance functions are facilitated by the AXE structure.

- extensions
- functional changes
- software maintenance
- maintenance of the central processor subsystem

Extensions

Extension means that the number of devices is increased in an exchange carrying live traffic. The devices added to the exchange are of the same type as the ones that already exist, which means that no new functions are added. The extension covers two parts, the hardware and the software.

The packaging structure is strictly hierarchical having the levels: circuit board, magazine and magazine group. The magazine is called extension module (EM). Depending upon the size of the extension and on whether space already exists, boards only, or extension modules need to be installed.

A principal block diagram of a magazine group is shown in figure 7. The group contains two regional processors and a number of extension modules up to a maximum of 16.

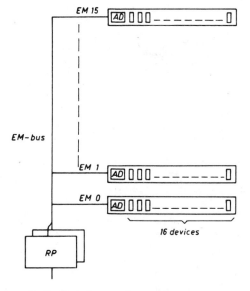

Fig. 7   Block diagram of a magazine group

An extension module is a selfcontained unit which has an adaptation part for connection to the bus from the RP and a number of devices, e.g. 16 trunk circuits. The wires needed to connect an EM are normally speech-wires, bus-wires and -48 V power. Normally the DC/DC supply units and the tone generators are located within the EM and no additional wiring is needed.

To make extensions easy, the system has a minimum of wiring which is specific to the individual exchange.

When the equipment has been installed it can be tested with test traffic generated from test equipment. For larger extensions the testing can be arranged as shown in figure 8.

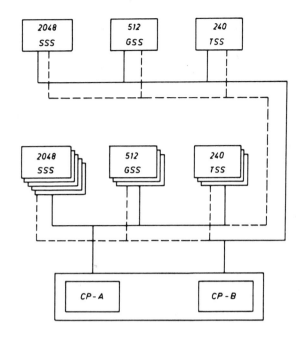

Fig. 8   Testing principle at extensions

the stores independent of other blocks and is thus, if needed, easily relocated on line during any necessary repacking.

When replacing function blocks it is practical to have both the new and the old block in the exchange at the same time, thus testing the new block while the old is still in operation. (See figure 9.) The new block is then taken into service by a command which also removes the old block from service.

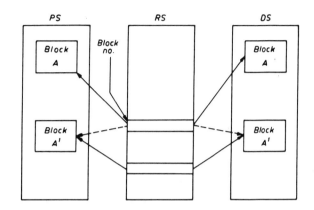

———— references when both the new and the old block are operational

- - - - references when only the new block is operational

Fig. 9   Method for replacing function block

The new equipment installed and its RP:s is connected to one side of the central processor and the extension can thus be tested as a separate exchange. The other side continues with normal traffic handling.

From a software point of view the extension requires additional space for data. If more storage is needed additional store modules have to be installed. To get the necessary continuous free space in the data stores repacking is often necessary. The repacking is performed as a function in the AXE operating system and is initiated by commands. The repacking is done without disturbing the traffic handling. When enough free space has been obtained the expansion of the data area is initiated. This function also is performed within the AXE operating system.

After the expansion has been carried out the new devices and data areas are put into operation. In order to load information about the new equipment the same method is used as described in chapter "Alterations".

To summarize, an extension in AXE means installing equipment with a minimum of individual wiring, testing of installed equipment and repacking and expansion of data areas.

Functional changes

A functional change means that an existing function is modified or that a new function is introduced in an exchange. For AXE, because of the SPC technique, this normally means changes in the software where most functions are performed.

The functionally modular structure and the black-box philosophy of AXE makes the functional change simple. The most important characteristics are:

a)   function blocks intercommunicate by means of well defined formalized software signals

b)   function blocks are completely relocatable

This means that it is possible to replace function blocks or to add new function blocks with a minimal effect on other function blocks. Because of the relocatability each function block can be located anywhere in

With the characteristics mentioned above, a functional change in an exchange is fairly easy to perform. The only thing needed is to select the correct blocks and load them into the processors.

Functional changes may also include introduction of entirely new functions. One of the advantages of SPC technique is the flexibility for future needs. To prepare for new functions the AXE structure is built up with modules in a hierarchy as described earlier. One reason for this is to restrict the changes to as few modules as possible in the system. When designing an entirely new function it is of course necessary to recompile all surrounding function blocks that are dependent on the new function. When the new function is to be introduced into an exchange, the procedures to load the function blocks and take them into service are the same as mentioned above.

Software maintenance

Software maintenance here means the handling of program errors that still may be left in an exchange after cut over. Large software systems are likely to contain some errors after cut over and therefore methods and tools must exist in order to be able to handle these errors and to correct them.

The AXE system structure and the black box philosophy are designed with this objective in mind. Here again the most important characteristics are the intercommunication procedures between function blocks. Checks also exist on the addressing so that no access is possible outside the areas defined for the function blocks in the stores.

When an indication of a software error is recognized it is important to be able to study the program on line. In AXE there are means for tracing a signal both to and from a function block and for tracing accesses to data within a function block. (See figure 10.) These means are built-in, hence they can be used to trace software errors during normal traffic handling.

ISS 74

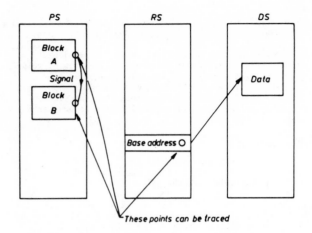

Fig. 10   Tracing of software errors

These points can be traced

When an error is located it must be corrected. Aids exist
in the AXE system to make the required corrections. One
method is to replace the function block containing the
error with a corrected version. Another method is patching
but replacement is preferred, as the operation and maintenance staff then does not have to make changes in live
programs. The correction is thus made with help of the
programing system and a new program is sent to the exchange and loaded. This is done as described in the
chapter "Functional changes".

Maintenance of the central processor subsystem

The central processor subsystem consists of two parallel
processor sides working in a synchronous mode.

Each processor side is built-up with units working together via a unibus system. This implies that all the
units have a standard interface towards the bus and each
unit can be handled by the maintenance system towards
this standard interface.

If an error should occur, the faulty processor side is
identified and the correct one continues to handle the
traffic. It is then important that the faulty unit within
the side is identified so that it can be replaced by a
spare unit.

The indication of an error is usually obtained through an
alarm from the comparison unit between the two processor
sides. When such an error indication occurs the alarms
are analyzed and the maintenance system tries to identify
the side containing the error. If necessary, the maintenance system executes checking programs to find out
which of the two processor sides works correctly. If this
cannot be determined, one of the sides is selected at
random to continue the traffic handling. Should the faulty
one be selected the error will recur whereupon the other
side will be selected. When the faulty processor side is
found it is necessary to identify the faulty unit. This
is done by means of taking one of the units at a time
into operation until an alarm occurs. The last unit taken
into operation is then the faulty one. After replacing
the faulty unit it is taken into operation according to
the procedure described above. If the new unit is fault-
free the whole processor side will return into operation
and the processor system will again be running synchronously in the parallel mode.

Should an error occur which cannot be eliminated by the
above mentioned method, tracing is performed from a
processor test unit. By means of the processor test unit
the internal registers in the processors can be reached
and a manual trace can thus be accomplished.

General administrative routines

The operation and maintenance functions described so

far are of a type special for SPC-systems and the structure of the system determines how the functions are
designed. In AXE there are of course the normal operation
and maintenance functions needed for the telephone
traffic handling. These functions are used for alterations, maintenance and statistics.

The operation and maintenance functions are implemented
in different function blocks, which are grouped together
to form packages. Each package contains a number of
related function blocks. A number of such packages is
defined.

The communication between operation and maintenance staff
and the exchange is performed by means of commands and
printouts. Some of the functions are initiated with
commands and some are fully automatic. The command language is based on telephony terms and knowledge of the
internal structure of the system is not required. Printouts are produced only when information really is needed
by the operator. Typewriters or displays are used for
communication with the system and are located either at
the plant or at a remote point, in the latter case connected via a modem.

Some examples of this type of operation and maintenance
functions are given below.

Alterations

The environment of an exchange changes constantly. Subscribers are moved, routes are expanded, new routes are
introduced, the routing is altered etc. Information
about the environment of the exchange is mapped in the
exchange data stores and the changes must be introduced
here.

Commands concerning subscribers contain information
about subscriber directory number, class of service
and multiple position.

Commands concerning routes contain information about
route characteristics and which trunks that form the
route. Routing commands contain information about
numbering plans and which routes to use to reach the
different destinations.

It is possible to check that the change has been correctly carried out, as information can be obtained by the
operator as to conditions both before and after the
change. This can also be used to retain the earlier
information, if the change has been incorrectly initiated.

Maintenance

Maintenance covers the functions and the necessary
activities to retain a high level of performance. Maintenance includes the means to discover, locate, isolate
and correct errors. In the following, maintenance related
to the traffic handling process is discussed.

Supervision functions continously check that a high
quality level of traffic handling is retained. When an
error occurs they discover and often also locate the
error. Errors are isolated by blocking functions which
often are automatically initiated by the supervision
functions.

The transmission quality of subscriber lines is checked
by means of a check circuit located in the extension
module of junctors (one check circuit per 16 junctors).
When a subscriber line with bad transmission quality
is found, automatic line measuring equipment may be
connected. The measuring equipment can also be used
after a repair.

The switching network is supervised on every call as
ascertain that through-connection without any cross-
connection has been obtained. When error indication
occurs automatic blocking takes place. Information is
printed out for the maintenance staff to replace the
faulty unit.

The trunks are supervised by means of error supervision per route. The software contains functions to check the signalling. In this way an exchange can discover not only its own errors but also those in interworking exchanges. The error supervision function can locate the error to an individual trunk and block it.

Supervision is also performed on the number of blocked devices per route, on the congestion per route, that every trunk has been used at least once a day, etc. Some supervission functions are realized by means of a quotient check, that is the number of errors discovered is compared with the number of successfully performed calls. When the quotient exceeds a preset limit, the maintenance staff is notified.

Statistics

In order to verify that an exchange is correctly dimensioned statistics are obtained from the exchange. It is also important to get statistics for the planning of future exchange extensions and for network planning. These statistics can be obtained by means of traffic measurements where any route may be measured. The traffic measurements can be performed both on routes and internal equipment such as code receivers, junctors etc.

Statistics can also be obtained on the dispersion of traffic between different destinations. This is of value for planning the routes in the network. The statistics are obtained from basic information stored in connection with the traffic handling functions. This information is available to the statistics functions and is processed in the desired way.

CONCLUDING WORDS

The operation and maintenance functions mentioned in this paper contain only a few of the operation and maintenance features available with the AXE-system.

As the philosophy of operation and maintenance will develop for SPC-systems as well as within administrations, new features will be added to the AXE-system.

The main objective, ease of handling, has governed the design of the AXE-system and will continue to do so in future.

ISS 74

Paper 26

Telephone Electronic Switching System No. 10 (D10)

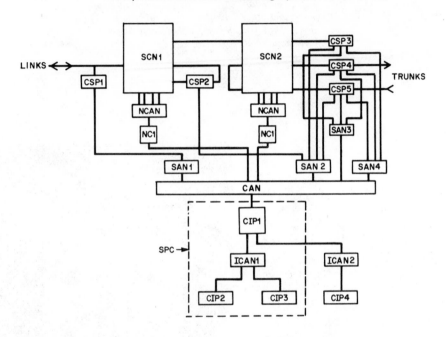

SCN1 = LINE LINK NETWORK
SCN2 = TRUNK LINK NETWORK
CAN = SIGNAL RECEIVER AND DECODER
CIP1 = CENTRAL CONTROL
CIP2 = PERMANENT MEMORY
CIP3 = TEMPORARY MEMORY
CIP4 = MAGNETIC DRUM MEMORY
CSP1 = LINE CIRCUIT
CSP2 = INTRA-OFFICE TRUNK
CSP3 = SERVICE CIRCUITS
CSP4 = OUTGOING TRUNK
CSP5 = INCOMING TRUNK

ICAN1 = MEMORY BUS
ICAN2 = CHANNEL MULTIPLEXER
NC1 = SPEECH PATH CONTROLLER AND
        REGISTER (N+1)
NC2 = NETWORK MAP
SAN1 = LINE SCANNER AND SCANNER
SAN2 = TRUNK SCANNER AND SCANNER
        DRIVER
SAN3 = RELAY CONTROLLER AND REGISTER
SAN4 = SIGNAL DISTRIBUTOR
SPC = CENTRAL PROCESSING SYSTEM

Outline of D10 Electronic Switching System

Koichi Sato*
Itsuo Masumura*
Kazuhiko Wakabayashi*
Michio Tokunaga*
Hirotoshi Shirasu*

ABSTRACT: The D10 electronic switching system is a large-capacity stored program control type electronic exchange whose specifications have been authorized by the Nippon Telegraph and Telephone Public Corporation (NTT) for application to commercial service. It features versatile functions peculiar to electronic systems and overall economical advantages comparable to conventional crossbar exchanges. The new switching system offers many entirely new kinds of services to the subscribers and enables telephone offices to improve and rationalize construction, operation, maintenance, and other activities. The same benefit accrues also to the exchange manufacturers; that is, streamlining and saving of labor can be realized in every stage of design, manufacture and inspection.

INTRODUCTION

RESEARCH and development activities on electronic switching systems in Japan have been carried out since 1964 by Nippon Telegraph and Telephone Public Corporation's Musashino Electrical Communication Laboratory with the cooperation of four companies—Nippon Electric Co., Oki Electric Industry, Fujitsu Limited., and Hitachi, Ltd. As a product of the joint work, the DEX-21 electronic switching system[2] was developed by modifying the DEX-2, following the DEX-1 and the DEX-2[1] which were previously described in this journal. The DEX-21, installed at the Shinkasumigaseki Telephone Office as a field test machine, has been in operation since December 1971. Based on the experience in manufacturing the DEX-21, Nippon Telegraph and Telephone Public Corporation (NTT) worked out a standardized design of the electronic switching system for large offices, set forth specifications, and named the system "D10"[3]. In October 1971, Hitachi supplied the first D10 electronic switching system to NTT's Hirokoji Telephone Office in Nagoya. The system started service in October 1972. This article outlines the D10 electronic switching system. Fig. 1 gives a view of the D10 system installed in the machine room of Hirokoji office.

BASIC FEATURES OF SYSTEM
Stored program controlled system

Basically an automatic telephone exchange has the function of switching a great number of telephone circuits, and its control system must be an on-line real-time system.

Fig. 1– View of installed D10 electronic switching system. A special feature of the system lies in the extremely small installation space required.

That is, a subscriber telephone set, as data terminal equipment, has the functions of transmitting line data (such as on-hook, off-hook, and answer) and data for connection (such as dial number); while an automatic telephone exchange receives these data, and promptly performs data processing including count, translation, selection, and control. Such functions exist also in the conventional step-by-step exchange and crossbar exchange. Exchange systems have been implemented with the same technologies suitable at the time of development, technologies for exchange systems have advanced along with the modernization of switching systems. The conventional switching systems were based upon electromagnetic technology alone

* Totsuka Works, Hitachi, Ltd.

Reprinted with permission from *Hitachi Rev.*, vol. 22, no. 6, pp. 247–252, 1973. Five companion articles on the D10 Electronic Switching System are published in *Hitachi Rev.*, vol. 22, no.'s 6 and 7.

because semiconductor technology was still undeveloped. The telephone switching logic was implemented by mechanisms or relays in wired logic fashion, whereas today in the electronic switching system based on the stored program controlled system, it is implemented by software. An automatic exchange therefore, may be regarded as a special control machine in itself.

In 1946 Von Neuman proposed an electronic computer with program control, and later its industrialization was achieved by the progress of semiconductor technology. But many years went by before telephone communication engineers recognized the electronic computer as a means applicable to their own field. If telephone calls may be regarded as a direct reflection of social activities, then it is natural that automatic exchanges designed to perform management of phonecalls should be required to have functions corresponding to social changes. Thus it was generally believed that, in order to meet such demands, the primary target in electronifying the automatic exchange should lie in the stored program controlled system. The advantages of the stored program controlled system have been recognized worldwide. This is the basic thought underlying the development of the D10 electronic switching system.

Although the control system for electronic switching shares the same basic thought and technologies with the electronic computer, it has the definite purpose of telephone switching. So, it is important that, in the basic concept of maintenance and operatability, the control system should inherit the system and tradition of the conventional exchange technology. Accordingly in setting forth the specifications for the D10 as a commercial model, much effort has been exerted for partial modification so that the D10 may easily be adopted into the existing maintenance and operation system.

The program of the electronic switching system in the stored program controlled system corresponds to the circuit of a crossbar exchange. Therefore, administration of program corresponds to that of the circuit. Under conditions where a switching system is to control functions of a great number of exchange offices, the system is subject to restrictions that are different from those of commercial computer software. Accordingly, it is more logical to regard the character of the whole control system as similar to that of a crossbar exchange.

Special features of D10

The D10, a standard large-capacity system for line switching and toll switching following the C400 and the C82 crossbar exchanges, has the following special features in addition to the previously mentioned general features inherent in stored-program control.
(1) The system uses newly developed miniature crossbar switches of the mechanical latching type and miniature relays of the magnetic latching type in its speech paths together with full stored-program control, so that

control of the speech paths is highly flexible.
(2) High-speed core memories and high-speed CSL type integrated circuits enable the central control to achieve the highest performance as a processor in commercial electronic switching systems and to have a high traffic processing capacity as large as 9×10^4 BHC (without additional processors).
(3) Installation space has been vastly reduced by adopting integrated circuits, magnetic drums, small-size equipment for the speech path, and high-density mounting.
(4) Data channels to which various computer input-output devices can be connected have given greater flexibility in data exchange between the system and the outside.
(5) An economical memory system and reduced installation space have been made possible by introducing magnetic drums. Moreover, various features not included in other systems are made possible; namely rewriting of office data on an on-line basis, high-speed program loading, periodic logging of systems information for provision against trouble, electronic metering, the $N + 1$ redundant system of the main memory, and economical variable abbreviated dialing. Thus the system has outstanding economy and performance.

These are features that the D10 can well be proud of to the world. 35 million-bits floating head magnetic drums, which have made the above various features possible, have been manufactured by Hitachi, Ltd. under the joint study of NTT's Musashino Electrical Communication Laboratory.

Flexibility required in total network

With the advance of human society, sophisticated functions are being required of communication service. In addition to conventional telephone switching services, the following new services are being considered. And the D10 has sufficient flexibility to provide the new services:
(1) New telephone services: The D10 makes it possible to afford economically such new telephone services as variable abbreviated dialing, transfer of terminating calls, overriding, and add-on, which have been uneconomical in conventional switching systems. Especially in centrex service, new services are in great demand for raising business efficiency, so that new applications are expected in this field.
(2) International subscriber toll dialing: International subscribers dialling requires the system to handle internationally determined special procedures regarding the numbering plan, signaling system, and charging. Furthermore, these procedures are not only complicated but also subject to change in future. Stored program control in this aspect, is quite advantageous because of its flexibility. Advances in satellite communication and tightened relations between nations will rapidly diffuse international subscriber toll dialing in the foreseeable future.
(3) Video telephone: Since video telephone requires ex-

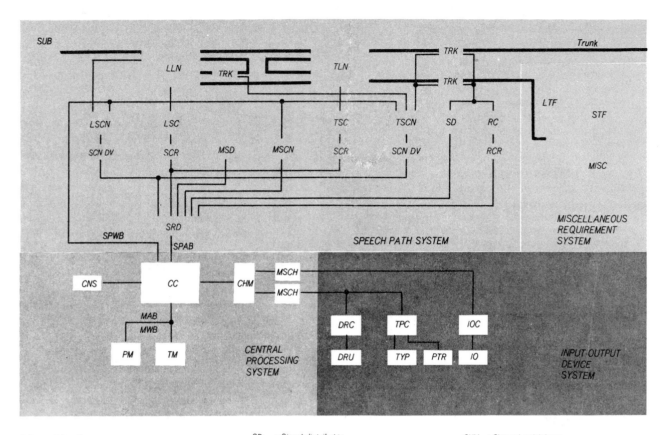

SUB	: Subscriber	SD	: Signal distributor	CHM	: Channel multiplexor
LLN	: Line link network	LSC	: Line-link speech path controller	MSCH	: Multiplex subchannel
TLN	: Trunk link network	TSC	: Trunk-link speech path controller	DRC	: Magnetic drum controller
TRK	: Trunk	RC	: Relay controller	DRU	: Magnetic drum unit
LSCN	: Line scanner	SPAB	: Speech path address bus	TPC	: Typewriter paper tape reader controller
TSCN	: Trunk scanner	SPWB	: Speech path answer bus	PTR	: Paper tape reader
SRD	: Signal receiver and distributor	CC	: Central control	TYP	: Typewriter
MSD	: Maintenance signal distributor	CNS	: Test console	IO	: Input output device
MSCN	: Maintenance scanner	PM	: Semipermanent memory	IOC	: Input output device controller
SCR	: Speech path controller register	TM	: Temporary memory	LTF	: Line test frame
SCNDV	: Scanner driver	MAB	: Memory address bus	STF	: Supervising and test frame
RCR	: Relay controller register	MWB	: Memory answer bus	MISC	: Miscellaneous equipment frame

Fig. 2—System configuration of D10 electronic switching system.
The speech path system consists mainly of electromagnetic components, and the central processing system
and input-output device system are of a construction similar to electronic computers.

pensive wide band transmission channels, attempts have been made for effective utilization of the channels. The control and charging of the system, however, also present problems. Moreover, various services including conference telephone and information service must be made available, in addition to simple face-to-face telephone.

(4) Data exchange, data service: Data exchange is made in two forms—line switching, and store and forward switching. The former is expected to be possible in any switching system because telephone switching itself is a kind of line switching. The latter should be possible by using the central processing system. Also of interest is the adaptability of the switching system to various data service. The possibility must be explored.

(5) Development into total network: How to implement

the above-mentioned services in a public communication network is a matter of importance. The switching system, which is placed at the switching point of the network, constitutes the nucleus of communication service functions. Flexibility of D10 will be given full play in this respect.

Construction

Fig. 2 depicts the standard D10 system configuration. The system is divided into four systems, namely the speech path system, the central processing system, the input-output device system, and the miscellaneous equipment system. The speech path system performs establishing and releasing of connections between subscribers and trunks. The central processing system controls the connection. The input-output device system is used for supplying data to and taking them from the system and for man-machine interface. The miscellaneous equipment system consists of accessory equipment.

The interface between the speech path system and the central processing system consists of an address bus (32 bits) and answer bus (32 bits). Designation of equipment in the speech path system is performed by the decoder in the speech path control system so that changes in the mode of speech path control might not affect the central processing system. This is to enable possible future system changes to be made independently in each system (because techniques for the central processing system are slightly different from those for the speech path system, so that the techniques are unlikely to be developed at the same pace), and to make the interface suitable for general uses as far as possible. As the interface between the central processing system and the input-output device system, the 1969 Japan Standard Input-Output Interface is adopted, so that general-purpose input-output devices can be connected.

The miscellaneous equipment system is closely related to maintenance of the office. Careful consideration is given so that as much equipment in the C400 crossbar exchange as possible may be used in much the same way.

Economy of system

The D10, with all the new functions, is required to be compatible with the conventional C400 crossbar exchange also in economy. At the stage of development, about 40% of the overall cost reduction was achieved by eliminating the redundancy of the DEX-2, reducing drastically the number of component parts through system improvement, and cutting down on component cost. As a result, we obtained the prospect that the D10, when mass-produced, will be comparable in economics to the C400 as installed in large offices. While in the cases of high traffic and in terms of new service features, the D10 is advantageous, for centrex service satisfying the above conditions, the D10 is expected to be less expensive than the C410 in the range of almost all applications.

In evaluating economics, one should consider installation space, power consumption, and installation cost in addition to the equipment cost. Installation space required for the D10 has been vastly reduced—to less than one-third of that for the C400. This would be helpful in reducing the office and building cost when increasing the number of terminals in offices in large cities. As for power consumption, introduction of noncurrent holding type speech path elements such as crossbar switches and trunk pattern relays has greatly reduced electric power that increases in proportion to traffic, thus resulting economical power supply equipment. Installation cost has measurably been saved by reducing the number of frames and interface wiring, and by using connectors for wiring and computer programs for installation tests. In overall economics, including the above, we obtained the prospect that the D10 will merit comparison with the C400 in a wider range of applications.

Environmental conditions

The No. 1 ESS, DEX-1 was designed so that an air conditioning system would not be required, following the tradition of electromagnetic switching system. This condition, however, resulted in higher electronic component cost especially for core memories and electronic circuit packages. It would be difficult to provide economical high-speed memories without the use of air conditioners, so that it would be disadvantageous in overall economics. Therefore the DEX-2 was provided with a sectionalized air conditioning system—a duplicate system. In the DEX-21, economical air conditioning was achieved by using an air conditioner for the office building and an additional air conditioner. The temperature and humidity are $10-40^\circ$C and 30–80 RH even in the worst case where one air-conditioning system is shut down. With the D10, in accordance with the actual conditions of existing telephone offices, the temperature and humidity were set at $5-35^\circ$C and 45–85% RH respectively, which conform with the relevant JIS specifications for normal temperature and humidity.

Direct-current power is supplied in two voltages, viz. −48V and +50V. Other voltages are derived from the −48V, the conversion being performed within the frames as far as possible. This is because supply of low-voltage large currents through a common bus would impose severe restrictions on frame arrangement because of voltage drops. As for alternating currents, those for the magnetic drum drive, which does not permit a moment's interruption, are supplied by inverters in the frame, while for other uses, commercial AC sources are employed.

Details of equipment design will be described in a companion article. For the DEX-21 and the D10, the small-scale high-density mounting method for the DEX-2 was improved. Since the existing telephone offices have sufficiently high ceilings, the frame height was set at 2,740 mm as in the case of the carrier system and the crossbar system, to use the space effectively. Moreover, to facilitate manufacture and maintenance, two-side mounting with movable gates as in the DEX-2 was discarded in favor of one-side mounting. As for cable wiring, the free-access floor was abolished for economical reasons; a frame-mounted rack of plate-rack construction was adopted.

FEATURES

As a special feature of the stored control program system, the D10 employs common hardware, which is used for various purposes by varying the type of software. The programs divide largely into three series—the D100, D160, and D180. The D100 series programs are for on-line processing in an exchange; with a duplicate central processing system, high-reliability continuous operation is performed as an on-line real-time system. The D160 series programs are for non-real time batch processing with a single or duplicated central controls. The D180 series programs, with the single central processing system and input-output devices, perform general-purpose off-line batch processing, like a general-purpose computer.

New services for subscribers

The capabilities of new telephone services have been discussed previously in this article. To start with, the D10 is now providing the same types of services as being offered by the C400 and the C410 crossbar exchanges. In line with the NTT policy, programs are being added to make various new services available for the benefit of subscribers, and to help create new demands for telephone.

In introducing new services into the C400 crossbar switching system, it was necessary to install special magnetic drums at the office and adapters at the subscriber terminals. In the case of the D10, the originally installed magnetic drums can be jointly used, and reswitching in the speech path unit equipment is available, so that no adapter is needed at the subscriber terminal. Therefore, the economical dividing line between the C400 and the D10 depends upon the subscriptions to new services.

New features in maintenance and operation

In addition to new services to subscribers, the electronic switching system offers a major advantage in improvements in the fields of installation, maintenance, and operation on the part of NTT. The following new features will be made possible:

Improvement of charge calculation: In the conventional electromagnetic switching system, call frequency is registered in a charging meter provided for each subscriber, and data are read from the meter. In the D10, the call frequency is accumulated and registered in an area corresponding to each subscriber in the magnetic drum, and the data can be transferred to magnetic tape any time. In foreign countries an automatic message accounting (AMA) system is adopted rather than magnetic drums, and this system requires frequent changing of magnetic tape. In terms of operation, the electronic charging meter system with magnetic drums is thought to be better than the AMA system.

Improvement of traffic measuring: Like charge data, traffic data are stored in the magnetic drum and read out on magnetic tape as occasion demands. In traffic measuring, data must be recorded at specified times, so that, when charging meters are used, maintenance men must be on hand to do the job. In the D10, by contrast, data recording is performed by program operation.

Processing of the measured data for statistics is accomplished by simply feeding the magnetic tape to a computer.

Improvement in office subscriber data renewal: In the traditional crossbar exchange, jumper field wiring is required to be altered, when setting and changing office data (e.g. concerning numbering plan, trunking plan, equipment allocation) and subscriber data (e.g. on correspondence of telephone number and equipment number, and subscriber service class.) Such routine work for maintenance and operation of a switching system can be performed by typewriter operation in the D10 so that operatability is improved to a great extent. The D10 has such a high degree of freedom that there is hardly any hardware restriction in

setting the numbering plan and trunking plan, and subscriber services are available in many classes. This will be advantageous in office design and operation.

A change in the charge system can be met simply by altering office data or programs. Such a functional change, which must be carried out in a specified period of time, presents difficulties in preparation and execution if it involves a large amount of hardware changes, but it is very easy if accomplished by software switching.

Simplification of machine maintenance: Electronic equipment, which makes up the bulk of the control section, uses high-reliability components with sufficient allowance on performance, so that errors and faults are extremely limited. If any error or fault occurs, it is localized by means of a diagnostic dictionary, so that swift repair is possible.

When subscriber and trunk lines are to be tested from the test board, it is possible to test all circuits successively by program; periodical and unscheduled tests are effected efficiently. All connection tests in offices can be conducted by means of a typewriter.

Modernization of installation: Owing to high-density mounting of equipment, the D10 electronic switching system requires very few frames. In the D10, one frame is equivalent to several frames in conventional systems so that most cable wiring (formerly made during installation work) comes completed in the equipment. Interframe cable wiring has been drastically reduced by the above fact and the characteristics of time-sharing use of signaling wire. Since plug-in connectors are used for interframe wiring, cable connection tests can be completed before installing the frames. Moreover, connector wiring can be performed by the automatic wiring machine, without haman aid.

After installation and cable connection, thorough debugging is carried out with a system test program, as to the central processing system, the input-output device system, and all speech paths, all terminals, and all trunks; and trouble locations are typed out. Such thorough installation tests are difficult with crossbar exchanges.

Following the system test for hardware, on-line program tests are started by loading on-line programs and office data. By complete debugging of the programs and data, smooth cut-over is possible.

The procedures described above make it possible to speed up installation work, save labor, and assure better quality of installation work. On the other hand, advanced technology is required in analyzing trouble because sophisticated components, devices, and complex programs are involved.

As discussed above, improvement has been made on several points. The system will surely contribute much to modernization in construction, maintenance and operation at telephone offices.

Reliability

The life of a telephone exchange is usually regarded as 40 years, and a 2-hour system-down-time is usually allowed in this lifetime. Since these values might result in higher costs,

Outline of D10 Electronic Switching System

the conditions were reviewed and relaxed at the design of the DEX-21. Reliability requirements of components and redundancy of equipment were determined to meet the following targets:

Life .... 22 years
Frequency of trouble
    .... 2 times/week for 20,000-terminal office (excluding electromagnetic components for speech path)
Down time .... Not more than one system down lasting over 30 minutes in 10 years

As a result of specific design based on the above figures, the following calculation values were obtained:
Mean time between failures
(MTBF) of system .... about 100 (30,000 terminals) or 150 (10,000 terminals) hours
Expected value of accumulated down time
(30 minutes and above) .... 0.6 hour/20 years

Better values are being shown in actual operation, which means that the reliability of components is better than expected.

The most salient feature of the D10 redundancy design is the redundant system of the memories. While in early models, memories were completely duplicated, the DEX-21 and later models adopt the $N+1$ redundant system in which one spare unit is provided for all memories. In the $N+1$ redundant system, copies of the temporary memory data and the semipermanent memory data are stored in magnetic drums; when one memory fails the copy of the data in the faulty memory is read out into the spare memory, which thus replaces the faulty one. In this way much saving is accomplished by using an inexpensive magnetic drum to take the place of costly memories. Since the content of the temporary memory changes momentarily, new data are transferred to the magnetic drum every several seconds. When switching over to the temporary memory, processing must be interrupted for 10 seconds. However, this does not affect calls that have already come through, but only those in the process of dialing or connection. The probability of being affected by interruption is far smaller than the misoperation rate allowable (2×10^{-4}) for an ordinary switching system, so that we regarded the processing interruption as allowable.

STREAMLINING IN MANUFACTURING STAGE

For exchange manufacturers, the shift from crossbar exchanges to electronic switching systems has brought on streamlining in all production activities including design, manufacture, and inspection.

In the field of design, design automation by computers is widely adopted; the central processing system, logics, and other electronic devices are designed chiefly by this method. As input information, a logic circuit designer prepares logic cards that determine logic, and assign cards that assign logic circuit elements to the circuit board. Then detailed design is made using the design automation system; circuit diagrams, wiring tables, print pattern data, data for automatic wiring machine, and data for test equipment are all prepared automatically. If these operations are made entirely manually, such a method will require complex and long procedures, and inevitably will entail trouble due to human error. With the automation system, design of extremely high quality is obtained assisted in part by the various check systems incorporated in the system.

While the recent rise of personnel wages is forcing mechanization and labor-saving in manufacture, fortunately electronic equipment which largely makes up the electronic switching system is of a construction that lends itself to automation, so that there is the possibility of wide range of automation. Introduction of automation is being considered for various manufacturing steps including wiring of electronic equipment and manufacture of packages.

Since the electronic packages use plug-in connections, inspection of individual units (such as packages and wiring) in process is made easy. As test data to be used in the inspection, information obtained from the stated design automation system is fed as input to the tester, and tests are conducted at the intermediate stages of packaging, wiring, etc. Finally these construction elements that have undergone tests are assembled. Then, program tests are conducted on the basis of programs incorporating specified test conditions.

In this way, labor-saving is realized in each stage of manufacture and inspection, and fully automatic examination by program is performed, so that products of high quality can be manufactured. By applying software to switching functions, very few kinds of equipment will suffice, and various functional requirements do not much affect hardware specifications, so that steady production plans can be formulated.

As stated, manufacture of electronic switching systems lends itself to labor saving—a major requirement of the times and which will lead to improvement of product quality.

CONCLUSIONS

It has been seen that the D10 electronic switching system has several unique features and excellent economies. Extensive introduction of the system is expected to contribute to the advances in NTT's total communication network. Striving for further cost reduction and higher function of the system, the authors hope to develop electronic equipment for the next generation, based on the D10 manufacturing techniques. The authors wish to express their sincere thanks for the guidance provided by members of Nippon Telegraph and Telephone Public Corporation and the companies taking part in the joint research and development work on electronic switching systems.

REFERENCES

(1) Kubo, et al.: *Hitachi Hyoron* **51,** 951–984 (Oct. 1969)
(2) Yamauchi, et al.: Communications Laboratory, Communications Laboratory Report 20, 3
(3) Ishii, et al.: D10 automatic switching system, Shisetsu 23, 3.5–9

Supplementary Bibliography for Paper 26

D10

SOFTWARE

COMMAND LANGUAGE FOR D10 ELECTRONIC SWITCHING SYSTEM
OGATA H + NAKAJO T + AWAJI K
P80 OF CONF SOFTWARE ENGRG FOR TELECOMMUN SWITCHING SYST.,
APR 1973, INST ELECT ENG (LONDON), CONF PUB 97

OPERATIONAL SOFTWARE FOR D10 ELECTRONIC SWITCHING SYSTEM
DOKE K + TAMAKI K AND OTHERS
HITACHI REV. 22 (7): 292-8 (1973)

COMPUTER-AIDED DIMENSIONING OF D10 ELECTRONIC SWITCHING SYSTEM
FOR LOCAL OFFICE USE
KODAIRA K + OHARA K + OSANO I
REV. ELEC COMMUN LAB 20: 951-961 (NOV/DEC 1972)

PRODUCTION AND MANAGEMENT OF D10 PROGRAM FILE (SWITCHING SYSTEM)
TAKAMURA S + NAKAJIMA H + MORIYA K
JAP TELECOMMUN REV. 15 NO. 2: 85-92 (APR 1973)

DESIGN PRODUCTION AND MANAGEMENT OF D10 SOFTWARE SYSTEM
TAKAMURA S + HONMA Y + MORIYA K
P170 OF CONF SOFTWARE ENGRG FOR TELECOMMUN SWITCHING SYST.,
APR 1973, INST. ELECT ENG (LONDON) CONF PUB 97

STANDARDIZED PROGRAM SYSTEMS FOR D10
ELECTRONIC SWITCHING SYSTEM
KOTARO DOKE
KENSO TAMAKI
SHOICHI MURASE
MUTSUO IKUTA
HITACHI REVIEW VOL. 24 (1975) NO. 11 P435

COMPONENTS, EQUIPMENT, HARDWARE AND PRODUCTION

CENTRAL PROCESSING SYSTEM AND INPUT OUTPUT DEVICES OF D10
ELECTRONIC SWITCHING SYSTEM
ARAI Y + KOONO Z + MUNETAKA H AND OTHERS
HITACHI REV. 22 (7): 253-65 (1973)

SPEECH PATH AND MISCELLANEOUS EQUIPMENT FOR D10 ELECTRONIC
SWITCHING SYSTEM
ISHII E + GONO M + KUWAHARA H + SEKI S + MUKAEMACHI T
HITACHI REV. 22 (7): 266-75 (1973)

PACKING AND ASSEMBLY OF D10 ELECTRONIC SWITCHING AND ITS
COMPONENTS
TAMURA A + TACHIBANA Y + KASUGA K AND OTHERS
HITACHI REV. 22 (7): 305-15 (1973) HITACHI HYORON 54 (11):

1009-17 (1972) (IN JAPANESE) BTL TRANSLATION NO. 61:33P
(1973)

FIELD EXPERIENCE AND MTC

SERVICE EXPERIENCE OF D10 ELECTRONIC SWITCHING SYSTEM
IKETANI H + TANNO T
JAP TELECOMMUN REV. 15 (4): 231-7 (OCT 1973)

D10 ELECTRONIC SWITCHING SYSTEM 5 (MAINTENANCE)
NAKATANI K + MORIYA K
JAP TELECOMMUN REV. 14: 123-30 (JUL 1972)

D10 ESS TRAINING SYSTEM
TAKAHASHI T + KURIHARA T
JAP TELECOMMUN. REV. 16 (2): 111-15 (APR 1974)

D-10 STANDARDIZED PROGRAM FEATURE AND FIELD TEST REPORT
T. MURATA, H. HATAKEYAMA, H. ISHIKAWA
JAPAN TELECOMM. REVIEW - JAN. 1976 - P11-16

_____

Paper 27

Telephone Electronic Switching System No. 20 (D20)

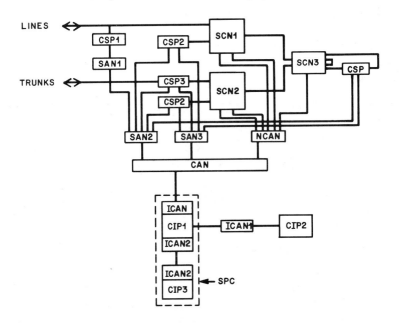

SCN1 = LINE LINK NETWORK
SCN2 = TRUNK LINK NETWORK
SCN3 = JUNCTOR LINK NETWORK
CAN = SIGNAL RECEIVER DISTRIBUTOR
CIP1 = CENTRAL CONTROL
CIP2 = MAGNETIC DRUM
CIP3 = TEMPORARY MEMORY

CSP1 = LINE CIRCUIT
CSP2 = SERVICE CIRCUITS
CSP3 = INCOMING AND OUTGOING TRUNKS
ICAN1 = MAGNETIC DRUM CHANNEL
NC   = SWITCH CONTROLLER
SAN1 = CALL DETECTOR
SAN2 = SCANNER
SAN3 = SIGNAL DISTRIBUTOR AND
          RELAY CONTROLLER
SPC = CENTRAL PROCESSOR

D-20 Electronic Switching System (Part 1)
—System Description and Objectives—

By Sumio Yazu*, Hiroshi Iketani**,
and Takenobu Tanno**

MUSASHINO ELECTRICAL COMMUNICATION LABORATORY, NTT*
ENGINEERING BUREAU, NTT**

The newest type of electronic switching system based on the DEX-A11, called the D-20, has been developed. The D-20 complements the D-10 by offering economical electronic switching service for small-medium size telephone offices. This paper describes the objectives and system outline of the D-20.

1. Introduction

Japan's telecommunication network has over 20 million telephone subscribers, and provides new telephone services such as "abbreviated dialing" and "call waiting" in addition to the basic telephone services.

The higher level of social activities has brought about the need for new kinds of telecommunication service. Especially, the rapid spread of electronic computers has accelerated new lines of communication between "man and machine" or between "machine and machine" in addition to those between "man and man". This tendency is expected to lead to prosperity in the data communication and video communication fields.

In order to offer such a variety of communications, it is thought that electronic switching systems with stored program control would be the most appropriate, and are now expected to form the nucleus of the total communication network in Japan.

As a first step, a large size electronic switching system, called the D-10, has been developed, and many D-10 central offices are already in commercial use.

In order to expand the applicable range of stored program control electric switching systems to small offices, NTT's Electrical Communication Laboratory made a start in 1969 on a project for a small-medium size electronic switching system.

In general, it has been said that the stored program control switching system is not economical for small-medium size office use because of the cost of the central processor, especially the high cost of memory devices.

However, economy is achieved by simplifying the central processor and by storing even the call processing programs in an economical file memory (magnetic drum memory) to reduce the high cost random access memory.

In 1971, a laboratory test model called the DEX-A1, was built to study implementation of the stored program control techniques with frequent use of a drum memory, and its practicability was proved through on-line tests.

A field trial model called the DEX-A11, an improved version of the DEX-A1, was next developed and has been operating successfully since customer service started in November 1973.

Based on the DEX-A11, the newest type called the D-20 has been finally developed, and a commercial test is planned for 1975.

In the following, the D-20 will be briefly presented with the emphasis on objectives and system description.

Reprinted with permission from *Japan Telecommun. Rev.*, pt. 1, pp. 243–249, Oct. 1974.

Details of the hardware and software will be described in the next issue.

2. Objectives

2.1 Range of Applicability

A large size electronic switching system, called the D-10, has been developed and many D-10 central offices are now providing good service. Since the number of small-medium size offices of less 10,000 lines is about 80% of the total in Japan, it is uneconomical to apply the D-10 to all of them. The D-20 is designed for local switching systems with about 10,000 lines.

Moreover, it is possible for the system to provide four-wire toll service and video-telephone service by replacing the speech path equipment.

2.2 Flexibility

It is becoming apparent that flexibility is extremely important for an electronic switching system. Many services provided today had not been conceived of even 20 years ago when our crossbar switching system was designed.

In accordance with the rapid advance in social activities, the electronic switching system will be required to provide various new services not known today. For such requirements, the D-20, with stored program control, will provide new services economically in small-medium city areas.

2.3 Maintenance and Administration

The new system should be equally dependable and more efficient in maintenance and administration, compared with existing systems. Therefore, the D-20 electronic switching system uses highly reliable components in package form, and an appropriate redundancy structure. Also, the D-20 system improves maintenance and administration by use of stored program control.

For instance, although the method of locating troubles in a switching network is logically almost the same as for crossbar systems, the maintenance personnel has only to replace faulty packages by the aid of a diagnostic program instead of repairing the hardware itself. Also, changing information on customers, such as class of telephone service, and various kind of traffic measurements, are easily carried out through teletypewriter input commands.

Because of its intended use in nonmetropolitan areas, the D-20 is designed to be largely unattended. That is, maintenance tests, traffic measurements, and so on, are designed to be remote controlled.

Needless to say, repair or replacement of packages, connections in MDF, and so on, give rise to work in the exchange offices.

2.4 Miniaturization of the System

The reduction of the space required for switching systems in nonmetropolitan areas, as well as in metropolitan areas, is extremely urgent, because within 15 years telephone traffic will rise to several times its present level. The use of miniaturized components and compact assembly reduces the number of frames, the system taking up one-third the floor space of the C-460, which is the standard medium size crossbar system in NTT.

2.5 Economic Considerations

The cost of the system should be as low as possible to meet the preceding objectives.

Since the D-20 is intended for small-medium size offices in nonmetropolitan areas, and the expected demand for new services will not be very great, the realistic objective is to make it competitive with the standard C-460 crossbar system in terms of installed first cost, without the advantages of new services.

In order to attain this objective, the D-20 adopts various kinds of techniques: frequent use of a low cost drum memory, suitable switching network for small-medium size offices, adopting the Call Detector which concentrates line scanning points, simplification of the central processor, and so on.

Besides, by improvement of maintenance and administration, the annual cost is expected to be reduced, compared with conventional crossbar switching systems.

3. System Description

3.1 General Description and Main Features

The general formation of the D-20 is classified roughly into two main parts: The switching network (SP system) to make up speech paths and the central processor (CP system) to control the switching network. The outstanding attributes of the electronic switching system would be fully achieved by applying the stored program control.

As mentioned before, the stored program control is not considered economically applicable for small size offices because of the cost of the central processor, especially the high cost of the memory.

The cost tendency of the electronic switching system is shown in Figure 1. The SP system grows in comparatively small steps, and its cost increases gradually in proportion to the number of lines.

In the stored program control, however, the CP

Table 1. Main Features of the D-20

Field of Application		Local switching
Maximum size	Network capacity	800 erlangs
	Call-handling capacity	About 12,500 busy-hour calls
Speech path	Basic components	Miniature crossbar switch (8 x 8) and miniature relay
	Network construction	Junctor folded six-stage
	Network growth unit	50 erlangs (1,280 lines)
Central processor	Basic components	Logical IC, IC memory and magnetic drum (floating head)
	Maximum amount of temporary memory	65,536 words (16 + 1 bits per word)
	Maximum amount of magnetic drum memory	20 megabits
Customer services		Standard telephone service. abbreviated dialing service, call waiting service, international D.D.D. service, and so on
Reliability		Less than one hour in 20 years
Call processing Irregularities		Less than 2×10^{-4}
Floor space		One third of C460

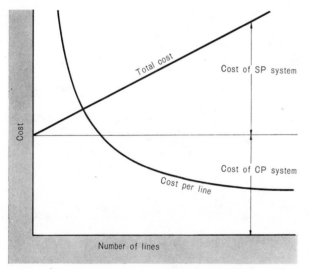

Figure 1. Cost tendency of the electronic switching system

system, especially memory units, are in general to be provided with the maximum call-handling capacity of the system from the initial state.

The cost of the CP system, therefore, remains nearly constant regardless of the size of the office, and so the system installed cost per line is relatively high in the first stages.

To cope with this problem, approaches in the following two directions were reviewed:

(1) Frequent use of low cost memory devices

(a) To store most of the programs in the file memory (magnetic drum) and transfer as many programs as required to the temporary memory if necessary.

(b) To execute all the programs stored in the magnetic drum cyclically.

(2) Reduction of the quantity of the memory itself

(a) To adopt a wired logic control in a part of the system

(b) To adopt complex instructions

The review has resulted in the following conclusions:

The handling capacity of the system decreases in (1–b).

The flexibility deteriorates in (2–a).

Memory quantity is not reduced as expected in (2–b).

On the other hand, the design objectives of both economy and flexibility are satisfied in (1–a).

That is, in the D-20, the magnetic drum with a low bit cost is used for storing most of the programs, including call processing programs as well as maintenance programs, administration programs, and various other data.

Program segments stored in the magnetic drum (DR) are transferred through the magnetic drum channel (DRCH) into the temporary memory (TM) to be executed by the central control (CC), as shown in Figure 2.

According to the size of an office, the D-20 switching system memory devices are arranged on an economical basis. At a small office, in order to reduce the high cost temporary memory, most of the call processing programs are stored in a file memory (magnetic drum) instead of the temporary memory, and as the size of the office increases, additional TMs (8 kilo-

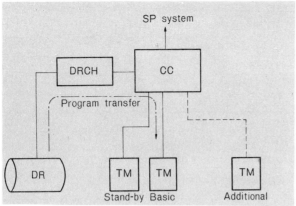

Figure 2. Block diagram of processing by transferring programs

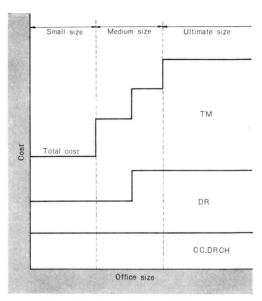

Figure 3. Cost tendency of CP system

words each) are provided to store the frequently used call processing programs. Additional DRs are installed with growing subscriber data.

By using the several techniques described above, a cost reduction of the CP system was attained. Figure 3 shows the cost tendency of the CP system for each size of office.

Three kinds of system files are provided according to the size of an office: small, medium and ultimate size files. Office file renewals can be easily carried out with the use of the standby magnetic drum memory maintaining continuous system operation.

3.2 Hardware

A block diagram of the D-20 is shown in Figure 4. The basic configuration of SP system is essentially the same as that of the D-10.

From the point of its being suitable for a small-medium size office, the switching network is composed of a junctor folded six-stage network, as shown in

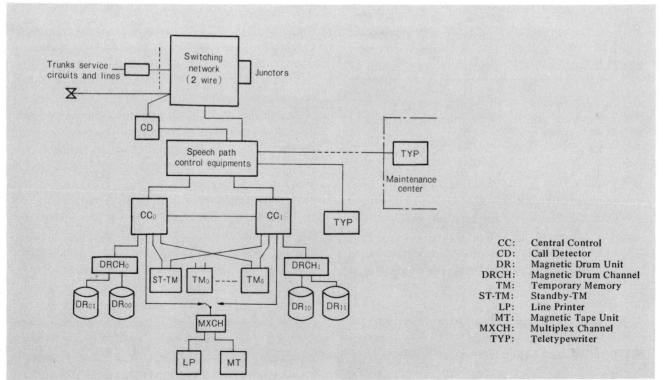

Figure 4. D-20 block diagram

CC: Central Control
CD: Call Detector
DR: Magnetic Drum Unit
DRCH: Magnetic Drum Channel
TM: Temporary Memory
ST-TM: Standby-TM
LP: Line Printer
MT: Magnetic Tape Unit
MXCH: Multiplex Channel
TYP: Teletypewriter

226

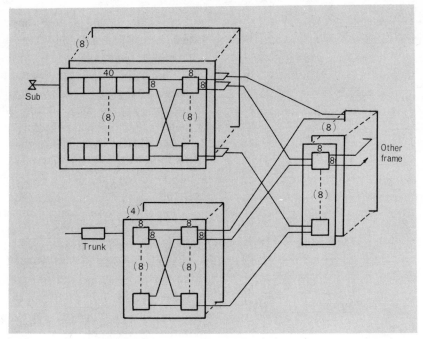

Figure 5. D-20 network fabric (2-wire network)

Figure 5.

One unit of the network, which has a traffic capacity of 108.8 erlangs, is mounted on a switch frame (SWF).

Ultimately the D-20 system consists of eight SWFs which can carry over 800 erlangs of traffic. The switch of a network is made up of 8 x 8 mechanical latch crossbar switches.

The call detector (CD), which concentrates line scanning points when the subscriber calling rate is low, is provided every 256 lines. By using the CD, the cost of scanners and scanning processing time are reduced.

Trunk circuits (TRK) are almost the same as those of the D-10, except for a few special circuits and they are compatible with those of the D-10. Interfaces between the SP system and the CP system are concentrated in the speech path control (SPC), and each subsystem may be easily improved independently.

The CP system consists of central controls (CCs), magnetic drum channels (DRCHs), magnetic drums (DRs) and temporary memories (TMs), and a multiplex channel (MXCH).

Although one CC unit is enough to control a system, CC is duplicated for emergencies, and the redundancy structure of TM is economically designed by adopting the n + 1 standby system.

Each CC, DRCH and DR is directly associated and designed as a single switchable entity. This reduces both the quantity of equipment required and the number of programs required for the administration.

The basic central processor frame (CPF) contains duplicated CCs, DRCHs and DRs (524 kilo-words each), eight TMs (8 kilo-words each) and a MXCH. In addition to the basic frame, a growth frame which allows for expansion of the two DRs (524 kilo-words each) is available.

In the normal state, the CCs operate in synchronous mode and the main execution results of both CCs are compared by using the arithmetic circuits, whereby expensive matcher circuits are avoided.

In synchronous mode, both CCs send commands to one of the DRCHs, only the command from the CC connected to the DRCH being effective, thus synchronous operation can be made easily.

The arithmetic word length of the system is 16 bits and 53 basic instructions are prepared. The typical equipment-layout of the D-20 is as shown in Figure 6.

3.3 Software

The software configuration of the D-20 is composed of execution control (EP), call processing (CP), fault recovery (FP), administration (AP) and diagnostic programs (DP). Programs for not only maintenance and administration, but also for call processing are transferred from the DR to the TM.

The EP supervises the real-time ability and the periodicity for call processing, and controls program execution.

The role of the CP is to control the progress of the switching operation in accordance with the call status.

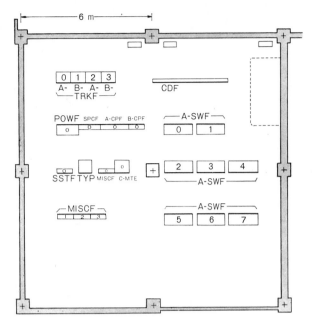

SWF: Switch Frame
TRKF: Trunk Frame
SPCF: Speech Path Control Frame
CPF: Central Processor Frame
TYP: Teletypewriter
MTE: Magnetic Tape Equipment
SSTF: Supervisory Supply & Test Frame
MISCF: MISC Frame
POWF: Power Frame

Figure 6. Equipment layout plan

The FP is simplified as much as possible while maintaining high reliability (less than one hour down time in 20 years).

The formats of the commands, used for man-machine communication through the teletypewriters, are the same as those of the D-10. These are interpreted and executed by the AP.

The DP has been designed on the individual unit resolution basis, taking advantage of a smaller system and fewer circuit packs per unit, compared with the D-10.

Figure 7 shows programs and call data transferring method. The tasks which control the switching operation are composed of task tables and task macros. The task macros are called and executed by the task control program, using the task tables scheduling the call processing.

All the information on each call, such as call status, charging index, subscriber class, path identification information, and so on, are concentrated in a task control block (TCB). When a call is originated, the idle TCB is allocated on the TM. The contents of the TCB are held in the DR during the ringing and talking period, and recovered to the TM when the called party answers or when the conversation is finished. This procedure reduces the quantity of TM required.

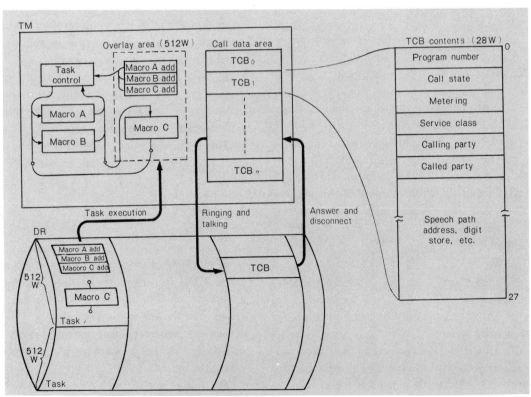

Figure 7. Programs and call data transfer

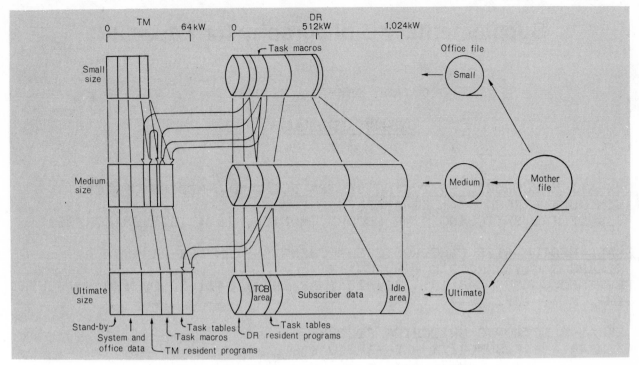

Figure 8. An example of memory allocation and size of office

Figure 8 shows the memory allocation in each size office file and the mother file configuration. Additional TMs are installed as the lines increase and task macros and task tables are gradationally stored in the TM. In the ultimate file, main tasks are allocated in the TM, and the processor call-handling capacity is estimated as about 12,500 busy hour calls (BHC). Additional DRs are installed in proportion to the growth of subscriber data.

In order to simplify file generation and management, the D-20 adopts an automatic program generator which automatically generates program files from the mother file.

4. Conclusion

It is generally known that the stored program control switching system is very advantageous for reducing the work of maintenance and operation and for adding new service features, because of its high stability, maintainability and availability. In order to provide these advantages all over the country, the D-20 has been developed with an eye to making it economically useful for small-medium offices.

In this sense, the D-20 is expected to play a significant role in building up an improved telephone network suited to the coming new society.

5. Acknowledgment

The work of developing the D-20 has been carried out with the cooperation of four manufacturers, Nippon Electric Co., Hitachi Ltd., Oki Electric Industry Co., and Fujitsu Ltd. The authors wish to thank all the people in both NTT and the manufacturing companies who collaborated in the work for their contributions to this project.

References

(1) M. Yamauchi, H. Iketani, and E. Shikiba: "D-10 Electronic Switching System (Part 1) — General and Hardware —", JTR Vol. 13 No. 3, 1971.

(2) M. Shiromizu, J. Jinguji, and S. Kondo: "D-10 Electronic Switching System (Part 2) — Software and Support System —", JTR Vol. 13 No. 4, 1971.

(3) E. Shikiba, A. Tajima, and H. Nakajima: "D-10 Electronic Switching System (Part 4) — New Service in Electronic Switching System —", JTR Vol. 14 No. 2, 1972.

(4) H. Akimaru and K. Yamamoto: "Small-Medium Size Electronic Switching System, DEX-A1", Review of E.C.L., NTT, Vol. 19 No. 3, 1971.

Supplementary Bibliography for Paper 27

D20 (AND DEX-A1, A11)

SYSTEM GENERAL

DEX-A11 ELECTRONIC SWITCHING SYSTEM FOR SMALL-MEDIUM OFFICE
SHIMIZU K + KOONO Z + KUWABARA H
P259 OF INT SWITCHING SYMP RECORD, MUNICH, 1974 (621.381537/159)

SMALL-MEDIUM SIZE ELECTRONIC SWITCHING SYSTEM DEX-A1
AKIMARU H + YAMAMOTO K + MUROGA K
REV ELEC COMMUN LAB 19: 204-10 (MAR 1971) P411-20 OF INT SWITCHING
SYMP, MIT, 1972 (E173 1597)

DEX-A1 ELECTRONIC SWITCHING SYSTEM
AKIMARU H + KUSUNOKI K + YAMAMOTO K
REV ELEC COMMON LAB 21 (7/8): 430-7 (JUL/AUG 1973)

DEX-A1 SYSTEM TRAFFIC DESIGN
FUJIKI M + ITOH M
REV ELEC COMMON LAB 21 (7/8): 438-47 (JUL/AUG) 1973

DEVELOPMENT OF SMALL-MEDIUM SIZE AND REMOTE CONTROL ELECTRONIC
SWITCHING SYSTEMS (D20, DEX-R1, R3)
YAZU S
REV ELEC COMMUN LAB 22 (9-10); 761-5 (1974)

DEX-A11 ELECTRONIC SYSTEM
KUSUNOKI K + YAMAMOTO K + SHIMIZU K
REV ELECTR COMMUN LAB 22 (9-10): 765-73 (SEPT/OCT 1974)

DEX-A11 SYSTEM TRAFFIC DESIGN
ITOH M + NUNOTANI Y + UEDA T
ELEC COMMUN LAB TECH J 23 (5): 781-94 (1974) (IN JAPANESE)

COMPONENTS AND HARDWARE

D-20 ELECTRONIC SWITCHING SYSTEM, PART 2: HARDWARE AND SOFTWARE
KUSUNOKI K + INAMASU M + IINO Y
JAP TELECOMMUN REV 17 (1): 14-23 (JAN 1975)

DEX-A11 SPEECH DATA SYSTEM (ELECTRONIC SWITCHING SYSTEM)
SHIMIZU K + TOKUSHIMA H + MORI A
REV ELEC COMMUN LAB TECH J 22 (9-10): 784-9 (1974)

DEX-A11 (ELECTRONIC SWITCHING SYSTEM TEMPORARY MEMORY)
HIYAMA Y + WAKABAYASHI Y + ISHIKAWA T AND OTHERS
REV ELEC COMMUN LAB TECH J 22 (9-10): 803-9 (1974)

DEX-A11 MAGNETIC DRUM MEMORY
KAMEYAMA T + KAWACA T
REV ELECTR COMMUN LAB 22 (9-10) 810-17 (SEPT/OCT 1974)

SOFTWARE

DEX-A11 (ELECTRONIC SWITCHING SYSTEM) CENTRAL PROCESSOR
MORIKAWA Y + AIZAWA K + KOINUMA T
REV ELEC COMMUN LAB 22 (9-10): 790-802 (1974)

DEX-A11 (ELECTRONIC SWITCHING SYSTEM) SUPPORT PROGRAMS
MIYOSHI R + HORI Y + MASUMORI T AND OTHERS
ELECTR COMMUN LAB TECH J 23 (5): 923-36 (1974) (IN JAPANESE)

DEX-A11 CALL PROCESSING PROGRAM
YAMAMOTO K YOSHIDA Y + NODA N
REV ELECTR COMMUN LAB 22 (9-10): 827-35 (SEPT/OCT 1974)

DEX-A11 EQUIPMENT AND PROGRAM TEST
TOKUSHIMA H + TONAMI S + YOSHIDA Y
ELEC COMMUN LAB TECH J 23 (5): 897-908 (1974) (IN JAPANESE)

FIELD TRIAL EXPERIENCE AND MTC

DEX-A11 (ELECTRONIC SWITCHING SYSTEM) FIELD TEST
HARYU A + IKEDA N + KASAI S AND OTHERS
REV ELEC COMMUN LAB 22 (9-10): 850-6 (1974)

DEX-A11 (ELECTRONIC SWITCHING SYSTEM) FAULT PROCESSING PROGRAMS
NAKAYAMA T + KOYAMA M + HASHIDA Y AND OTHERS
ELEC COMMUN LAB TECH J 23 (5): 871-84 (1974)

DEX-A11 FIELD TEST
HARYU A + HASHIMOTO K + IKEDA N
REV ELECTR COMMUN LAB 22 (9-10): 850-6 (SEPT/OCT 1974)

DEX-A11 MAINTENANCE AND ADMINISTRATION
TOKUSHIMA H + TONAMI S + ABE H
ELECTR COMMUN LAB TECH J 23 (5): 885-95 (1974) (IN JAPANESE)

_____

Paper 28

Processor Reed Exchange—PRX 205

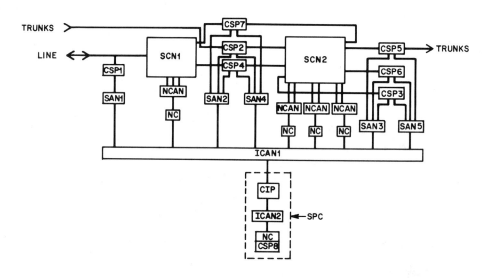

SCN1	= LINE LINK BLOCKS	ICAN1	= CONTROL CHANNEL
SCN2	= TRUNK LINK BLOCKS	NC1	= MARKER
CIP	= CENTRAL PROCESSING UNIT	NC2	= NETWORK MAP
CSP1	= LINE CIRCUIT	SAN1	=
CSP2	= INCOMING TRUNK CIRCUITS	SAN2	= } TESTER
CSP3	= SENDER	SAN3	=
CSP4	= A-JUNCTORS	SAN4	= } TESTER DRIVER
CSP5	= OUTGOING TRUNK CIRCUITS	SAN5	=
CSP6	= RECEIVERS	SPC	= CENTAL CONTROL UNIT
CSP7	= B-JUNCTORS		
CSP8	= CORE MEMORY		

GENERAL INTRODUCTION TO PRX 205

Dipl. Ing. F. J. Schramel and Ir. A. W. van't Slot
N. V. Philips' Telecommunicatie Industrie
Hilversum, The Netherlands

ABSTRACT: The PRX 205-system is a computer controlled local telephone exchange using reed-relays as crosspoints in the switching network and duplicated stored-program computers operating in a synchronous manner in the control part of the system.

In addition to a description of the system layout and elements, special attention is given in this paper to the expansion philosophy of an exchange.

The growth possibilities of the switching-network and the introduction of more than one control complex during the life-time of a particular exchange, is described in more detail.

1. Description of system-layout.

The general block diagram, as shown in fig. 1, comprises four main parts viz. the Switching Network, the Interface equipment, the Utility equipment and the Central Control. For the transfer of information to and from the peripheral equipment two highways with different transfer rates are available, namely a system Control Channel and Data Channel.

1.1. Switching Network. The "local blocks" LB contain a three stage linked network and concentrate subscriber and PABX lines via standard multiple arrangements to two groups of junctors A and B for originating and terminating traffic respectively. The heart of the network is basically a transit center consists of a six-stage linked network composed of identical expanding and compressing "transit blocks" A and B. The relay sets required for trunk lines from other exchanges and large

PABX's, for junctions from the subscriber local blocks and remote concentrators are intermixed and connected without multiple arrangements, partially via an IDF, to the inlets of the transit blocks; the same applies for the outgoing sets. This arrangement improves the traffic overload properties and makes the system configuration independent of the relative distribution between originating, terminating and transit traffic.

In order to avoid inflexible and inefficiently used separate concentration stages, the receivers and senders for MFC, tone push button dialling and PABX indialling are connected to the transit blocks in the same manner as the relay sets and are temporarily switched through to them during the processing of a call. The three-stage network in the local and transit blocks is constructed from plug-in crosspoint units, which comprise of either one 8 by 8, or two 8 by 4, or two 4 by 8, or four 4 by 4 matrices.

By connecting them in parallel all required switch sizes are made as 8 by 16 etc. Inside a block a third contact per crosspoint is used during the marking process and to convey the holding current for the relays, which are held in series.

Outside the blocks, however, all the interconnections in the switching network are on a two wire basis, which allows a fully independent operation and "vertical" control of all devices and consequently a great flexibility in the call processing. The network configuration, the free/busy/out of service states of all the devices and links and their current interrelation-

Reprinted from *1972 IEEE Int. Switching Symp. Rec.*, June 6–9, 1972, pp. 348-357.

ships are contained in a so called "System Map" which is stored in the memory of the Central Control.

The indicated data links (DL) are used for "common channel" signalling to and from other exchanges (CCITT No. 6) and for the transfer of data to and from remote maintenance and/or administrative centers. They are generally of the half or full duplex type with transfer rates ranging from 50 to 2400 Band.

1.2. Utility equipment. In addition to the above mentioned data-links, local man-machine communication for operational and maintenance purposes is provided by means of a system control and display panel (SCP), processor control and display panels (PCP) and "slow" utility equipment connected to the Control Channel. The latter, consists of a teleprinter (TEP) with low speed reader and punch, an optional high speed paper tape reader and punch (TAR) in order to load non-resident overlaid programs and to retrieve bulk data, and a testpanel (TPA) for the manual test of switching network and interface equipment.

The "fast" utility equipment, connected to the Data Channel, is mainly used in an off-line configuration of the Central Control for program development purposes (assembly, debugging etc.) and serves magnetic tape units, lineprinter etc.

The shown extension memory is an optional magnetic disc memory which is used on-line in a large exchange when the subscriber data, e.g. abbreviated dialling data, exceeds the max. capacity of the fast memory of the Central Control Unit.

1.3. Interface Equipment. The interface between the Central Control and the switching network, utility equipment and data links consists of a restricted number of standard control devices. A number of them are in common to a bus terminal CST, which converts the signals sent to and received from the Control Channel. The controls for data links and utility have the ability to transfer autonomously information to and from the central processors, while those for the switching network are "passive" and under direct control of the processors. The last group can be devided in three types:

a) Tester TR. Signals received in relay sets and subscribers line circuits are first integrated and then offered as valid signals via a standard boundary to a tester. The testpoints, constructed as resistor-capacitor gates, are arranged in a matrix of max. 64 words of 16 points, which can be fully addressed by interrogation instructions from the processor. The test result is transferred to the processor and used as "last look" condition during call processing or if it takes part in a scan procedure, compared with the old state stored in the processor memory. The test rate and sequence are determined by the central control, while the response time amounts a few microseconds.

b) Driver DR. Under stringent real time conditions a "fast" driver is used to operate and release reed-relays or flipflops in peripheral units which consists of a matrix of max. 64 half-words of 8 flipflops. These flipflops can be controlled individually or in groups by set and reset instructions, which have an operating time equal to the tester.

For economy reasons non time critical points to a maximum of 8192 are driven by a slow driver, qhich contains a buffer register and address decoders controlling reed-relay matrices for access to the peripheral relay sets.

The overall operating time to set or reset a relay is less than 8 msec, including checks.

c) Marker MR. The marker is basically a slow driver operating 3 relays in series, since the free-path selection is performed by the central control. Reed-relay matrices give access to the outlets and multipled vertical control wires of the speech path network via which the crosspoint relays are operated and checked stage for stage in a coincidence configuration. The operating time for establishing a connection or releasing a standing connection is less than 12 msec. The marker can handle a max. of

4096 subscr. or 1024 trunk lines.

The matrices of all described subsystems are housed in the same cabinets of the equipment to be controlled, which reduces the installation wiring. The controls, including the CST's, are common to a maximum of 4 cabinets and connected via connector terminated cables.

1.4. System Channels. In order to connect the central control to the peripheral subsystems, two types of channels are available.

a) Control channel. This channel is designed for general use and bridges lond distance at a basic speed of 200.000 words per sec. in spite of the relatively high-noise environment of an existing telephone exchange. The transformer coupled twisted pair bussystem comprises 8 address and 16 data lines outgoing from the central control and 16 data lines incoming, accompanied by parity and control lines.

b) Data channel. This channel is introduced if the number of datalinks for "common channel" signalling to and from other exchanges exceeds the max. of 7 to be served by the Control Channel. In larger exchanges it is used to connect the internal datalinks to and from colocated Central Control units via the couplers CCUC in a multi-central control configuration and/or to connect extension memories such as magn. discs.
In a off-line configuration for the purpose of program development etc. high speed utility equipment such as magn. tape units, line printer etc. are connected to this channel.
The basic transfer rate of 500.000 words per sec. and the multiplexed autonomous direct access to the memory greatly reduces the loading of the central processor required for the handling of a great number of data messages. The coaxial cabled channel comprises 16 data lines outgoing and 16 data and 18 memory address lines incoming, accompanied by parity and control lines, and serves a maximum of 8 data multiplexer terminals DMT's. The DMT terminates the cables run to and from a distant multi-

plexer DM, which interleaves the transports of a number of data sources and destinations.

1.5. Central Control. The Central Control consists of two realtime processors and the terminals CPT and DMT for the system channels. The processors operate instruction synchronously in a dual mode and are continuously compared. The configuration is governed automatically by a program controlled alarm and switch-over unit ASU and manually by the system control panel SCP.

a) Processor Terminal PT. This device provides as well as the terminal CPT for the control channel as the circuitry for interrupts IA and autonomous data transport requests ATA. Hardware allotters determine the priority between simultaneous interrupts or requests. Groups of interrupts are masked by a register which is set by program in accordance to its software priority.

b) Data Channel Control. The DCO allots the autonomous transport requests, received from the data multiplexer terminals DMT's, and checks data and addresses before admitting them to the memory registers of the processor.

c) Input/Output-unit. The IO-unit is to some extent independant of its corresponding CPU and allows an asynchronous cooperation with the peripheral equipment. It contains six registers, three of them are used to store the data required for the autonomous scan procedure. This program initiated hardware subroutine reduces the loading of the CPU due to the fact that the I/O unit autonomously increases the current address and seizes the registers of the CPU to perform compare, load and store functions at the moment that the new status of the interrogated peripheral testpoints is received. About the same procedure is applied to autonomous data transports on the control channel.
A test-access connection to the neighbour processor is provided via which a faulty processor can be investigated by means of diagnostic programs in the on-line machine.

d) Central Processing Unit. The CPU is a binary

one-address machine with a word and instruction length of 16 bits and 6 program-accessible registers. The general purpose instruction package comprises 26 memory reference and 58 control, transfer and logic instructions. Modification and indirect addressing is specified per instruction and full addressability of the memory is obtained by relocating the 8 bit address field via an addition of the contents of a 18 bit relocation register, which is loaded per program module. Interrupts, autonomous transports and scans, received via the I/O unit have hardware priority over instructions. In this program "hesitating" technique the control decides after each completed instruction, which next operation shall be done. The crystal clock provides 16 time-slots with an interval of 110 nsec.

e) Memory ME. Each Processor has its own memory which is used unstratified for program and data but a write protect bit per word is used to avoid mutilation of program or fixed, data. Moreover, hardware protected areas are reserved for data channel transports and special programs such as bootstrap etc. The capacity is extensible to a maximum of 16 modules of 16.384 words each. A module contains a stack of ferrite-core matrices driven according to the coincident-current principle with a common current source, which allows a dissipation as low as 60 Watts. Access time to any word is 600 nsecs and the read-write cycle takes 2 microsecs. The cooperation with the CPU is asynchronous by means of the processor stop clock facility. The data channels have access priority over the CPU and operate with the cycle-stealing principle.

f) Real-time clock. The period is 12,5 msec, which can be halved or doubled by means of straps. This basic interval and multiples of it are used to schedule the autonomous scan-procedure in accordance to the real-time requirements of the peripherals, to measure the recognition time of signalling systems, to guard the operation time of slow subsystems such as markers and drivers etc.

2. Modularity and extension philosophy.
The use of well dimensioned modules, plug-in units, factory wired cabinets, together with connector terminated cables for the interconnections in the interface area and intermediate distribution frames allows an economic and smooth on-line extension philosophy of the switching network to meet the demand in traffic growth.

The same applies for the central control area, where the introduction of more central control units in order to share the load of an extending system causes no basic interference with the operating already installed system. The modularity aspects of major system parts will be described briefly.

2.1. Subscriber blocks. A LB-type I cabinet can house two blocks of 512 subscribers each, extensible in steps of 64 lines. The 3-stage network has switch sizes of 8 by 4, 8 by 4 and 8 by 4 in the respective stages, while in the first stage transposition is applied over 16 subscribers. The max. average both way traffic per line amounts 0,07 Erl. and by adding 8 by 4 switches in parallel to the third stage on factory prewired positions this value can be increased to a maximum of 0,13 Erl.

For larger traffic a type II cabinet is available, which contains 3 blocks of 256 subscribers with a 3 stage arrangement 4 by 4, 8 by 4 allowing a max. traffic of 0,15 Erl. By adding 8 by 4 switches to the third stage the traffic can be raised to a max. of 0,29 Erl. The individual traffic per line can be higher than the mentioned average traffic figures but by translation in the central control the average over the first stage can be kept below the stated maxima.

In order to adapt to the actual traffic in the project the outlets of the blocks are run either straight or in multiples of two to the junctors AJ and BJ.

2.2. Junctors and relaysets. A cabinet for junctors can house 96 AJ's and 96 BJ's, while two AJ's or BJ's are combined in one unit. The extension step is 4 junctors, which is the size of the translation groups to the inlets of the TB-blocks and to the outlets of the LB-blocks. The cabinet for incoming and outgoing relaysets has the same structure and figures as the junctor cabinet.

2.3. Receivers and senders. This equipment is stored in a cabinet which has room for 80 units. Each unit location is generalised in order to accept a great variety of sender and receiver units, such as MFC incoming, MFC outgoing, Keytone, PABX-indialling, etc. The size of the extension and translation group is again four.

2.4. Transit network. The transit network is based on one standard cabinet, which is used on the A and the B side and comprises 4 basic type 0 blocks with 64 inlets and 128 outlets; the three stages have the sizes 4 by 8, 4 by 4, 4 by 4 respectively.
By adding 4 by 8 switches to the first stage on prewired locations in the cabinet two adjacent type 0 blocks are merged to a type 1 block, with 128 inlets and 256 outlets and stage sizes 8 by 16, 4 by 4 and 4 by 4.
In the same manner 4 by 4 switches can be added to the second stage by merging two type 1 blocks to a type 2 block, with 256 inlets and 512 outlets and stage sizes 8 by 16, 8 by 8, and 4 by 4. The links between the A and B side are evenly distributed over the blocks in order to equalize the traffic and are arranged such that the procedure in the central control for the selection of a free path between an inlet and outlet of the network can be based upon an algorithm rather than linked tables. The links are distributed by means of connector terminated cables, comprising four links, which are plugged in factory wired IDF-connectors, mounted at the rear of the TB-cabinets. The cables running between TB cabinets standing in one row are supported by horizontal cable ducts,

incorporated in the cabinets.
In large exchanges the interconnections between the blocks housed in different rows of TB cabinets are run via an auxiliary cabinet, standing at the end of each row, and an overhead cable ducts, tying those cabinets together. In order to restrict the required space for easy access and manipulation, auxiliary cables of 48 pairs are used with at both ends a connector block; this block allows 12 IDF cables to be plugged in, which leave or enter the row ducts. The described block types and IDF capabilities provide the means for a gradual extension of the transit network accordancing to the following strategy.
In order to obtain full accessibility to the outlets of the network the number of links between an A and B block has to stay over 16 if the average efficiency of the inlets and outlets amounts to 80%; in small exchanges with an average efficiency lower than 70%, due to small trunk groups, this value can be 8. In a table the growth of the max. number of inlets/outlets is shown in relation to the merge steps, which are recurrently first applied to the A-blocks.

max.cap.	nA_p	$n B_p$	x	m
1024	$16 A_0$	$16 B_0$	24	8
512	$8 A_0$	$8 B_0$	24	16
1024	$8 A_1$	$16 B_0$	28	16
2048	$16 A_1$	$16 B_1$	32	16
4096	$16 A_2$	$32 B_1$	36	16
8192	$32 A_2$	$32 B_2$	40	16

The meaning of the parameters is:
n, the max. number of blocks before the next merge; p, the type of block; x, the number of crosspoints per inlet per side A or B; m, the min. number of links between two blocks.

2.5. The multi-control unit concept. A single central control unit, comprising two parallel operating processors, can handle depending upon the type of telephone signalling a maximum of 36.000 to 43.200 calls per hour, which means 1000 to 1200 Erl. on the inlets of the transit network with an effective holding time of

100 second per call. In those calculated and in practice measured figures an allowance is incorporated for an unexpected 20% future traffic growth of already installed subscriber lines and a 10% loss due to a multi-control unit configuration.

As is described above the transit network can be extended as one traffic unit far beyond the power of one central control unit, so more CCU's are introduced in a configuration as shown in fig. 2.

The system is subdivided in a number of control areas and each CCU controls its own switching network as a self contained exchange in the same configuration as a smaller exchange with single CCU and so it has no access to or responsibility for the switching network in other control areas.

The data related to the building-up, supervision and release phase of a call, which is handled by two CCU's, is transferred over a high-speed internal parallel data-link. Rather than using a common highway the data links are applied on a point to point basis and connected via the multiplexer DM to the data channel of a CCU. The messages contain the same type of telephony events and directives as defined in the CCITT No. 6 signalling system and are formatted in a standard way such that the program load for packing and unpacking is kept to a minimum, and also by the lack of error detecting and correcting procedures, required for external data links. The permanently initiated CCUC's transfer the messages from and to the memories and communication with the call processing program is achieved by means of "scanning" of soft transport indicators by the master control program rather than with interrupts. As a result the response times are in the order of tens of microsecs. and the impact on processor loading is restricted below 10%, independent of the number of CCU's.

The handling of an incoming trunk call on control area 0 and destined for a B subscriber on control area 2 will now be briefly described. As is explained in the corresponding "software"

paper the call-processing program is structured as if the system was split in the middle of the transit network. Incoming calls are handled by A-side programs and data is stored in a corresponding call record; in the same manner outgoing calls are handled by B side programs and call records.

Communication between A and B side and vice versa is established by transferring data between the call records, which happens inside the same memory if the call belongs to one CCU or via the datalink if the call belongs to two control areas.

When in our example the appropriate signalling program for the IT has stored enough digits in the associated call record, analysis indicates that the required B subscriber belongs to CCU 3. A message is sent to CCU 3 comprising the numbers of the CCU(0), the A-call record, the TB-A block to which the IT is connected and the B-subscriber. If the B-subscriber is free the CCU 3 selects a free LB-path and BJ and a B-call record and determines the free links running between the TB-B block concerned and the TB-A block in control area 0.

For this purpose the CCU's "know" the numbers of the TB-blocks belonging to the other control areas. The CCU 3 sends back to CCU 0 a message with the numbers of the CCU (3), the A-call record (CCU 0), the B-call record, the TB-B block to which the BJ is connected and the free links stored in two words. The CCU0 selects a definite link and sends its conclusion to CCU 3 together with the numbers of CCU0 and the B-call record; CCU 3 in turn switches its connection followed by CCU0 on a return message from CCU 3. The subsequent messages comprising telephone events and directives as "answer" etc. have simply the addresses of the CCU and the A or B call record.

Calls for outgoing trunks are handled in the same manner except that the traffic is first offered to the trunks belonging to the same control area before it is offered as overflow to an adjacent control area.

2.6. Resulting traffic range. For practical reasons such as the size of the equipment room the max. number of CCU's is restricted to four or five allowing a maximum traffic on the TB inlets of 5000 to 6000 Erl. Together with an economic lower limit of 100 to 200 Erl. on the TB-inlets the system offers a range large enough to cover nearly all types and sizes of local and rural exchanges, including the reserve required for a traffic growth over a period of 30 to 40 years.

In the near future a more powerful processor with reduced cycle-time and wider wordlength will be available, which has an upward software and channel compatibility with its slower version. Together with the same multi-control unit concept it will reduce the number of CCU's in large exchanges.

3. Summary of main features.

3.1. Stored program control. The stored program control concept, optimized for line and message switching, together with a defunctionalised peripheral switching network offers a "future proof" system.

3.2. Network flexibility. The switching network as a transit centre with separate subscriber concentration stages, either locally or remotely controlled, can cope with divergent situations ranging from a simple terminal exchange to either a main transit centre in a large local network or a combined local and trunk exchange. The message switching capability allows the introduction of a vast number of "common channel" data links.

3.3. System range. The system can be economically exploited starting from initial capacities of 100 to 200 Erl. and can be installed and extended up to a max. capacity of 5000 Erl. to 6000 Erl. The extension procedure, including the introduction of the multi-central control concept, has a minimum effect on the already operating equipment.

3.4. Installation. The time for on site installation, expansion and testing of the system is reduced due to the factory prewired cabinets the application of connector terminated cables and the use of X-ray test programs.

3.5. Electronic components and reed-relays. The use of hermetically sealed integrated circuits and mini-reed contacts, the latter for all "hard" contact functions, makes the system greatly insensitive for air contamination and relative humidity. The system dimensions are reduced by a factor two to three, compared with conventional systems, without forced cooling in the cabinets.

3.6. Reliability. Uninterrupted service in the unattended operation system is attained by the application of derated long-life components, worst case design, independent duplication of important equipment, automatic change-over procedures, short repair times, etc.
The dual operating processors in a control unit and the high independence of the control units in a multi-control unit concept contribute to this image.

3.7. Administrative and technical maintenance. The system can be exploited from a remote centre via a simple telegraph line or a more sophisticated datalink.
The regular change of soft data such as subscr. criteria, the retrieval of data, the loading of programs for traffic measurements or diagnostics etc. can be performed by those means. Moreover maintenance is simplified by well-ordered and standardized equipment, plug-in units, connector terminated cables in all control areas, the aid of diagnostic programs and test access to all equipment from a central location in the exchange.

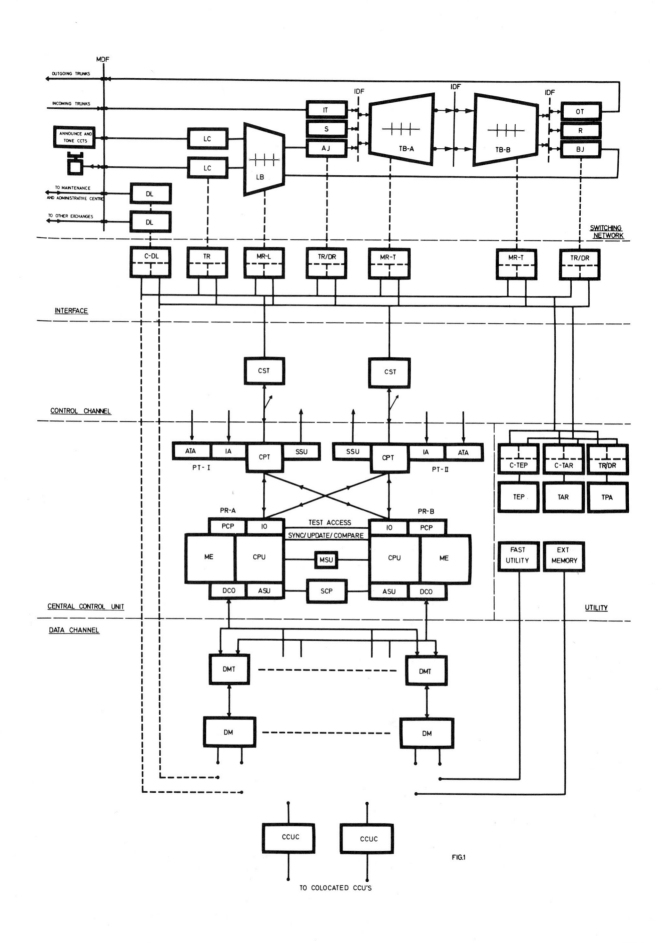

FIG.1

240

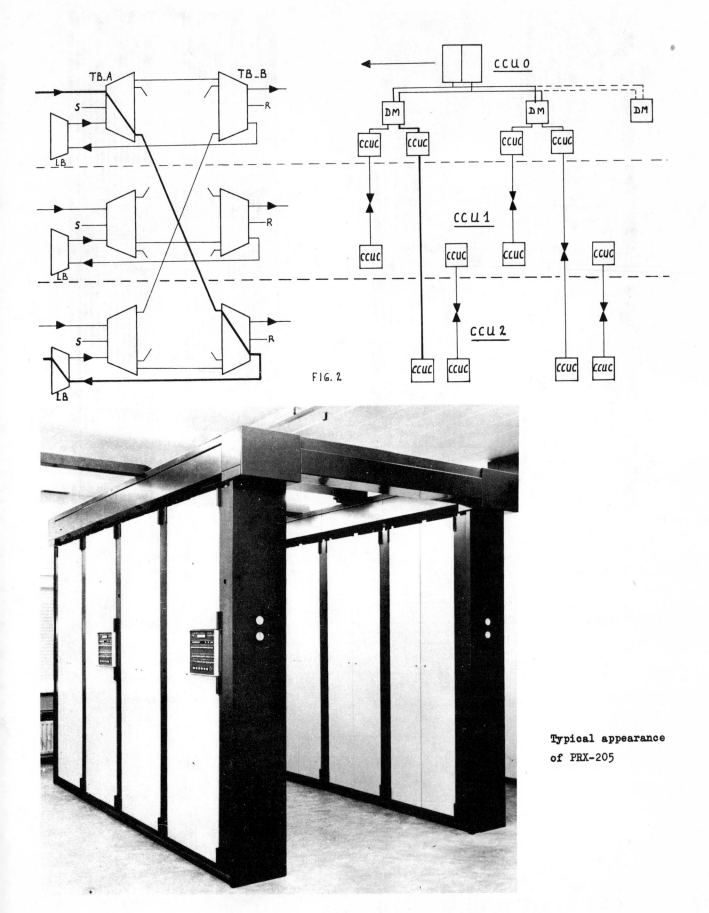

FIG. 2

CCU0

CCU1

CCU2

Typical appearance
of PRX-205

Partial View
Local Block Cabinet
for 1024 subscribers.

Pulled cards indicate
from top to bottom:

I.C. logic of Marker
Tester matrix 4x16 points
Switch 8 by 4 with 8 subsc. circuits
Switch two times 8 by 4.

Partial View
Processor Cabinet

Showing:

Busterminal, Int. Allotter
I/O unit, CPU, ASU
Processor Control Panel
Two memory modules.

Supplementary Bibliography for Paper 28

PRX-205

SYSTEM GENERAL

PRODUCTION AND TESTING OF PRX EQUIPMENT (PHILIPS' COMPUTER
CONTROL TELEPHONE EXCHANGE)
RAVNDAL J
TELEKTRONIK, NO. 4: 340-5 (1974) (IN NORWEGIAN)

SEMI-ELECTRONIC TELEPHONE SWITCHING SYSTEM PRX-205
VAN'T SLOT A W
IEE CONF SWITCHING TECHNIQUES FOR TELECOMMUN NETWORKS APR 1969
CONF PUB NO. 52 P217-25

TRAFFIC CONSIDERATIONS AND MODULAR SYSTEM GROWTH (PRX SWITCHING
SYSTEM)
BORCHERDING J + YFF B
PHILIPS TELECOMMUN REV 31 (2): 77-80 (SEP 1973)

PBX 205 LARGE SCALE INTRODUCTION IN THE DUTCH TELEPHONE NETWORK
MALTHA RAD & GOEBERTUS HJ,
PHILIPS TELECOMMUN REV 33 NO. 3: 125-37, SEP 1975

SOFTWARE

CALL HANDLING PROCEDURE (PRX SWITCHING SYSTEM)
KAMERBEEK GJ
PHILIPS TELECOMMUN REV 31 (2): 73-6 (SEP 1973)

SYSTEM SOFTWARE (PRX SWITCHING SYSTEM)
HIEMSTRA JH. + RESCOE HL.
PHILIPS TELECOMMUN REV 31 (2): 61-72 (SEP 1973)

FIELD EXPERIENCE AND PRODUCTION EXPERIENCES

RELIABILITY AND MAINTENANCE ASPECTS (PRX SWITCHING SYSTEM)
BRAKEL JA + EKAS WG + GOEBERTUS HJ
PHILIPS TELECOMMUN REV 31 (2): 85-92 (SEP 1973)

THE OPERATIONAL MAN/MACHINE CONVERSATION (PRX SWITCHING
SYSTEM)
VAN DAM WA + SCHREUR H + STEENHUISEN AC
PHILIPS TELECOMMUN REV 31 (2): 81-4 (SEP 1973)

THE FIELD TRIAL EQUIPMENT OF THE NETHERLANDS PTT ADMINISTRATION
VAN DE NIEUWEGIESSEN D TELECOMMUN J 41 (2): 130-2 (FEB 1974)

Paper 29

Electronic Switch (Wahler) System No. 01 (EWS 01)

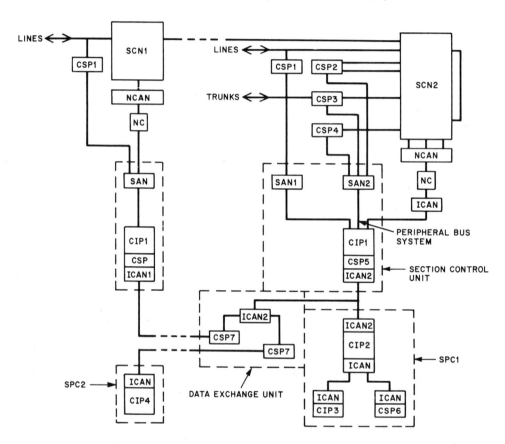

SCN1 = REMOTE SWITCH UNIT OR CONCENTRATOR
SCN2 = SWITCHING NETWORK
CIP1 = SECTION CONTROL
CIP2 = CENTRAL PROCESSOR
CIP3 = PROGRAM STORE
CIP4 = SERVICE COMPUTER
CSP1 = LINE CIRCUIT
CSP2 = INTRA EXCHANGE CIRCUIT
CSP3 = INTER EXCHANGE CIRCUIT
CSP4 = DIGIT CIRCUIT (FOR EMS)
CSP5 = CALL STORE
CSP6 = DATA STORE
CSP7 = BUFFER
ICAN2 = CENTRAL BUS SYSTEM
NC = CONTROLLER
SAN1 = IDENTIFIER
SAN2 = PERIPHERAL BUS SYSTEM
SPC1 = CENTRAL PROCESSOR
SPC2 = SERVICE COMPUTER

Design and Service Features of the EWS Electronic Switching System from the Administration's Point of View

By Heinz Kunze

The development of the local-office version of the EWS Electronic Switching System has advanced so far that a detailed description of the system's design and service features should now be presented. Three EWS telephone switching centers have already been constructed and put into operation, which shows how far the development has progressed.

This article appears by kind permission of the editors of the journal "Der Ingenieur der Deutschen Bundespost", from which it has been taken (Vol. 22, 1973, No. 3). It is the revised version of a lecture given by the author at the 1973 VDPI (Association of German Post Office Engineers) conference in Hannover.

Dipl.-Ing. Heinz Kunze,
Abteilungspräsident in the Fernmeldetechnisches Zentralamt of the Deutsche Bundespost, Darmstadt

Prime considerations

There is no doubt that the design of the EWS Electronic Switching System affects the type of service features which it offers, and vice versa, but since the required service features have a fundamental influence on the design, it is as well to deal with these first. They can be divided into three main categories (see Table 1):

a) Predominantly *subscriber-oriented features* should be easy to activate and should offer the subscriber a number of new services. If these conditions are fulfilled it means less work both for the subscribers and administrative personnel. Pushbutton dialing can reduce the dialing time by about half, and is also a prerequisite for subscriber-activated change-over to special services. The 2×1-out-of-4 code is also used for paystation signaling and for the simple type of data transmission which will be possible later on. Abbreviated dialing makes it far more convenient to dial frequently required numbers, and this can also be used as a basis on which to select the authorized subscribers in long-distance traffic. Independent equipment/directory-number allocation allows subscriber lines to be relocated, for technical reasons for instance, without the directory number having to be changed. Another highly significant feature is the possibility of direct inward dialing into medium-sized and small PABXs with economic use of the limited number of directory numbers available at the same time.

Features which are latent in the system include in-call suffix dialing, conference calls (when the necessary transmission hardware has been developed) and various delay system features. For this group of features the system must be designed to permit access to individual subscriber-related data and to allow existing features to be modified and new ones to be introduced as flexibly as possible.

Table 1
Subscriber-oriented features of the EWSO version

Basic features

• Pushbutton dialing, making for ease of operation and serving as a means for signaling and transmitting data

• Abbreviated dialing using one or two-digit abbreviated directory numbers

• Subscriber-initiated activation of special-service features: customer ordering services with different acknowledgment signals

• Directory/equipment-number allocation in the control area

• Direct inward dialing even into medium-sized and small PABXs

Other possibilities

• In-call suffix dialing

• Conference calls

• Call waiting if the called subscriber is busy (tone applied) or in the case of ATB

Reprinted with permission from *Telefhon Rep.*, vol. 10, pp. 121–131, July 1974.

b) Predominantly *operation-oriented features* (see Table 2) will enable the administration to rationalize its technical, planning and wiring operations. Because the system components are of uniform design and extensive use is made of automatic test equipment, maintenance can be centralized with the aid of a service computer. The service computer is vital for the performance of various functions within the system and as an interface unit to integrated data processing systems. Gradings are no longer permissible, but it must still be possible to expand the switching network in small stages. The quasi-full availability of all the trunk groups and two-way operation ensure optimum line utilization. Malicious-call identification in local and long-distance traffic and automatic charge registration throughout the invoicing process are obvious requirements.

c) The main *technical features* (see Table 3) must serve to permit optimum use of the system during the introductory phase and to render it future-proof by allowing for other types of switching systems to be incorporated later on. The increased range of the subscriber line plant, the use of growth concentrators in conventional switching centers and the possibility of remote-controlled switching centers are decisive features for the introductory phase. The use of concentrators in the connection area and automatic alternative routing at the earliest possible stage, namely the originating switching center, will result in better utilization of the subscriber lines (ASL) and interexchange trunks (OVL). Multiple-path selection

means that the probability of internal congestion will be very small, and it guarantees the quasi-full availability of the serving trunk groups. The absence of any but PCM signals on local and long-distance trunks and the equivalent path selection feature for all system versions will be of special importance for the future application of PCM. It will also be possible to use a video switching network without any problem. As indicated in Table 3, less than 50% of the space used for today's systems is required for the new system. This feature has since become an imperative necessity.

Studies have shown that these desirable service features can best be provided by a system with centralized, *stored-program control* (SPC). With an SPC system, all the logic operations which occur during the large number of switching positions involved in a connection are also realized by means of stored programs, which are activated in accordance with a set scheme. In contrast to this, present-day systems "note" the individual switching positions with the aid of specific relay combinations. The high degree of centralization of the control functions, which must be performed on the one-at-a-time principle for all the connected equipment, makes it necessary to adapt the "slow" periphery to the "fast" central processor by means of defined interfaces within the system. It is also advisable to provide for the pre-processing of signals in the periphery so as to keep time-consuming dynamic processing procedures away from the central processor and large data flows from the

internal data links. This is a prerequisite for the remote control which is called for.

The EWS system is divided into three, function-related levels, which will be explained in detail following this brief survey of the various versions of the system:

EWSO: For the *local system* the remote control of switching centers (VST) must be possible. This requires the formation of control areas consisting of a controlling local switching center (STOVST) with a central processor, and several controlled local switching centers (GOVST). The data exchanged between the switching centers are routed via special duplicated data links with multiple-path choice.

EWSF: For the *long-distance system* central processors must be available which permit the control of four-wire switching networks with a large number of trunks and numerous routes. A system of associated switching centers will serve to deal with the few instances involving large volumes of nodal traffic to be handled. This entails forming several independent control areas interlinked by means of special connecting paths for overflow traffic, similarly to present-day solutions with meter pulse senders. For rural areas the design must be such as to permit handling of a) the four-wire switching network of the long-distance switching center, b) the two-wire switching network of the local switching center (OVST) in the same locality and c) the GOVST of the open terminal switching center (EVST).

telefon report 10 (1974) No.4

Table 2
Operation-oriented features of the EWSO
and EWSF versions

- Standardized technology with internally defined hardware interfaces and specific software

- Extensive use of automatic test equipment

- No gradings in the switching network, but unrestricted expandability (in small stages as well)

- Full availability to all outgoing trunks

- Identification of calling subscribers (malicious call identification) in local and long-distance traffic

- Use of a service computer for the technical service office and as an interface to the equipment which processes telecommunications data

- Automatic charge registration with facilities for remote call-down and registering special charges

Table 3
Basic technical features of the EWS system

- Increased range for subscriber lines with a diameter of 0.4 mm at a distance of more than 6 km

- Multiple use of subsriber lines due to concentrators of various sizes

- Use of growth concentrators in conventional switching centers (using noble-metal uniselectors and two-motion selectors)

- Direct inward dialing with economic use of directory numbers

- Automatic alternative routing in the local network, and for separating bulk short-haul traffic at the originating switching center

- Two-way trunk utilization

- No need for dc signals for registers and trunks due to common signaling channels

- Equivalent path-selection procedure for space and time-division multiplex

- Loss reduction due to multiple path selection

- Remote control of switching centers

- Space saving of more than 50% in the control area

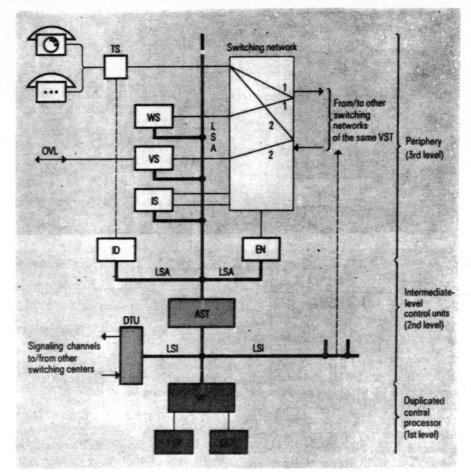

AST	Section control unit	LSI	Central bus system
DSP	Data store	OVL	Interexchange trunk
DTU	Data exchange unit	PSP	Program store
EN	Controller	TS	Subscriber line circuit
ID	Identifier	VE	Processing unit
IS	Intraexchange circuit	VS	Peripheral circuit
LSA	Peripheral-bus system	VST	Switching center
		WS	Digit circuit

Fig. 1
Basic structure of the EWS Electronic Switching System

The periphery contains all the circuits needed for employing the CCITT signaling methods for international switching centers.

EWSD: In the *digital version* the switching network consists of fast-switching integrated circuits. An additional function besides the physical connection of two PCM links is that of effecting a single or multiple time-slot shift when required. Despite the different design of the periphery the structure of the system should be retained to enable the same central processor to control both space-division and time-division multiplex switching networks.

Structure of the EWSO

Fig. 1 shows how the component parts of the EWS system are divided into three levels according to the functions they perform. The *first level* comprises the duplicated central processor, which consists of the actual processing units (VE) and the program and data stores. Changeover units for the central and peripheral domain also belong to this level. The central processor (ZST) is a process control computer which has to carry out the switching tasks on a real-time basis. The instruction repertoire is limited to the tasks involved in the performance of switching operations. This computer unit is required to give a 24-hour service. The principle of parallel operation (micro-synchronization) is employed in the EWS system to provide for this. The two VEs carry out the same operations at the same time.

The first level is linked to the *second level*, comprising the intermediate-control equipment, via a defined central bus system (LSYZ) with the aid of the central bus system. To this second level belong the section control units (AST), data

Fig. 2
Switching unit ABC of the EWSO

ASL Subscriber line
OVL Interexchange trunk
ZWL Link

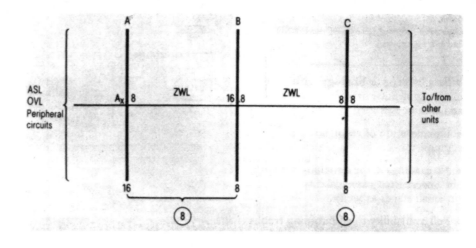

exchange units (DTU) and operators' consoles (BPL), which are not shown in the diagram. The section control unit constitutes the link between the devices of the peripheral section and the central processor. In the case of the local system, one AST normally serves two switching units ABC, i.e. approx. 4000 subscribers. Every 5 ms the AST is interrogated by the ZST for information from the periphery awaiting processing or is supplied with instructions for the periphery. Each AST is capable of addressing a maximum of 1024 peripheral functional devices (PEF). The 5 ms interrogation interval can be reduced if need be. The chief functions of an AST are as follows: finding and connecting PEFs, buffering messages, coding and decoding the signals transmitted between the central and peripheral bus system (LSYP) and accommodating the differing voltage and power levels of the central and peripheral area to one another. Each switching center is composed of several AST areas.

All the data traffic of a control area (STB) to other local and long-distance EWS switching centers flows via the data exchange unit (DTU). The messages are distributed in the DTU among the various paths assigned to each route. The bytes comprising a particular message are transmitted simultaneously, i.e. in parallel, along the available trunks. The opposite DTU recognizes the assigned bytes from special signals and reassembles them into messages. The data are transmitted at a speed of between 1200 and 4800 bit/s. This use of common signaling channels makes it possible to avoid transmitting dc signals on the interexchange trunks.

The operator's console (BPL) contains the input/output devices which permit the maintenance personnel to exchange information with the ZST. Normally, however, the system is accessed via the service computer.

The *third level* is connected via the peripheral bus system (LSYP). The periphery comprises all sections of the system which are connected to trunks or whose functions include the immediate control of trunks, namely the switching network and controller (EN), identifier (ID) and subscriber line circuits (TS), digit circuits (WS) and line circuits (VS and IS) for traffic to EMD switching centers and traffic to and from other EWS switching centers.

A large number of special-service circuits are also employed (testing network, customer service, etc.). Irrespective of the tasks which these perform, the accessing of various addresses takes place via the same peripheral bus system.

The structure of the switching network which is designed as a reversed trunking scheme makes gradings unnecessary and permits full availability. All the trunks in the connection area, for local and long-distance traffic and to digit circuits (registers) are connected to the inputs on an equal status basis. The switching network accordingly contains the concentration or expansion stage (ASL) and the route switching network (OVL), and also performs the line-finder functions of

conventional register switching networks. Reversal is necessary for each connection, for subscriber lines, trunks and circuits are connected to one and the same side of the network. The other side only contains terminals for connecting several trunking units of the same switching center. Only the two speech wires are through-connected since the requirements call for centralized path selection and signaling.

Fig. 2 shows the trunking scheme of a switching unit ABC for approx. 2000 subscriber lines with a traffic intensity of approx. 0.08 erl/subscr. As a basic rule, a number of x inputs, which can be selected in stages, can access eight links (ZWL). Where the local version is concerned, x is always greater than or equal to 8 (concentration/expansion). The system is wired in such a way that the permissible traffic intensity of this "eight-line trunk group" is not exceeded. It is possible to achieve an even traffic distribution by rearranging the connection scheme of the subscriber lines and peripheral circuits at the switching network, and without having to change the directory numbers. This is because the terminal location of the subscriber lines at the switching network is not tied to the directory number. A switching unit AB (KGAB) consists of 16 switching matrices A with 8 outputs each and 8 switching matrices B with 16 inputs. In the case of $A_x = 16 \triangleq 0.08$ erl/subscr., the KGAB has 256 inputs, and 512 inputs are available if the number of switching network terminals is increased to 32. Eight KGABs and eight switching

Fig. 3
Growth concentrator in the EWSO

EKT-ST Growth-concentrator control unit
HL   Concentrator trunk
SS   Interface
ST   Control unit

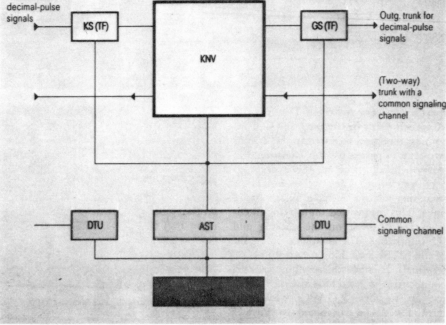

AST   Section control unit   KNV   Four-wire switching network
DTU   Data exchange unit   KS (TF) Incoming circuit (for VF signals)
GS (TF) Outgoing circuit (for VF signals) ZST   Central processor

Fig. 4
Signaling paths in an EWSF switching center

matrices C (KVC) make up the KGABC, with approx. 2000 subscribers. This means that there are a maximum of 64 different paths available for each desired connection, which permits better utilization of the switching network due to multiple path selection. Several KGABCs are connected via groups of eight KVC outputs. Trunking considerations therefore allow the formation of a switching network consisting of up to nine KGABCs, without parallel connection. This scheme provides for full availability, irrespective of the terminal locations. A KGAB, remote-controlled from a controlling switching center, can be operated as a growth concentrator (EKT) (Fig. 3).

It is possible to use EWSO line units (AE), connected via 64 concentrator trunks and two control trunks, in conventional switching centers for "expansion" purposes. The maximum range of 1800 Ω must include the line section in the conventional area. With present ranges already being fully utilized, only the difference will be available. Other types of concentrators for approx. 20 and 100 to 150 subscriber lines will be used to relieve the strain caused by the scarcity of main cables in the loop plant (ASB).

The controller (EN) (Fig. 1) accesses the crosspoints via the rows and columns of the crosspoint matrix. The crosspoints, consisting of bistable relays, defined by the trunking coordinates are then actuated or released.

In the EWSO system, the subscriber-line addresses are recognized via the identifier (ID) and forwarded to the ZST. This makes it possible to provide such required facilities as central charge registration and malicious-call identification. (The question of OLD/NEW and NEW/OLD signaling methods is dealt with in the EWSF section.)

Structure of the EWSF

This, too, is structurally divided into three levels (Fig. 4). For clarity's sake the incoming and outgoing trunks are shown on both sides of the 4-wire switching network (KNV). The two, fundamentally different signaling methods, OLD/NEW (NEW/OLD) and NEW/NEW are included in the diagram.

Trunks for decimal-pulse signals contain, e.g. VF circuits which route the pulse trains from the EMD equipment to the ZST via the peripheral bus system, AST and central bus system, and vice versa. Two-way trunks to EWSF switching centers no longer contain any signaling equipment. The signals are transmitted via the appropriate route selected by the DTU (data exchange unit) and via common signaling channels. The EWSF differs from the EWSO chiefly with respect to the peripheral level and the associated programs.

Fig. 5 shows the trunking principle of the EWSF switching network. Through-connection is on a 4-wire basis, and only

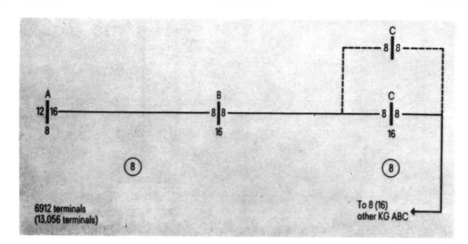

Fig. 5
Trunking principle of the EWSF switching network

KG ABC   Switching unit ABC

speech wires are switched. The crossing of speech paths in the outgoing and incoming direction required in the case of two-way operation for transmission reasons takes place at the switching-network input. The twelve inputs of switching matrix A have access to 16 links. This means that high traffic intensities are possible on the offering and serving trunks. The switching unit ABC of the EWSF switching network has 768 terminals. It is possible, without parallel connections in switching matrix row C, for up to nine KGABCs with 6912 terminals to be combined to form a switching network. The diagram (Fig. 5) also indicates an expanded C-row, in which case the switching network is comprised of 17 KGABCs with up to 13,056 terminals. Fig. 6 shows the connection of two KGABCs in greater detail. This arrangement also ensures full availability. With EWSF a total of 128 paths are available between any two terminals, and multiple path selection results in minimal internal congestion.

All the system versions must be provided with automatic test equipment for the switching network and peripheral functional devices (line circuits). Fig. 7 should help explain the principle of the internationally recommended method of testing the through-connection of the switching network, shown as an example. The terminals are here allotted a characteristic resistance R, which is measured by an automatic tester for 4-wire switching network (APRE:KNV). The nominal value is $R/2$. The 4-wire switching network is also used as an access switch.

The measured resistance serves to ascertain whether a through-connection attempt has failed ($R_{actual} = R$) or whether parts were in faulty contact during through-connection ($R_{actual} < R/2$). By setting specific switching-network configurations it is also possible to use the APRE:KNV to locate a faulty crosspoint and block it in the store against further seizures.

The peripheral circuits are tested by means of an automatic peripheral circuit tester (APRE:S). The switching-network side is accessed as in the case of the APRE:KNV. For accessing of the trunk side the peripheral circuits can be reached via a ring lead which is connected to the trunk side by means of instructions from the ZST. There are appropriate versions of both these APREs for EWSO and EWSF.

The EWSF must also be provided with adaptation circuits which simulate the multi-wire interface used for modern relay repeaters and trunk group selectors on the line side. Automatic testing of long-distance trunks is carried out by devices which are controlled by the ZST and which, as access selectors and test finder switches, use the 4-wire switching network (KNV) again. This equipment can interoperate with the devices in switching centers with electro-mechanical equipment. The other devices, such as the AST, BPL and DTU, correspond to the equipment in the O version. If necessary, a special DTU for long-distance switching centers with more than 16 possible routes must be used.

Structure of the EWSD

In this case, too, the requirements (path selection) mentioned at the beginning have influenced the system structure.

It is possible to control a space-division multiplex and a time-division-multiplex switching network using the same ZST. This again requires a purpose-designed periphery and a differentiated program volume. Only this system structure makes it possible to introduce the digital switching system coordinated with the economic requirements for the PCM transmission systems. (The digital version is dealt with in another article in this issue.)

Service computer

The system design is influenced to a considerable extent by the service computer (BR), which functions as a transition point to other processing equipment for telecommunication data as well as performing technical-service operations. This centralized data processing system has two essential tasks to perform:

• Acting as a computing and storage aid for the EWS system;

• Handling the tasks of the individual telecommunication offices (e.g. maintenance, fault-clearance, customer and intercept services).

The ability of the service computer to act as a computing and storage aid means that all the data and programs not immediately required for the switching procedures can reside in the service computer. These can be transferred at any time to the various central processors (ZST) by

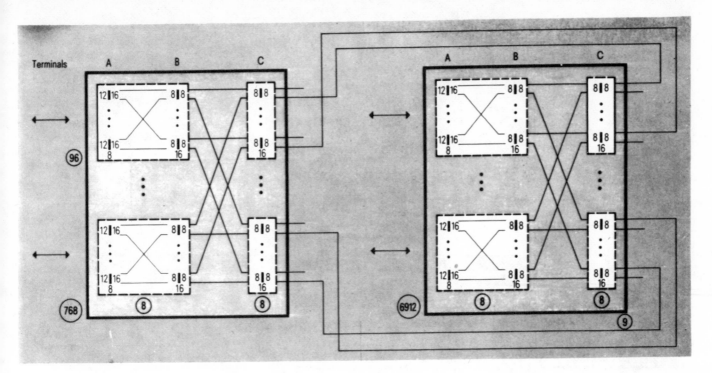

Fig. 6
Structure of the switching network
in the EWSF

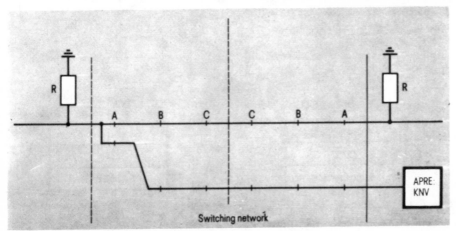

Fig. 7
Testing the through-connection
of the switching network in the EWSF

APRE:KNV Automatic tester
for 4-wire switching network

means of call-down signals or special instructions. Because of the service computer, the capacity of the ZST core memories can be relatively low, besides which the storage of data at another location considerably increases the overall reliability of the EWS system. The tasks performed by the service computer as a computing and storage aid include the following:

● Storing infrequently required switching-system programs and data (e.g. routine-test programs and traffic-measuring programs).

● Accepting data for the purpose of present-day meter comparison and traffic measuring equipment (traffic intensity scanners and traffic flow measuring equipment) and malicious call identification, etc.

● Storing data for the intercept service in the case of changed directory numbers.

● Accepting data for controlling recorded-announcement units for subscribers.

● Managing the wake-up job data file and initiating the automatic wake-up procedure.

● Matching the addresses of the EWS functional devices to their geometrical location in the rack row, rack frame and module frame.

The handling of operations for the telephone maintenance service (FEUST), the telephone fault-clearance service (FEEST) and the customer service (FEAD) is so closely linked to the computing and storage aid and the switching system that it would be impractical to treat it as a separate function.

FEUST operations must be handled in such a way that fault clearance, testing and other related tasks can be performed in a straightforward manner with minimum personnel requirements. When a fault has to be located the service com-

puter uses interpretation and diagnostic programs to isolate the fault down to the plug-in module stage, and initiates its display at the video data terminal. The service computer also has numerous service data at its disposal, such as equipment data, cable-routing data, MDF wiring data, terminal allocation data and capacity data relating to the switching matrices A (KVA).

The handling of operations for FEEST requires, among other things, a minimum response time for the overall system during fault sectionalization. Where fault acceptance and fault testing take place at the same desk, immediate access to the subscriber-store data must be possible. Switching and acceptance test procedures are also initiated from this position. The conventional testing network has been replaced by remote-controlled test circuits in each switching center, which are controlled via common

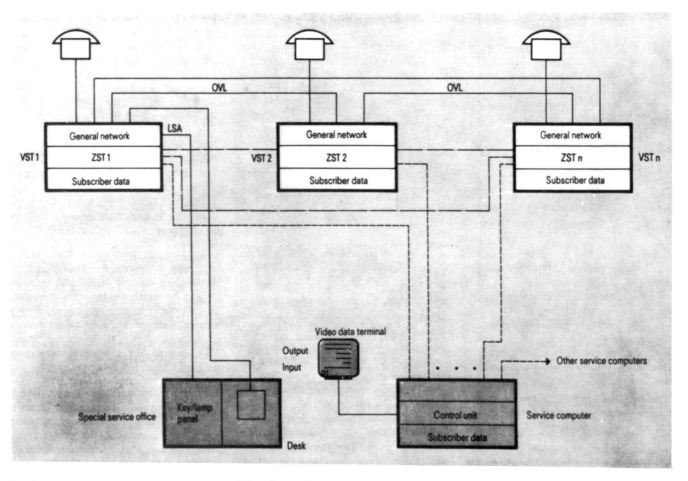

Fig. 8
Incorporation of EWS into the integrated
data processing system

LSA   Peripheral bus system
OVL   Interexchange trunk
VST   Switching center
ZST   Central processor
———   Speechpaths
– · – · –   Connection paths between the
         EWS switching centers
– – – –   Connections between the EWS
         switching centers
         and the service computer

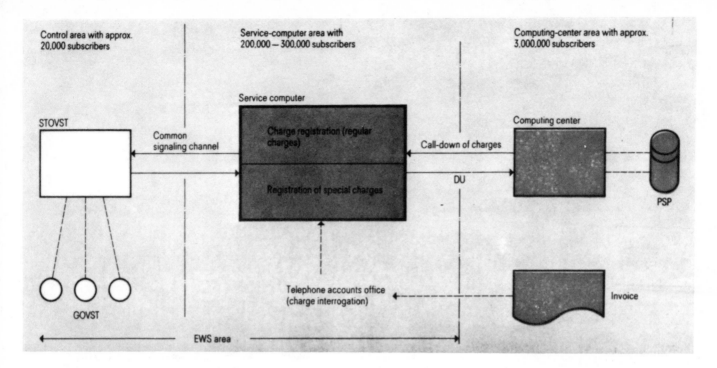

DU	Data transmission
GOVST	Controlled local switching center
PSP	Disk storage unit
STOVST	Controlling local switching center

Fig. 9
Charge registration in the EWSO

signal channels. Fig. 8 shows the interoperation of the system, the service computer and the FEEST special-service office in greater detail.

Up to 20 EWS control areas comprise a service-computer area with 200,000 to 300,000 subscribers. The desks belonging to the special-service office are connected to one of these controlling local switching centers (STOVST) via speech wires and the peripheral bus system. The video data terminals (DSS) of the service computer are permanently assigned to these desks. When a call is made to this office, the ZST1 performs the functions of the call-waiting panel and desk-access control. After the desk has been selected it is accessed via the switching network. The ZST1 transmits the desk data to the service computer via a data channel so that it can prepare the associated DSS for service by supplying it with the appropriate forms. When this configuration has been established the desk is able to transmit instructions for the EWS testing network via the peripheral bus system and to interrogate the service computer for subscriber data or modify subscriber data stored in the service computer. The transfer of modified data from the service computer to the applicable ZST is effected automatically with the aid of protected procedures.

The handling of customer-service operations is highly dependent on their synchronism with the normal sequence of switching operations within the connection setup. When the intercept service is activated the information which has to be passed on to the caller appears on the screen of the video data terminal the moment the desk is accessed. This is due to the fact that the identification data of the desired subscriber line are transferred, e.g. from ZST2 to ZST1 and transmitted to the service computer.

The high degree of night-time concentration, which is desirable on account of its operational advantages, can be easily achieved if service computers are intermeshed. A standard interface to the telecommunication-data processing equipment can be provided by means of data channels to other computers.

Fig. 9 illustrates charge registration as a good example of the interplay between EWS and service computer.

The registered charge data (GE) are transmitted to the service computer, arranged according to location, via the common signaling channel in a 24-hour cycle. The service computer then rearranges and adds up the data for directory-number-related storage. The data of special charges, accruing from subscriber-initiated changeover operations and the like, are immediately transmitted to the service computer and stored there separately. The computing centers can now call down the charges independently. The telephone accounts offices can interrogate the stores for individual subscribers at any time without clearing the stores.

This last section deals with the *EWS program system*. This can be divided into three program groups: the operating system, the user programs and the hardware check programs.

Table 4
Program organization
of the operating system in the EWS

• *Control system*
Sequence control
Input/output
Program selection
Timing program

• *Safeguard programs*
Function test programs (routine)
Error messages
Fault locating
Changeover to standby
Configuration
Diagnosis
Reconfiguration

• *Translators*	
EWS assembler	
Program generators	
	EWS operating
• *Utility programs*	system 4004
Linkage editor	
Simulation	
Library	

Fig. 10
Translation principle in the EWS

LK Punched card
LS Punched tape
MB Magnetic tape

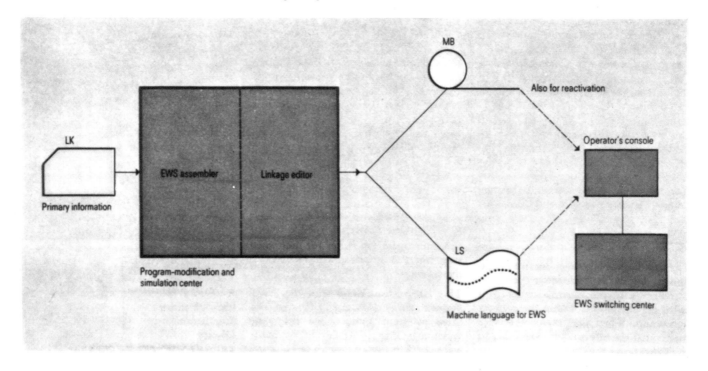

The *operating system* (Table 4) comprises the various control systems. These control all the program runs within the system, including the selection of programs for all the operating procedures: scanning the AST in a 5-ms cycle, treatment of messages via the central bus system, calling down the timing programs and other programs belonging to the message. The safeguard programs, which are the most significant in this group, allow the technical services to be carried out extremely efficiently. Error messages may be transmitted on the basis of routine tests or during normal program runs. Due to special programs the ensuing procedure is aimed at locating the individual module in which the fault originated. The system design incorporates the principle of redundancy. Fully automatic changeover to standby equipment reduces the effects of faults to a minimum. Various test configurations are set by the operating personnel to produce diagnostic reports. When the fault has been diagnosed and eliminated, e.g.

by plugging in replacement modules, the original configuration can be reestablished and the module can be returned to service. Program modifications and other tasks require translating and utility programs, although these are only needed in the domain of the service computer.

Table 5 shows the organization of the *user programs*. This group contains switching programs which are related to individual devices. Each peripheral functional device (circuits, controller, etc.) has a specific program. The subprograms on the other hand are task-related. They are called down when recurring tasks are repeatedly required independently of the devices. The user utility programs are used for the operation and administration of switching centers. They normally only reside in the service computer and enable the tasks listed in Table 5 to be carried out (among other things). The programs for storage organization control the location of associated storage cells, e.g. on the basis of identifier or path-selection messages.

The last group comprises the *programs required for checking the hardware prior to cutover and expanding the switching centers*. They are normally only required during the relevant phases. The off-line tests are arranged in precisely defined sequences which permit the central and peripheral sections to be put into service quickly and efficiently. When expansions are undertaken it is necessary to write in the data for trunk-group linkages. Expanding the stores entails shifting entire areas, which in turn necessitates other measures such as changing the base addresses for address computation.

The maintenance of this software presents the administrations and the manufacturer with entirely new tasks. The practical experience of other operators has shown that the software packet is undergoing a constant process of optimization. This calls for the availability of a central test facility (Fig. 10), where the primary information required for modification or for the data input is produced with the aid of punched cards

Table 5
Organization of the user programs
in the EWS system

- *Switching programs*
Evaluating information
Operating the device store
Generating instructions
- *Subprograms*
Path selection
Device selection
Controlling time clock
Data treatment
- *Utility programs*
Traffic measurement
Reading out charges
Meter comparison
Record keeping
Program treatment
- *Storage organization*
Address computation
Directory/equipment-number allocation
and other functions

and other material. After the symbolic language has been translated by the EWS assembler and the individual parts (tapes) have been linked, the programs are accepted in machine language, e.g. on magnetic tape. The data must be fed in at the operator's console the program subjected to a trial run in the test switching center before modifications or new programs can be approved. These tapes can be used in any controlling switching center, e.g. for the introduction of a new service feature.

References

Gerke, P.: EWS – A Solution for Digital Telephone Networks. telefon report 10 (1974) pp. 145 to 153

Bretschneider, G.; Widdel, K.-H.: EWS – The Starting Point for Integrated Data Processing in the Telecommunications Sector. telefon report 10 (1974) pp. 137 to 143

Supplementary Bibliography for Paper 29

EWS (OR SYSTEM IV)

GENERAL AND APPLICATIONS

EWS: GERMANY'S ANSWER TO ESS
KUNZE H
IEEE SPECTRUM NOV 1975 – P51-54

LITERATURE ON THE EWS ELECTRONIC TELEPHONE SWITCHING SYSTEM
TELEFON REP 10 (4): (JUL 1975)

INTRODUCTION OF THE EWS ELECTRONIC SWITCHING SYSTEM IN THE NETWORK THE DEUTSCHE BUNDESPOST
ELIAS D
TELEFON REP 10 (4): (JUL 1975)

DEUTSCHE BUNDESPOST PREPARES WAY FOR NEW ELECTRONIC SWITCHING SYSTEM
BAUR H
SIEMENS REV 40 (10): 451-4 (OCT 1973)

WEST GERMANY'S TELEPHONE NETWORK ADDS NEW GENERATION SWITCHING SYSTEM
TELECOMMUN EURO/GLOBAL 7 (5): 60E-60F (MAY 1973)

NOW IN OPERATION: THE EWS SWITCHING CENTER IN MUNICH-REFLACK
ANON
TELEFON REP 10 (4): (JUL 1975)

DIGITAL TRANSIT SYSTEM

EWS: A SOLUTION FOR DIGITAL TELEPHONE NETWORKS
GERKE P
TELEFON REPORT 10 (4): (JUL 1975)

INTRODUCTION AND REALIZATION OF THE PCM SWITCHING NETWORK
IN THE EWS 1 ELECTRONIC SWITCHING SYSTEM
SLAPON R
NACHRICHTENTECH Z (NTZ) 28 (3): 102-7 (MAR 1975)

SERVICE COMPUTER

A MONITORING COMPUTER IN THE EWS 1 (ELECTRONICALLY CONTROLLED
ROUTING SYSTEM FOR TELEPHONY)
HOLZOREBE H
FERNMELDE-PRAXIS 52 (1): 9-22 (10 JAN 1975) (IN GERMAN)

SERVICE COMPUTERS FOR EWS 1: THEIR APPLICATION IN SPC TELEPHONE
EXCHANGE NETWORKS OF THE DEUTSCHE BUNDESPOST
SCHULZ K
NACHRICHTENTECH Z 28 (5): K185-8 (1975)

RATIONALIZED TELEPHONE SERVICE: AUTOMATING OPERATIONAL
AND ADMINISTRATIVE TASKS WITH THE EWS SERVICE COMPUTER
TELEFON REPORT 2/75 VOL. XI NO. 2 DECEMBER 1975 (SIEMENS)
PP60-63

Paper 30

Nobel Metal Crosspoint (Edelmetall-Schnellrelais Kontaki) Switching System No. 10,000 E with Electronic Control 801 (ESK-10,000 E)

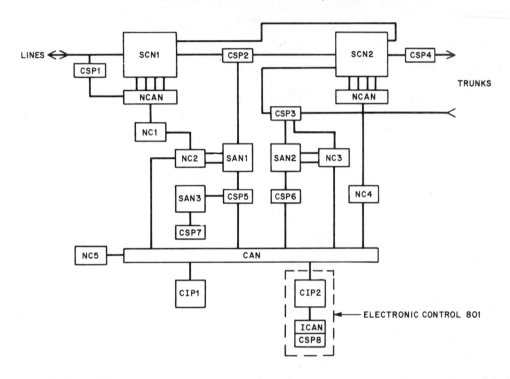

SCN1 = SUBSCRIBER SWITCHING NETWORK
SCN2 = ROUTE SWITCHING NETWORK
CIP1 = TRANSLATOR L
CIP2 = CONTROL UNIT – STS
CSP1 = LINE CIRCUIT
CSP2 = ORIGINATING RELAY SET
CSP3 = INCOMING OR TRANSIT RELAY SET
CSP4 = OUTGOING RELAY SET
CSP5 = ORIGINATING TRAFFIC REGISTERS
CSP6 = INCOMING OR TRANSIT REGISTERS
CSP7 = PUSHBUTTON RECEIVERS
CSP8 = BUFFER REGISTERS
NC1 = LINE MARKER
NC2 = ORIGINATING REGISTER LINK CONTROLLER
NC3 = INCOMING REGISTER LINK CONTROLLER
NC4 = MARKER/PRE TESTER
NC5 = BUS ALLOTTER
SAN1 = ORIGINATING REGISTER LINK
SAN2 = INCOMING REGISTER LINK

ESK 10000 E —
A Family of Systems for Public Telephone Exchanges

By Ferdinand Schalkhauser

The advent of the high-speed relay with noble-metal contacts (ESK relay) made available to the telephone engineer a component which enabled him to obtain the best solutions to switching tasks and problems. In consequence of its high switching speed the ESK relay is also very suitable for interoperation with electronic control equipment [1].

The variety of possible applications which the ESK relay offers in the field of switching has resulted, first of all in the domain of PABX's, in a family of switching systems which has a homogeneous structure and comprises exchanges of all sizes [7, 10, 18, 19]. A corresponding development has taken place in the field of switching systems for public exchanges: these systems have become known under the collective name

Siemens ESK 10 000 E crosspoint system

(Fig. p. 109) [32, 33]. In addition, there have been new developments in the field of telegraph switching centers – systems which are likewise designed on the crosspoint system and which have appeared commercially under the designation "TWK" [43, 44, 46].

All these switching systems have resulted from the basic research and the development carried out by

Siemens in the last ten years and which have produced the various possible implementations of a modern switching system [1a].

The family of systems of the Siemens ESK 10 000 E crosspoint system encompasses exchanges of any size, from the small rural exchanges with only a few subscribers up to the large local exchanges which, for appropriate values of traffic intensity, can serve as many as 100,000 subscribers. To this family of systems belong also the automatic exchanges with four-wire switching which handle national and international traffic, starting with small systems which switch only a small number of trunks and ending with a full trunking system for switching a total of 19,200 connecting paths.

This broad spectrum of possible applications in the public sector has been achieved by the logical application of a "building-block principle" which – with the ESK relay as the fundamental component – extends from the trunking and control system concepts via the construction principle up to the exchange layout. The great flexibility of the ESK 10 000 E system is not the least of the advantages which have resulted from the application of these principles.

Fundamentally, the equipment of the

ESK 10 000 E system may be classified into three groups:

- Speechpath network and individual relay sets,
- Centralized equipment, such as registers and markers,
- Central control.

In the case of local automatic exchanges the trunking scheme for the speechpath network is, in principle, the same whatever the size of the exchange. A subscriber switching network (TW) is provided for the purposes of traffic concentration and expansion, while the traffic distribution is performed by a route switching network (RW). A different arrangement is, however, adopted in small exchanges serving not more than 600 subscribers. In this case it is more economic to combine the two switching networks into a common "subscriber/route switching network" (TWR).

Subscriber switching network

All exchanges serving more than 600 subscribers have a subscriber switching network with a four-stage trunking scheme (ABCD) [35]. The link selection is conjugate. All four stages are used for both outgoing and incoming traffic. 1100 subscriber lines

Reprinted with permission from *Rep. on Telephone Eng.*, vol. 2/3, pp. 106–113, 1969.

with 1000 directory numbers may be connected to one trunking unit of the subscriber switching network (TW trunking unit). The spare 100 lines may be allocated to PBX linegroups, for example, the lines of which, as is well known, have a common directory number. Partial-capacity arrangements and also expansions can each be realized in groups of 100, if required also 20, subscriber lines. The switching stages C and D are made up of groups of 50 terminals – these may be outlets or inlets. The terminal groups connect to the feeding relay sets and in the case of the incoming traffic are seized by the route switching network (RW).

Full availability exists between the subscribers and the D-stage terminals. For the outgoing traffic the internal blocking is negligibly small, since an idle feeding set is generally found in a second switching attempt. In the case of the traffic to the subscribers, the small internal blocking depends on the number of links and the input load on the D stage. By varying the number of links between the A and B stages the traffic capacity can be matched to the traffic intensity for all values which occur in practice. Five capacity stages are available. In this way it is possible to handle traffic intensities from about 7 to 22 erl for 100 subscribers (incoming plus outgoing traffic). This is achieved in a simple way by combining standardized modules to form wiring units and combining these to form a TW trunking unit.

Each TW trunking unit has at its disposal a marker which controls the switching of the speechpath network. The control functions of a TW marker can, if necessary, be undertaken automatically by the marker of another trunking unit.

Route switching network

Whereas in the case of the subscriber switching network (TW) every desired traffic intensity can be handled as a result of the flexibility of the link arrangement, the traffic intensity to be handled in the case of the second large building block of the system, the route switching network (RW), can be considered to have practically the same value for all exchanges of the ESK 10000 E family of systems [36].

The load on a route switching network lies between 0.6 and 0.8 erl per inlet. The design of the trunking scheme must take these values into account. As already mentioned, the route switching network is responsible for the traffic distribution; it therefore handles not only outgoing and incoming traffic but also transit traffic. It follows of necessity therefore that the traffic volume and the number of traffic routes are the determining factors in obtaining the most economic solution to the problem as to how this traffic should be handled. These considerations have resulted in a two-stage trunking unit with fan-type trunking, having 50 inlets and 198 outlets, for use with exchanges having a full capacity exceeding 600 subscribers. The number of trunking units required in an exchange is dependent on the number of inlets required in the route switching network (Fig. 1). Internal blocking is reduced to a minimum by application of the re-entry principle. If one wishes to increase the number of outlets, either one can introduce an interconnection scheme or connect such building blocks as 1st and 2nd route switching stages in series. On the other hand, it is always possible to enlarge a trunking unit in stages. The subscriber capacity of the exchange spectrum which can be built up from these standardized units depends on the total subscriber traffic to be handled, ranging from a few hundred subscribers up to about 8000 subscribers for average traffic intensity.

Another type of RW trunking unit results for exchanges with an initial partial capacity of about 3000 subscribers and whose full capacity does not exceed 20,000 subscribers (the traffic intensity to be handled is, of course, to be taken into account here also). The trunking scheme in this case is of the four-stage meshed type. The link selection is conjugate over all four stages. Full accessibility exists between each RW inlet and each outlet. Serving trunks are connected to one outlet only, so interconnecting schemes or parallel connections extending over many racks are no longer necessary. Such a trunking unit possesses 600 inlets and 600 outlets; partial capacities are of course possible. On the other hand, many trunking combinations may be realized using these building blocks. From the constructional point of view there are no difficulties in doubling the number of outlets of the D stage. Thus two such trunking units can be combined into a double unit and two double units can in turn be connected together by means of reentry trunkgroups. These four-stage RW units have only small internal blocking, so the trunks connected to them may be designed as practically full-availability trunkgroups.

With regard to layout, the A/B stage is housed in one rack and the C/D stage in a second. Such a rack pair caters for 150 inlets and 150 outlets. The capacity stages 150, 300, 450 therefore lead to the trunking unit with 600 inlets and outlets.

In an analogous fashion to the above implementation of the route switching network, another type of trunking unit was built, having 2400 inlets and outlets, for exchanges with an initial capacity of about 10,000 subscribers and also, in particular, for long-distance exchanges. Eight such building blocks can be combined in a similar fashion to that used in the

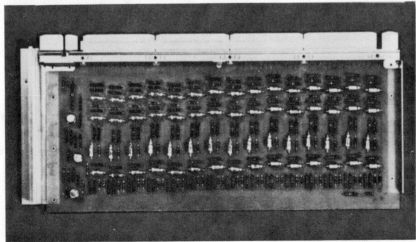

Fig. 1
Module from the control equipment
for the route switching network
with output elements

*Switching equipment
of the Siemens ESK 10000 E
crosspoint system*

trunking unit described above. In this way exchanges with a maximum of 120,000 subscriber lines may be realized for suitable values of the subscriber traffic intensity. The construction and layout follow the same scheme as before: A/B rack, C/D rack. However, such a rack pair caters for only 120 inlets and outlets since the smallest capacity of a trunking unit here extends via the stages 600, 1350 to 2400, and for these large possible expansions proportionally more space must be provided in the racks.

The same building-block principles are followed in the design of route switching networks for four-wire switching in DDD exchanges. In this case likewise a four-stage trunking unit with 600 inlets and outlets is used, having the same trunking options and scope for expansion as for local exchanges. Since we have here eight-wire working, it is possible to serve 150 inlets and outlets by using two A/B and two C/D racks. The large four-wire trunking unit stands in an analogous relationship to the two-wire version. With full capacity this unit can likewise serve 2400 inlets and outlets. In this design five A/B and five C/D racks provide for 300 inlets and outlets. In respect of the trunking possibilities the same considerations apply. Since, from the point of view of the control equipment, the large four-wire trunking unit likewise affords combinations involving eight trunking units, complete route switching networks in DDD exchanges have a total of 19,200 four-wire connecting paths.

All TW and RW trunking units work on −48 V. The four-wire route switching networks work, in addition, on −60 V.

As has been shown, the multiplicity of trunking-scheme building blocks of of the ESK crosspoint system covers a broad spectrum. They are neutral as regards the design and the type of signaling of the individual systems and can thus be used universally for the entire ESK 10000 E family of systems.

Relay sets

In contrast to the building blocks of the trunking scheme, the design of the peripheral relay sets and the registers depends to some extent on the way in which external switching signals are processed in a particular system. The data and information needed for the establishment of a connection are supplied to a register via the individual relay sets for outgoing, incoming and transit traffic, stored there until required, and then transmitted in

coded form to the central control equipment. This equipment prepares (edits) information for automatic alternative routing, zoning, regulation of the processing sequences, etc. in a logical fashion according to predetermined programs and transmits the results to the control equipment of the route switching networks in the form of switching instructions, the appropriate register for the further establishment of the connections receiving at the same time the requisite program sequences.

The individual relay sets assigned to the different trunks are connected to the registers via two-stage connectors which switch eight or twelve wires per connection. The building blocks of the connectors are made up of switching units, each of which has 72 inlets and 25 outlets. Since the outlets of the switching units may be interconnected, the number of inlets and outlets of a connector can be adapted so as to meet all requirements over a wide range.

One rack accommodates either four switching units of the eight-wire connector with a total of 288 inlets or two switching units of the twelve-wire connector with a total of 144 inlets. These connectors are building blocks which are likewise independent of the design and the type of signaling of the various systems.

Central control equipment

As already mentioned, the choice of a route switching network from among the types available depends on the initial capacity of an exchange and the desired full capacity. If for a particular case the optimum RW implementation is adopted when planning an exchange, the central control equipment to be chosen is also specified. Its operating speed, call density, route selection possibilities, etc. should likewise accord with the size of the exchange [37].

Thus for exchanges in which the two-stage type RW is used as the route switching network or in which the same building block is used as 1st and 2nd RW, central control equipment has resulted – consisting of a translator L and a central marker – which can satisfy all demands in respect of automatic alternative routing, zoning and program sequences. The translator and central marker transmit their edited programs and setting instructions to the register or to the marker of the relevant RW trunking unit, which in turn control the further establishment of the connection. Since the frequency of seizure of the central control equipment for the type of ex-

change under discussion falls well short of that at which the ESK relay can operate, the translator L and the central marker have been implemented with ESK relays throughout, except for a few electronic output amplifiers. Since, in addition, it is possible to increase by stages the service features allowed for in the hardware-logic program, this solution certainly represents the optimal solution from the economic point of view for the size of exchange considered.

In exchanges in which the type 600 RW trunking unit is employed, and which therefore have a full capacity of 12,000, 15,000 or 20,000 subscribers – depending on the traffic intensity – the call density and the switching speed of the central control equipment already play an important role. For this system therefore a control has been developed with electronic components, nearly all of which are discrete ("Electronic Control 501"). This central control equipment consists essentially of three units, the translator L (ZUL), the pretester (RWV) and the marker (RWM). The pretester and the marker are each assigned to a trunking unit with 600 inlets and outlets. In the case of full capacity for an exchange with four RW trunking units, four pretesters and four markers are therefore required. An additional pretester and marker can, if necessary, perform the tasks of a device which has been taken out of operation. The translators L are grouped centrally. The number required depends on the traffic intensity to be handled by the exchange and the resulting traffic load on the translator rather than on the number of RW trunking units of an exchange. Each translator can sustain a maximum load of 0.8 erl. A second translator is generally included as a standby.

The central control equipment also contains an RW automatic tester (APRE), which supervises the switching of the connecting paths through the switching networks. Several test programs are available. These enable a continuous check to be made of all the important service parameters. A fault occurring during testing is displayed visually; the important data which enable the fault to be localized, however, may also be printed out on a pageprinter. From what has been said previously, it may be realized that emphasis has been placed on a stage-by-stage increase in capacity, appropriate to the size of exchange concerned, for this control also.

An "Electronic Control 801" is installed in exchanges whose capacity

Fig. 2   Electronically controlled central equipment with TTL circuits and stored microprogram for a four-stage route switching network (partial view)

The translator L (ZUL) forms the heart of the central control equipment. It edits, according to a given program, the data and information received from the peripheral equipment and required for the further establishment of a connection. These programs are stored in semi-permanent memories with hardware logic (Fig. 3). They can be adapted to new conditions in a simple way by inserting or removing wires. Two translators L are provided in an exchange, regardless of its size. The capacity of the translator may be increased in stages since the number of traffic routes, for example, among other factors, is functionally related to the exchange size.

The situation is different for the control unit (STS), which in practice represents the interface between the electromechanical registers and the devices of the electronic control and which acts as a buffer during the time necessary for automatic alternative routing and for switching of the route switching network. The number of control units needed in an exchange of a particular size therefore depends exclusively on the volume of traffic to be processed.

"Electronic Control 801" is provided with an automatic tester (APRE) which, together with the control unit, pretester/marker and translator L, performs the same tasks as were explained for "Electronic Control 501".

The exchange of information between the devices of the central control equipment takes place via a fast data transmission system (bus), which is associated with the appropriate devices by static alerting signals from the bus allotter. For reasons of redundancy, both the fast data transmission system and the bus allotter are duplicated in the exchange.

The structure of the devices which form the "Electronic Control 801" is similar to that of computers. The sequence of operations and the logical decision patterns of the information processing are stored in semi-permanent memories with hardware logic. This ensures easy adaptation to different types of exchange. The devices themselves are therefore practically neutral with respect to the system. This is also true, by the way, for the two central control equipment units already described. With regard to operation, it is especially noteworthy that all the devices of the "Electronic Control 801" to a large degree supervise themselves, by means of checking circuits, routine and diagnostic programs. Faults are signaled automatically; they can also be

provides from the outset for trunking units with 2400 inlets and outlets. The capacity of these exchanges can be expanded in stages from about 10,000 to 120,000 subscribers, depending on the traffic intensity. In this case the fully electronic central control equipment consists of integrated circuits, the high switching speed of which is a must for the processing with the correct phase relationships of the data flows in exchanges of this size (Fig. 2). As in the case of the "Electronic Control 501" the editing of information and switching operations are apportioned to different devices, the number of which depends on the size of the particular exchange. Thus the modular system is used in this type of control also.

Pretester and marker are combined into one unit in the "Electronic Control 801". Two pretester/marker units (RWVM) can test the outlets for their idle/busy status and take care of the link selection through the switching network arrangement of from one to four RW trunking units, depending on the traffic load.

Reports on Telephone Engineering 2/3-1969

Fig. 3
Memory cores of the read-only memory
for the program control unit
in the translator L
of the central control equipment

printed out on a pageprinter, however. If a changeover to the standby circuit of a device is necessary, this also takes place automatically.

The "Electronic Controls 501 and 801" are used not only in local exchanges but also for the control functions of the corresponding four-wire RW trunking units in DDD exchanges. They can also be used in mixed exchanges with two-wire and four-wire route switching networks. As a result of this great flexibility the two electronic control units make a valuable contribution to the total system.

The short outline of the trunking and control principles of the ESK 10000 E crosspoint system given above naturally gives only a rough survey of the complete principles of the system. However, the system exhibits numerous modern service features, which are equally important from the point of view of the subscribers, operation and administration. Thus even the basic equipment of local exchanges offers the following features:

Pushbutton calling for the subscriber; flexible assignment of almost 80 class-of-service combinations to the subscribers; favored treatment for privileged subscribers; absent subscriber

service (FEAD) which can be controlled directly by the subscriber (i.e. without the aid of the operator); automatic assignment of particular relay sets for subscribers with charge indicators or for coinbox telephones; subscriber identification and storage of the number of the caller in the originating register for special purposes; traffic equalization within a TW trunking unit (1000 subscribers) by changing the terminal location of a subscriber while maintaining his directory number; freely assignable PBX linegroups within a 1000-subscriber group; full availability of the serving trunks of the four-stage route switching network; multifrequency code signaling in the traffic to other exchanges; automatic alternative routing and zoning. The basic system also provides for the subsequent connection of equipment for automatic charge registration.

The provision of a translator "S" in addition to the basic equipment enables the realization of a number of service features in connection with emergency call numbers, changed number services, fault signaling, etc. If a translator "T" is used instead of the translator "S", this can perform the functions of the translator "S"; in addition further service features may

be realized. Included among these are the abbreviated numbers assigned to subscribers; the establishment of a connection without dialing; call forwarding; traffic equalization over more than one TW trunking unit, i.e. flexible assignment of subscriber terminal location while maintaining the subscriber directory number.

The translators "S" and "T" are central units. The technical effort for the translator "S" is relatively small. The translator "T", on the other hand, can become quite voluminous if all its technical possibilities are exhausted. Since it is a question of supplementary equipment in both cases, however, the customer can choose according to his own special economic viewpoint.

From the point of view of maintenance the ESK 10000 E crosspoint system has great merits. The high quality of the ESK relay and the electronic components used in the control system contribute greatly to this. Also, as already mentioned, the routine, test and diagnostic programs in the central equipments on the one hand relieve the exchange personnel to a large extent from supervision tasks and on the other hand provide the maintenance staff with the necessary information for assessing the technical condition of the exchange at any time. Since the construction of the system is exclusively based on plug-in modules, repairs and replacements are easily made when necessary. The modules in the racks are held by key-lock connectors; the high contact pressure possible with these devices guarantees excellent contact quality. The rack and exchange cabling is likewise designed to plug in [47 to 50]. Expansions may therefore be carried out very simply. These advantages justify the statement that Siemens have made a valuable contribution to the switching systems of public exchanges throughout the world with its ESK 10000 E crosspoint system.

References

[1] Rohde, K.: Siemens Crosspoint System. Reports on Telephone Engineering V (1969), pp. 101 to 105

[1a] Fischer, K.; Rings, F.: Developments in the Field of Electronic Telephone Engineering. Reports on Telephone Engineering V (1969) pp. 121 to 131

For further references see p. 105

Supplementary Bibliography for Paper 30

ESK - 10,000E

LOCAL SYSTEM

ESK-CROSSPOINT SWITCHING SYSTEM FOR LOCAL OFFICES
SKAWSKI H
NEC PROC 1966-P434-9

ESK 10,000E - A CROSSPOINT SWITCHING SYSTEM FOR LOCAL EXCHANGES
DEUTRICH KD
IEE CONF SWITCHING TECHNIQUES FOR TELECOMMUN NETWORKS
APR 1969 CONF PUB NO. 52 P331-9

TRANSIT SYSTEM

COMMON CONTROL OF LARGE CAPACITY TRANSIT EXCHANGES IN THE ESK CROSSPOINT SYSTEM
VOEGTLEN D
IEE CONF SWITCHING TECHNIQUES FOR TELECOMMUN NETWORKS
APR 1969 CONF PUB NO. 52 P320-4

CONTROL

ESK TRANSLATOR FOR NATIONWIDE DIAL SERVICE
VILLMANN W
SIEMENS REV 28 362-3 (1961)

COMMON CONTROL OF LARGE ESK 10,000E EXCHANGES
VOEGTLEN D
IEEE CONF REV 1969, P35-13 - 35-18 69 CP375-COM

Appendix A

THE CLASSIFICATION AND UNIFICATION OF SWITCHING SYSTEM FUNCTIONS

A. E. Joel, Jr

Bell Telephone Laboratories, Incorporated
Holmdel, N. J.

Introduction

At the 1966 International Electronic Switching Conference in Paris, Walter A. MacNair of Bell Telephone Laboratories, Incorporated stated,(Ref. 1) "My appeal is to develop our language of switching to make it adequate and not restrictive in the thinking process. The problems of switching systems of the future are going to be difficult enough to solve without the additional handicap of poor language tools. -----The urgency for the use of generic terms increases as the technology grows and gives the engineer multiple choice of method and apparatus to solve his design problems." In this paper, I would like to extend this appeal to one system of symbolism as well as nomenclature, and to illustrate its advantages by application to several different system structures.

Switching has been a most prolific area for innovation since the invention of the telephone. Early switching systems were designed around new devices. Starting about 35 years ago, with the introduction of the concept of common control, engineers began to look upon system organizations from broader viewpoints. Concepts like direct and indirect (or register control), bypath and common control entered the switching lexicon. The genesis of many of these concepts were contained in some of the earlier inventions but were developed primarily as a means to an end. The number of new system organizations introduced into commercial systems increased rapidly, accelerating with the application of electronic logic and memory At this point the stored program concept was added as a subclass of common control.

As these system concepts are applied, they result in different system designs. With different technology and different organizations, these systems provide telecommunication switching most economically in different line-size ranges and with different service features. The same system organization may be built with components of different vintages or by different manufacturers. The number of new system designs being proposed or placed in production has been accelerating since electronic components more suitable for switching system functions have become available in the past 25 years (Ref. 2).

The writer contends that if the industry is to make progress in understanding principles and find the bases for comparing and evaluating switching systems of the future, more sophisticated analytical methods are needed. There are probably as many approaches to this objective as there are students of the subject. It is in this spirit that the author offers the following contribution.

Much of our understanding comes through language. We have devised and given special meaning to many terms to describe our systems. The IEEE (Ref. 3) and International Teletraffic Congress have issued some standard definitions for the broader aspects of system services and features. Through the CCITT Working Committee XI/3 efforts are being made to standardize the high-level language of stored program switching systems (Ref. 4). However, we have no standard language to describe system functions and their organizations.

Block diagrams representing two identical or similar systems may be quite different. These differences are due in part to a lack of communication among designers and to a lack of a standard switching language.

Proposal - General

In this paper the author proposes that certain functions be recognized as fundamental in the design of telecommunication switching. Once these functions are agreed upon they would be utilized to provide high-level descriptions of switching systems. Such descriptions should prove most useful in delineating to the

Reprinted from *1972 IEEE Int. Switching Symp. Rec.*, June 6–9, 1972, pp. 446–453.

profession the differences among systems from an organization or architectural point of view. There will of course be other differences, particularly in the technical specification of devices (reliability, sensitivity, speed, etc.), equipment growth modules, service features, etc. It is an objective of this paper to stimulate others into joining this effort. To this end this paper proposes the following specific set of switching system functions and then illustrates their application to a number of electromechanical and electronic switching systems. Some analysis of the differences between system arrangements which this technique highlights is also described, but much more remains to be studied in this regard.

Specific Functions

Assume the following basic functions in a line or circuit switching system or office:

1. Call Signal Processing

2. Call Information Processing

3. Switching Networks and Their Controls.

For simplicity, the means for implementing service continuity or security, maintenance and administrative functions are omitted from this discussion, although their importance and influence on the system organization should not be minimized.

1. Call Signal Processing is the receipt, including registering (storage), and transmission of signals by the switching office. These signals are service requests, digital information such as the calling and called addresses, and call supervision.

2. Call Information Processing is all actions which are taken to interpret, to make decisions, to convert, and to control the internal movement of call information. Call information includes the calling and called address and the location and use of permanently recorded (translation) data concerning these addresses. As with all other functions, the function may be described independently of its form of implementation. For example, in stored program controlled systems it is not unusual for part of the Call Signal Processing and Call Information Processing function to be implemented with the same equipment.

3. Switching Networks and Their Controls. There are many functions within a switching office which the

author chooses to consider as switching networks for the purposes of this discussion. Some are listed below. They may use time or space division techniques to connect inputs (i) to outputs ($\emptyset$). Depending upon the relative size of the number of inputs and outputs, networks (in one or more stages) may be further classified as distribution (i = $\emptyset$), expansion (i < $\emptyset$), and concentration (i > $\emptyset$). Each network has its own control which is designated NC. The principal functions of a network control are to make busy-idle tests and to select, establish, and release paths through any type of switching network.

3.1 Switching Center Network (SCN) This is the principal network of the office used to interconnect lines and/or trunks to each other. There may be several separate divisions of this network such as the one switching lines to outgoing trunks (originating switching center network) or incoming trunks to lines (terminating switching center network).

3.2 Access Networks This is a second general class of networks which are used in register and common control systems. At least three network functions in this category can be identified. Some access networks are trivial, such as a concentrator connecting a number of registers to a single common control. Although they may be functionally identifiable, in many system block diagrams they may not be specified. Physically they are included in larger equipment units. With the greater degree of commonality found in electronic switching systems, sometimes more of these access networks are required. They might be described as connectives, associating a few control elements with a much larger number of call supervising and network elements.

3.21 Signal Access Networks (SAN) are used to connect lines and trunks with the call signal processing portion of a system. Register, Sender, and Service Circuit links are usually space division SANs passing information in two directions. Scanners and Signal Distributors are time division SANs passing information in only one direction.

3.22 Control Access Networks (CAN) are used within the control portion of a system and between the control and other portions of the system. Two specific subclasses of CANs have been identified.

3.221 Network Control Access Networks (NCAN) are used to connect network controls with the inputs, outputs, or links of any network being controlled.

3.222 <u>Intra Control Access Networks</u> (<u>ICAN</u>), are the networks used to provide paths for the movement of information between control functions. In systems with bulk memories, the circuitry which accesses particular memory addresses is considered to be an ICAN.

Application

The applications of these functions are described below in two types of system situations. First, there are the conceptual systems; those describing switching system principles and then there is the application of these functions to specific system designs.

Application- Conceptual Systems

There are <u>direct control</u>, <u>indirect control</u>, and <u>common control</u> conceptual system types with which switching system designers are familiar. Generally the noncommon control systems establish connections in the switching center network (SCN) in a progressive manner.

Figure 1 illustrates a progressive direct control system with line finders. The line circuit is a call signal processing (CSP) circuit which detects service requests. Through the allotter, (CAN), the line finder switch, (SCN), is controlled by its own control, NC. Each selector stage has a CSP which directly controls (NC) the selector switches (SCN).

By contrast, a direct control system with a common network control per stage is shown in Fig. 2. Experimental systems of this type were tested in the 1930's (Ref. 5). Note that there is a distinction between common network control and common control. A common control that "looks ahead" eliminating the progressive character of the control for a multistage SCN. It also eliminates the need for CSPs for each SCN stage.

Figure 3 illustrates the indirect control type of progressive systems. The register-senders are shown as CSP. Optionally it may have an individual translator (designated CIP) as in the Director System (Ref. 6), or a common translator as the decoder in the Panel System (Ref. 7) accessible through a control access network (CAN).

Application - Specific Systems

When these system principles are applied to meet specific cost, service and size objectives, then the basic functions are sometimes combined in a different way. In addition, many inventions have been made and many more will no

doubt appear which derive advantages for a particular combination of these functions. For example, in some systems the switching center network (SCN) is used for both its regular functions and for some or all of the signal access network (SAN) functions. Conceptually, control access network functions could be performed by the SCN. In systems with end-marked networks the SAN could also provide the NCAN function.

The principles involved in variations of the connectivity of functions of specific systems may be better understood when systems are portrayed in this manner. A number of similar and different switching systems are described below using these functions. These interpretations are only as accurate as the details of the information available to the writer from published material.

Figure 4 shows a system with a divided switching center network (SCN). One portion serves lines, the other trunks. This system is known as the Type 5005 (Ref. 8). It employs an end-marking form of network control so that the network control (NC) is shown as an intimate part of the SCN. This system has several separate CIPs, one for each SCN, a common translator and one for outgoing trunks. Outgoing senders are connected to registers through SANs.

A system with a common network control, known as the No. 5 Crossbar System (Ref. 9), is shown in Fig. 5. Here the NC and CIP are integrated. (For simplicity, combined rather than separate dial tone and completing markers have been shown.) This system also has a separate common translator (CIP). The outgoing senders are connected to the outgoing trunks. The originating register is accessed directly through the SCN. After call registration, the line is reconnected to the appropriate type of trunk (CSP). The four stages of the SCN are accessed for control through two separate NCANs.

Returning to systems with a divided SCN, Fig. 6 illustrates the No. 1 ESS (Ref. 10). For the first time the SAN functions are one-way electronic networks called "scanners" and "signal distributors." The stored program control (SPC) brings together a CIP and its access in this case to combined CSP/NC functions. These in effect are implemented in "call stores" where call signal information and a "network map" are stored. The high-speed electronic "buses" provide communication with the functions that are peripheral to the stored program control. The bus access is shown as an ICAN.

By contrast, another system, the PRX 205 shown in Fig. 7, (Ref. 11) like the system of Fig. 6 has a stored program control containing a "network map." However, note the two parts of the switching center network (SCN) are connected like those in Fig. 4. By using uniform symbolism and nomenclature these facts become much clearer. Note the differences between the names given to the one-way SAN functions by the different designers.

In both of the previously described systems there is only one active CIP, and therefore, only one is shown. To simplify system understanding, all redundancy as well as peripherals related to maintenance and administration have been omitted. However, the same approach could be taken here as has been done for the call processing structures. The quantities of each function provided for call processing vary with each installation. The maxima could be included in general descriptive literature. Similar simplified and uniform network topology diagrams could be drawn for all SCNs and CANs. Experience with such simplified diagrams might apply as well to call processing function diagrams such as described in this paper. Complex grading and slipped link connections are difficult to illustrate. If such disclosures are deemed desirable they may be described in footnotes or separate drawings.

The two remaining Figs., 8 and 9, illustrate electronic switching systems with an SCN configuration similar to the system of Fig. 7. Figure 8 is the No. 1 EAX system (Ref. 12). Broadly, the network control resembles the No. 1 ESS, but includes the SAN for controlling the CSP junctor circuits. (Note the addition of SCN$_2$ for use on intra-office calls.) The senders connect with the registers in the same manner as in the system of Fig. 4, except they also connect with the incoming registers since the system also serves tandem traffic.

Figure 9 is a diagram of the ESC No. 1 system using these names (Ref. 13). Here the network is similar to the systems of Figs. 4, 7, and 8. Like the system of Fig. 4 the SCNs are also controlled by end-marking. Note that the systems of Figs. 8 and 9, have many more blocks than the stored program controlled systems of Figs. 6 and 7. Also when there are many blocks simple functions are assigned to each. In the case of the system of Fig. 9 the information is passed serially. This means that the ICANs are time divided.

The above examples have been chosen to illustrate systems that share general similarities in architecture. The details of implementation are all different. Also note from the legends the large variety

and conflicting use of the same or similar terms. However, by maintaining a uniform level of detail and using a few basic symbols it has been possible to illustrate similarities in fundamentals. Traffic flow should be considered to achieve uniformity. In these examples lines were shown on the left and flow was generally from left to right.

The writer hopes that this exposition will encourage those designing and describing new switching entities to work toward uniform exposition by developing standard symbols and nomenclature. Perhaps this Symposium could produce the start of an industry-wide effort in this direction. Students of switching and those desirous of discovering switching principles should find an approach such as described a necessity. This effort might provide meaningful measures and methods for evaluating switching functions and for comparing systems.

References:

1. W. A. MacNair, Recent Trends in Electronic Switching Technology, Proceedings of the Colloquium on Electronic Switching, p51-61, Editions Chiron, Paris, 1966.

2. A. E. Joel, Jr., Twenty-Five Years of Switching System Innovation, Proceedings of National Electronics Conference, December 1970, p882-886.

3. IEEE Trial-Use Standard Definitions of Terms for Communication Switching - IEEE Transactions on Communication Technology - October, 1970 - p699-727.

4. Study Group XI Contribution No. 36 - Part 7, March 1970.

5. R. Taylor and C. E. Beale, Common Common Control System, Post Office Electrical Engineer's Journal - Vol. 24 - No. 2, July, 1931 - p125-131.

6. W. E. Hudson, The Director System of Automatic Telephony, Isaac Pitman and Sons, Ltd. - 1927 - London.

7. E. B. Craft, L. F. Morehouse and H. F. Charlesworth, Machine Switching Telephone Systems for Large Metropolitan Areas, AIEE Transactions, April, 1923, p320-334.

8. J. Isterling, The Type 5005 System - A New Thought in Crossbar Exchanges, A.T.E. Journal, Vol. 18, October, 1962, p149-162.

9. F. A. Korn and J. G. Ferguson,
    No. 5 Crossbar Dial Telephone
    Switching System, AIEE Transactions,
    Vol. 69, Part 1, 1950, p244-254.

10. W. Keister, R. W. Ketchledge, and
    H. E. Vaughan, New Electronic
    Switching System (ESS No. 1), IEEE
    SPECTRUM - Vol. 2, February, 1965,
    p87-94.

11: A. W. Van't Slot, The Semi-Elec-
    tronic Telephone Switching System
    PBX 205, Switching Techniques for
    Telecommunications Networks,
    Conference Publication No. 52, IEE,
    London, April, 1969, p217-225.

12. Paper at ISS 1972.

13. Paper at ISS 1972.

COMMON DIRECT-CONTROL SYSTEM

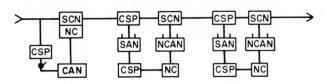

FIG. 2

INDIRECT-CONTROL SYSTEM

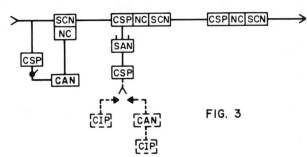

FIG. 3

DIRECT-CONTROL SYSTEM

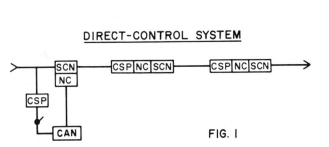

FIG. I

NO. 5005 CROSSBAR TELEPHONE EXCHANGE SWITCHING SYSTEM

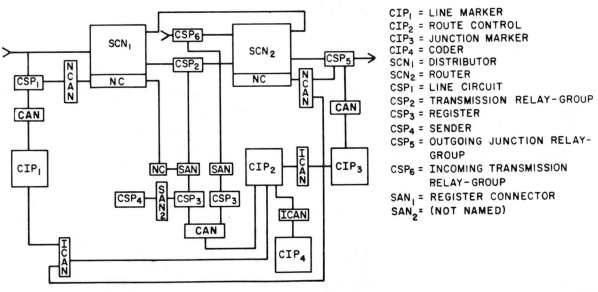

CIP$_1$ = LINE MARKER
CIP$_2$ = ROUTE CONTROL
CIP$_3$ = JUNCTION MARKER
CIP$_4$ = CODER
SCN$_1$ = DISTRIBUTOR
SCN$_2$ = ROUTER
CSP$_1$ = LINE CIRCUIT
CSP$_2$ = TRANSMISSION RELAY-GROUP
CSP$_3$ = REGISTER
CSP$_4$ = SENDER
CSP$_5$ = OUTGOING JUNCTION RELAY-
         GROUP
CSP$_6$ = INCOMING TRANSMISSION
         RELAY-GROUP
SAN$_1$ = REGISTER CONNECTOR
SAN$_2$ = (NOT NAMED)

FIG. 4

ISS 72

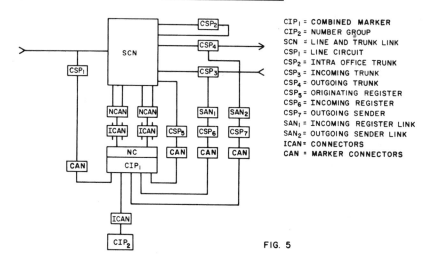

NO. 5 CROSSBAR SYSTEM

CIP₁ = COMBINED MARKER
CIP₂ = NUMBER GROUP
SCN = LINE AND TRUNK LINK
CSP₁ = LINE CIRCUIT
CSP₂ = INTRA OFFICE TRUNK
CSP₃ = INCOMING TRUNK
CSP₄ = OUTGOING TRUNK
CSP₅ = ORIGINATING REGISTER
CSP₆ = INCOMING REGISTER
CSP₇ = OUTGOING SENDER
SAN₁ = INCOMING REGISTER LINK
SAN₂ = OUTGOING SENDER LINK
ICAN = CONNECTORS
CAN = MARKER CONNECTORS

FIG. 5

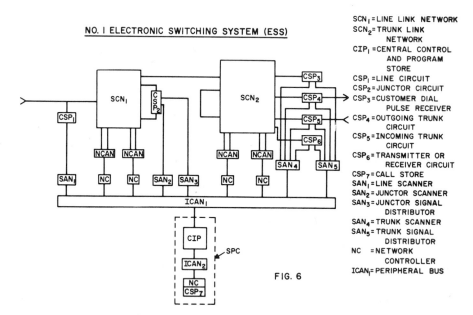

NO. I ELECTRONIC SWITCHING SYSTEM (ESS)

SCN₁ = LINE LINK NETWORK
SCN₂ = TRUNK LINK NETWORK
CIP₁ = CENTRAL CONTROL AND PROGRAM STORE
CSP₁ = LINE CIRCUIT
CSP₂ = JUNCTOR CIRCUIT
CSP₃ = CUSTOMER DIAL PULSE RECEIVER
CSP₄ = OUTGOING TRUNK CIRCUIT
CSP₅ = INCOMING TRUNK CIRCUIT
CSP₆ = TRANSMITTER OR RECEIVER CIRCUIT
CSP₇ = CALL STORE
SAN₁ = LINE SCANNER
SAN₂ = JUNCTOR SCANNER
SAN₃ = JUNCTOR SIGNAL DISTRIBUTOR
SAN₄ = TRUNK SCANNER
SAN₅ = TRUNK SIGNAL DISTRIBUTOR
NC = NETWORK CONTROLLER
ICAN₁ = PERIPHERAL BUS

FIG. 6

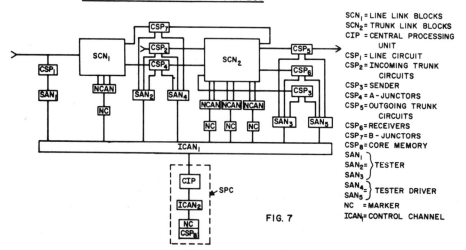

PROCESSOR REED EXCHANGE – PRX 205

SCN₁ = LINE LINK BLOCKS
SCN₂ = TRUNK LINK BLOCKS
CIP = CENTRAL PROCESSING UNIT
CSP₁ = LINE CIRCUIT
CSP₂ = INCOMING TRUNK CIRCUITS
CSP₃ = SENDER
CSP₄ = A - JUNCTORS
CSP₅ = OUTGOING TRUNK CIRCUITS
CSP₆ = RECEIVERS
CSP₇ = B - JUNCTORS
CSP₈ = CORE MEMORY
SAN₁
SAN₂ = } TESTER
SAN₃
SAN₄
SAN₅ = } TESTER DRIVER
NC = MARKER
ICAN = CONTROL CHANNEL

FIG. 7

NO. 1 ELECTRONIC AUTOMATIC EXCHANGE – EAX

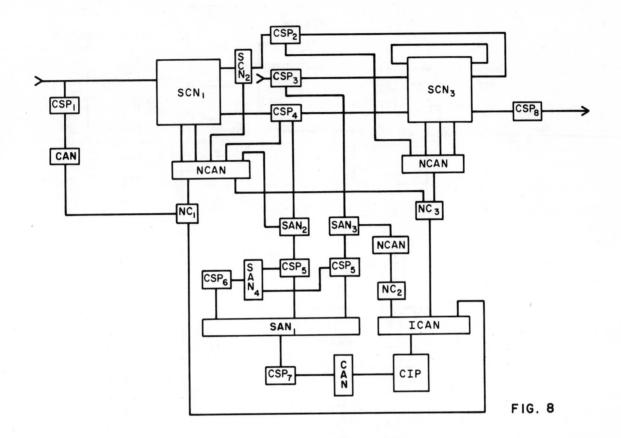

FIG. 8

SCN$_1$ = LINE MATRIX

SCN$_2$ = LINE MATRIX-STAGE C

SCN$_3$ = SELECTOR MATRIX

CIP = CENTRAL CONTROL

CSP$_1$ = LINE CIRCUIT

CSP$_2$ = TERMINATING JUNCTOR

CSP$_3$ = INCOMING TRUNK

CSP$_4$ = ORIGINATING JUNCTOR

CSP$_5$ = REGISTER JUNCTORS

CSP$_6$ = SENDERS AND RECEIVERS

CSP$_7$ = RS CORE MEMORY

CSP$_8$ = OUTGOING TRUNK

NC$_1$ = ORIGINATING MARKER–LINES

NC$_2$ = TERMINATING MARKER

NC$_3$ = ORIGINATING MARKER–TRUNKS

SAN$_1$ = MULTIPLEX

SAN$_2$ = R STAGE

SAN$_3$ = TRUNK REGISTER MATRIX

SAN$_4$ = SENDER–RECEIVER MATRIX

ISS 72

ELECTRONIC SWITCHING CENTER-ESC-I

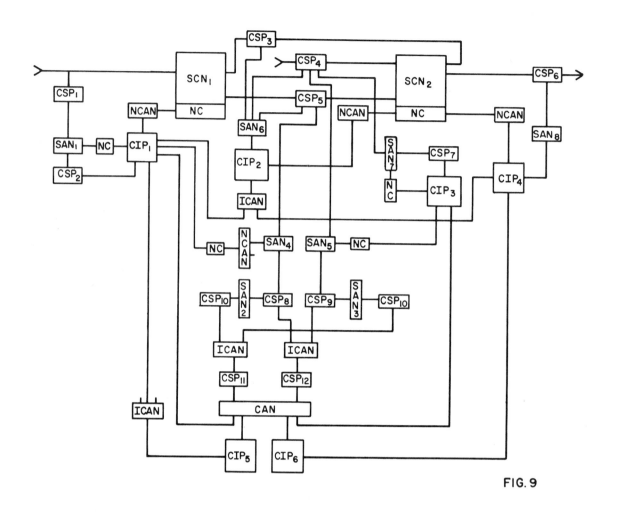

FIG. 9

SCN₁ = LINE LINK NETWORK
SCN₂ = TRUNK LINK NETWORK
CIP₁ = LINE MARKER
CIP₂ = JUNCTOR CONTROL
CIP₃ = TRUNK LINK NETWORK CONTROL
CIP₄ = OUTGOING TRUNK MARKER
CIP₅ = NUMBER TRANSLATOR
CIP₆ = CODE TRANSLATOR
CSP₁ = LINE CIRCUIT
CSP₂ = LINE SCANNER DETECTOR
CSP₃ = RINGING CONTROL
CSP₄ = TRUNK JUNCTOR
CSP₅ = LOCAL JUNCTOR

CSP₆ = OUTGOING TRUNK AND SERVICE CIRCUITS
CSP₇ = INCOMING TRUNK SCANNER DETECTOR
CSP₈ = LOCAL REGISTER
CSP₉ = TRUNK REGISTER
CSP₁₀ = SENDERS
CSP₁₁ = SENDER COMMON
CSP₁₂ = REGISTER COMMON
SAN₁ = LINE SCANNER
SAN₂ = (NOT NAMED)
SAN₃ = (NOT NAMED)
SAN₄ = SERVICE LINK NETWORK
SAN₅ = TRUNK SERVICE LINK NETWORK
SAN₆ = (NOT NAMED)
SAN₇ = INCOMING TRUNK SCANNER
SAN₈ = (NOT NAMED)

Appendix B
Production—Central Office—
Electronic Switching Systems

The following table lists the systems described in this book in chronological order. It also includes statistics on their utilization as best determined from published documents and requests to the manufacturers.

PRODUCTION

CENTRAL OFFICE

ELECTRONIC SWITCHING SYSTEMS

DATE OF FIRST SERVICE	SYSTEM CODE	COUNTRY(1)	INITIAL MANU-FACTURER	SWITCHING NETWORK	CONTROL	OFFICES(2)	LINES EQPD. X 10³ (3)	CHAPTER
1965	No. 1 ESS	U.S.A.	Western Electric	ML - Reed	SPC	671	13,200	1
1966	TXE 2	United Kingdom	Plessey	EH - Reed	EWL	701	877	15
1967	10C	Belgium	Bell Tele. Mfg.	EH - Reed	SPC	40	290	17
1968	No. 1 ESS - SP	U.S.A.	Western Electric	ML - Reed	SPC	472	NA	3
1968	No. 1 ESS - Tandem	U.S.A.	Western Electric	ML - Reed	SPC	NA	NA	2
1967	ESK 10,000E	Austria	L. M. Ericsson	ESK Relay	EWL	367	546	29
1970	ESK 10,000E	Hong Kong	L. M. Ericsson	ESK Relay	SPC - MP			
1970	ESC 1	U.S.A.	Stromberg-Carlson	EH - Reed	EWL	143	300	7
1970	E10	France	CGE	Digital TDM	EWL	25	100	20
1970	C1 - EAX	Canada	GTE - AE Canada	Crosspoint Switch	SPC	97	120	12
1970	No. 2 ESS	U.S.A.	Western Electric	ML - Reed	SPC	185	859	4
1970	NX - 1E	U.S.A.	North Electric	Crossbar	SPC	65	280	8
1971	SP 1	Canada	Northern Electric	Minibar	SPC	71	601	13
1971	AKE - 13	The Netherlands	L. M. Ericsson	Codebar	SPC - MP	14	80	23
1972	Metaconta L	France	CGCT	Metabar, ML - Reed	SPC	7	68	19
1972	No. 1 EAX	U.S.A.	GTE - AE	EH - Reed	SPC	52	347	9
1972	D10 Local	Japan	(4)	Mini-Crossbar	SPC	57	694	25
1972	D10 Toll	Japan	(4)	Mini-Crossbar	SPC	14	100	25
1972	PRX 205	The Netherlands	Philips	EH - Reed	SPC	28	107	27
1973	ARE	Denmark	L. M. Ericsson (6)	Crossbar	SPC	1	3	24
1973	EWS 01	West Germany	(6)	ML - Reed	SPC	4	3	28
1974	10C Toll	Australia	LCT	EH - Reed	SPC - MP	1	28	18
1974	SP1 - Toll	Canada	Northern Electric	Minibar	SPC	11	14.5	14
1975	ETS - 4	U.S.A.	North Electric	Codebar	SPC - MP	3	37	10

PRODUCTION
CENTRAL OFFICE
ELECTRONIC SWITCHING SYSTEMS

DATE OF FIRST SERVICE	SYSTEM CODE	COUNTRY(1)	INITIAL MANU-FACTURER	SWITCHING NETWORK	CONTROL	OFFICES(2)	LINES EQPD. $\times 10^3$ (3)	CHAPTER
1976	No. 4 ESS	U.S.A.	Western Electric	Digital TDM	SPC	4	97.9	6
1976	TXE 4	United Kingdom	STC	EH - Reed	SPC	1	4	16
1976	No. 2B ESS	U.S.A.	Western Electric	ML - Reed	SPC	5	NA	5
1976	E11	France	LCT	ML - Reed	SPC	1	9.6	21
1976	E10 - Tandem	France	CGE	Digital - TDM	EWL	1	1.6	22
1976	D20	Japan	(4)	Minibar	SPC	1	NA	26
1976	No. 3 ESS	U.S.A.	Western Electric	ML - Reed	SPC	1	NA	5
1976	TCS 5	U.S.A.	ITT - Telecomm.	PnPn	SPC	1	3.2	11
1976	AXE 10	Sweden	L. M. Ericsson	EH - Reed	SPC-MP	1	3	25

(1) First country of application
(2) In service as of 1/1/76
(3) Trunks for Toll or Tandem Systems
(4) Oki, Hitachi, Nippon Elec., Fujitsu, NTT - ECL
(5) In service as of 1/1/77
(6) Siemens, T&N, SEL, De Te We

EWL = Electronic Wired Logic
MP = Multiprocessor
NA = Not Available
SPC = Stored Program Control

CGCT - Compagnie Generale Constructions Telephonique
CGE - Compagnie Generale Electronique
GTE - General Telephone and Electronic - Automatic Electric
AE
LCT - Laboratorie Centrale Telephonique
STC - Standard Telephone and Cables

275

Author Index

Subject Index

A

ARM exchanges
  comparison with 10 C system, 138

C

Central office switching vii, 55, 89, 222
Centrex, 1, 13, 17, 30, 55
CITEDIS exchanges, 162
Classification
  of switching system functions, 265
Commercial electronic systems, 1
Common-controlled switching, 17, 55, 62, 89, 97
Communication switching, vii
Computer-controlled switching, 106
Crossbar switching systems, 55, 201

D

DDD toll network, 69
Digital exchanges, 162
Distributed common control, 47, 97
Dual purpose switching systems, 201

E

Electromechanical devices
  use in SP-1 system, 97
Electronic exchanges, 114, 138, 213
Electronic switching systems, 1, 114, 213, 222, 244
  with distributed control, 47
Electronic trunk systems, 138
ESK relays, 257
Exchanges
  see ARM exchanges, CITEDIS exchanges, Digital exchanges, Electronic exchanges, Large local exchanges, Local exchanges, Medium-size exchanges, Rural exchanges, Satellite exchanges, Telephone exchanges, Telex exchanges, Terminal exchanges, Time-division tandem exchanges, Transit exchanges, Trunk exchanges, Two-train tandem exchanges.

F

Four-wire transmission
  use in SP-1 system, 106

G

Geographical locations
  Australia—use of 10 C trunk exchange, 138
  Belgium—use of 10-C system, 129
  Canada—use of SP-1 system, 106
  Denmark—use of AKE 97, 193
  England—use of TXE 2 ESS, 114
  France—use of CITEDIS, 162, 169
    —use of E11 system, 169
  Japan—use of D10 system, 213
    —use of D20 system, 222
  Netherlands—use of AKE 97,193
  North America—toll network, 69
  Sweden—use of AXE system, 205

I

Inter-end office switching, 13
ITT switching systems, 149

L

Large local exchanges, 169
Local central office switching, vii
Local exchanges, 114, 129, 149, 169, 244
  computer controlled, 232
Local switching, vii, 13
Long-distance switching, 37

M

Medium-size exchanges, 149
Medium-size telephone offices, 23, 222
Medium-to-large telephone offices, 17, 62
Military switching, vii
Miniprocessors
  use in TCS system, 78
Miniswitch crosspoints
  use in Metaconta L system, 149
Muliprocessor-controlled switching, 69

N

Nomenclature
  of switching systems, 265

O

ONI (Operator Number Identification), 106

P

Picturephone ®, 17
p-n-p-n diodes
  use as crosspoints in TCS system, 78
Public central offices, vii
Public telephone switching systems, 162, 257

R

Reed switching systems, 129, 149, 205, 232
Remote-control switching, 129
Rural exchanges, 30, 47
Rural offices
  see Rural exchanges

S

Satellite exchanges
  use of TXE 2 system, 114
Smaller central offices, 89
Small–medium size telephone offices, 222
Space division switching network, 169
Sparsely populated areas, 30
Stored-program control, 23, 89, 129, 138, 169, 201, 205
  application in North American DDD toll network, 69
  common, 62, 97
  large capacity, 213
  use of ITT 1650 miniprocessors, 78
  use of ITT 1600 processors, 149

Editor's Biography

Amos E. Joel, Jr. (M'42–SM'48–F'62) was born in Philadelphia, PA. He received the B.S. and M.S. degrees from the Massachusetts Institute of Technology, Cambridge, in 1940 and 1942, respectively.

Joining Bell Laboratories in 1940, he worked for a time in the fields of relay engineering, crossbar system testing, and in the fundamental development studies of telephone switching systems. During World War II he was engaged in the design of circuits for early relay digital computers and for cryptographic and cryptanalysis machines. Subsequently he was concerned with the preparation of texts for and in the teaching of switching design, the design of automatic message accounting computer circuits, and the making of fundamental engineering studies of new switching systems. He was head of a department responsible for the development planning of the Bell System's first electronic telephone switching systems. He served as Director of the Common Systems Switching Laboratory from 1961 to 1967, which included responsibility for the development of the Traffic Service Position and Automatic Intercept Systems. At the present time, he is a Switching Consultant at Bell Laboratories, Holmdel, NJ. He holds more than 60 patents on his work, among which is the largest U.S. patent ever issued. He has authored numerous articles on switching subjects that appeared in the technical press and encyclopedias, and has lectured widely.

Mr. Joel has been active in both national and local IEEE affairs. He served as President of the Communications Society from 1974 to 1976, and is currently Chairman of its Advisory Council. He was also Chairman of the Board of Directors of the International Conferences on Communications. At present he is also the Liaison Representative between the IEEE Technical and Regional Activities Boards, and is a member of the IEEE Communication Switching Committee. Also, he has been a member of the Editorial Boards of the *Bell Laboratories Record* and the *Bell System Technical Journal*. He received the 1972 Achievement Award from the Communications Society in recognition of his inventiveness and leadership in the field of telephone switching. He is a licensed Professional Engineer in the State of New York, a member of Sigma Xi, the Association for Computing Machinery, and the American Association for the Advancement of Science. In 1972 he was co-recipient of the New Jersey Research and Development Council's Outstanding Patent Award for the concept of a new operator telephone traffic service system. In 1976 he was co-recipient of the IEEE Alexander Graham Bell Medal "For the conception and development of Electronic Switching Systems and their effective introduction into a nation-wide telephone system." He also represents the telephone industry on the American National Standards Institute Committee C42 "Definitions of Electronical Terms."